That *Bloody*

Cape Breton Coal

Miners installing friction steel support jacks for the Dosco Miner.
Princess Colliery, 1955.

Frontal view of a Dosco Miner showing the cutting jib, 1965.

That *Bloody* Cape Breton Coal

Stories of Mining Disasters in Everyday Life

Rennie MacKenzie

WITH PHOTOGRAPHS BY RENNIE MACKENZIE,
WARREN GORDON, LESLIE SHEDDEN,
AND FAMILIES AND FRIENDS OF THE MINERS

Breton Books

© 2004 Rennie MacKenzie

Editor: Ronald Caplan
Production Assistance: Bonnie Thompson
and Fader Communications

Our thanks to friends and families of miners who provided personal photographs for this book, including Marg Barnes, John Doyle, Kevin and Hilda Farrell, Fr. Frank Gaul, Brenda Tighe, Wallace and Joyce Tighe, Tommy and Polly Tighe, Paula Burke, June Attwood, Brian Marsh, Joe and Ada MacInnis.

Our thanks as well to Cyril MacDonald for permission to use photographs from the Leslie Shedden Photo Archives on pages i, ii, vi, 52, 100 and 130. The Front Cover photograph of a Dosco Miner crew and the Back Cover of a miner operating a Dosco Miner are also by Leslie Shedden.

The photo of Fabian Young on page 159 is by Warren Gordon, published with his permission.

 Canada Council **Conseil des Arts**
for the Arts **du Canada**

We acknowledge the support of the
Canada Council for the Arts for our publishing program.

We also acknowledge support from Cultural Affairs,
Nova Scotia Department of Tourism and Culture.

We acknowledge the financial support of the Government of Canada
through the Book Publishing Industry Development Program (BPIDP)
for our publishing activities. Canadä

PRINTED IN CANADA

National Library of Canada Catologuing in Publication

MacKenzie, Rennie, 1933-
    That bloody Cape Breton coal : stories of mining disasters in everyday life / Rennie MacKenzie.

ISBN 1-895415-57-8

    1. Coal mine accidents—Nova Scotia. I. Title.

TN311.M34 2004   363.11'9622334'097169   C2004-902251-2

CONTENTS

**Views in Cape Breton coal mines
by Leslie Shedden:
i, ii, vi, 52, 100, and 130**

Miner operating the Dosco Continuous Miner at the coal face.
The two hydraulic shafts prevent the roof from falling in.
Number 20 Colliery, 1959.

Introduction

YOU WON'T HAVE ANY TROUBLE finding information about major disasters in Cape Breton coal mines—disasters like the New Waterford explosion in Dominion Number 12 that killed 65 men in 1917, the runaway man rake that killed 22 miners in Princess Colliery, Sydney Mines, in December 1938, and the explosion in Number 26 Colliery, Glace Bay, that killed 12 miners in 1979.

This book, however, is a collection of stories about some of the disasters that never make history—about the lives of people who suffered the daily, ordinary knocks of working the coal mines, some of the reality that is rarely written down. The fact is that while the major tragedies are remembered and recorded, the deaths and injuries of individuals usually slip into oblivion.

From just 1950 to 1980, 61 miners were killed in the New Waterford coal mines alone. They died one after another, and are just as dead as those who died together in the well-known tragedies—but the loss of these 61 lives is not well remembered by the general public. For the families of those individual miners, however, their loss is often devastating—and it's suffered without the public support that usually comes in the wake of the major disasters.

The stories I tell here are not folklore or fiction.

No plot had to be planned or characters created. This is the hard-nosed reality of working underground. Rather than heightening interest by adding frightening details, I have actually had to cut back on many of the extremely unpleasant details out of respect for the families and relatives. Once they got the news, their lives collapsed emotionally in much the same manner as the roof collapses in the coal mine. They courageously picked up the pieces as they could, and carried on.

These dead and injured miners helped to build our communities. The coal mines are gone now, and our coal mining towns, like the families of the dead miners, are going on without their loved ones. In our continuing life as towns born from our underground bosom, may we never forget what gave us birth, and what it cost. Most of all, may we never lose the pride, honour and respect earned for us by the deaths and injuries of our loved ones—in the great disasters and in the individual disasters—disasters all.

We have often heard it said that "coal was in their blood." I have never accepted that idea. Much more to the point is that "their blood is in the coal."

Rennie MacKenzie
New Waterford
Cape Breton Island

William (Bill) Drake

IT WAS AROUND 1945 IN NEW WATERFORD, and I was in Grade 6 or 7 at Central School, not yet a teenager. I remember one of the things that helped bump me out of my childhood and into the brutal world of the coal miner. On Plummer Avenue on my way home from school I saw a grown man sitting in a child's cart, the same kind of wagon that I used to play with, but this guy was not playing—he was using it as a way to get around. He had a stick that he would jam into the ground alternately on either side of the cart to propel himself forward, much like paddling a canoe. I remember this so clearly because the man had no legs!

Sixty years later, I found out that this stick was a hardwood pool cue with about two feet of the tip

1

sawed off, and the wagon was a CCM cart bought at Sears. The man's name was Bill Drake.

Bill was born in Newfoundland in 1902, and he came over from Marystown to Cape Breton in 1922, looking for a job in the coal mines of New Waterford. He probably fished in Newfoundland during his teenage years, because before he got hired on at the mines in Cape Breton he went fishing for a while, and his Newfoundland talent for curing fish and seals was obvious.

Bill adapted in his own way. The term "Cape Breton Newfoundlander" might well be applied to him, because he carried a handgun, probably a result of the cultural adjustment this Newfoundlander made after he landed in Cape Breton. It is unlikely that Bill felt threatened in his hometown in Newfoundland, but getting beaten up in the early coal mining days of New Waterford was a real possibility. Bullying in this tough town was not confined to school yards. If you looked at a stranger for a few seconds without smiling, you would probably be asked: "Who in the hell are you looking at, b'y?" Also, stemmers [beggars] were all over the place, especially at the liquor store, and they could be more than a little abrasive if they were refused a "donation." Bill was prepared for any hostile situation.

His son Pat tells the story of Bill being confronted by one of the town's bullies and several of his friends. The tough guy "asked" Bill for a dollar—a lot of money back then. At first Bill tried to reason with him, told him he couldn't afford it because he was building a house, and told him his wife was pregnant. That didn't work and, backed by his supporters, the bully told Bill that if he didn't cough up the dollar they were going to put him in the hospital. Then Bill reached into his pocket, pulled out the handgun, and pointed it at his would-be assailant's head. Bill informed him that he had five bullets in the gun, which meant that he could probably kill two of them, and at least wound another three. Then he asked, "How do you like the odds now?" The guy's friends left in a hurry, leaving the bully in front of Bill. He was after going down on his knees, ashen-faced and sweating. The stakes had suddenly been raised from a dollar to the possibility of a bullet between the eyes. Still pointing the gun at the guy's head, Bill said, "I'll make a deal with you. You don't bother me any more, and I will let you go." This time, the guy was quite satisfied with Bill's reasoning. That was the end of that problem.

It was late 1922 or early 1923 when Bill got hired on at Number 12 Colliery. This would be about the time when coal mining methods were changing from the room-and-pillar system with pit horses hauling carloads of coal, to the longwall method with rope haulages. We don't know what Bill was doing for his break-in period, but most likely he had a few weeks as a trapper—the fellow who opens a door on the level just long enough to let the coal cars through, then closes it again to "trap" the air, so it will continue to circulate through the whole mine and not leak into just one level. It is also possible that after trapping, Bill would have been put to work hauling coal with a pit horse and looking after that horse in its stable, since back as late as 1926 there were still 25 or 30 pit horses in 12 Colliery. We don't know what other jobs Bill might have had in the pit, but we do know that in 1937 he was loading coal, and it is probable that he was loading long before that.

His son Pat says that although there were loaders as good as Bill, there were none better. The longwall system was well established now, and Bill was given the top section on the wall—the most envied section, since there was no one above him filling the shaker pan line. Bill had an empty pan line in front of him, and could not only load the coal as fast as he wanted, but he could also load the pan line when it was stopped, much to the displeasure of the loaders below him. When the pan line started up again, they had to wait until the coal Bill had heaped on it went down past them before they could start loading again. Consequently, Bill was always among the first of the 25 or 30 loaders on the wall who finished their section and were on their way home early—long before the eight-hour shift was up.

It was on an early trip [that is, boxcars full of coal] heading for the surface, one January day in 1937, that Bill lost his legs.

All the miners in 12 Colliery needed heavy coats, because the fresh, winter air went down 12 slope, making for a cold trip up to the surface, especially after sweating a lot. Most of the coats would be long, heavy army coats picked up at an army surplus store, where the price was right. It is likely that this was the kind of coat Bill had put on after he had walked out the level to the landing and was waiting for a drive to the surface. The man rake on the back deep went up every half hour, and likely

4

Bill was waiting for that; but it happened that a full trip was pulling off the landing on its way to the surface while Bill was there waiting. What happened next is uncertain, but it is possible that Bill hopped on the full trip for a quick ride to the surface. This was strictly forbidden by management, but a lot of us miners took the chance anyway. It is also possible that Bill was simply too close to the moving full trip. If he were on the landing, there would only be about three feet between the moving trip and the empty trip that had just landed. Whatever the situation was, it happened that Bill's long coat got caught in the moving full trip, and he was pulled by the coat so that his legs went under the trip and were run over by several full boxes, crushing, cutting and mutilating them. One leg was completely severed at the scene of the accident, but he made it to the hospital with the other one, where doctors tried in vain to save it. He lost both legs. The one severed in the coal mine was buried somewhere in St. Agnes graveyard in New Waterford, while the other one was amputated by the doctors, and burned in the hospital incinerator.

Months later, when the stumps healed, Bill was fitted with two wooden legs that had leather shoes on the feet of them, but the first time he tried them, he fell down, and felt so helpless and humiliated that he wouldn't wear them any more. Perhaps he intended to use them some day, but when he finally got around to it, he had become so accustomed to his height in the sitting position that he found himself too tall with the legs on, and actually felt a bit dizzy. So the wooden legs went into the attic, and stayed there. Pat Drake says that when he grew to a size that the shoes on the wooden legs would fit, his dad gave him those shoes, so they were not wasted.

Bill's "legs" became a child's heavy-duty CCM wagon bought at Sears, and when one wagon wore out, he would buy another one. We may wonder why Bill didn't use a wheelchair, since it would be more convenient than a wagon he had to propel with a stick. One possibility is that a wheelchair was simply too expensive, and perhaps not readily available in those days. Perhaps Bill believed a wheelchair would stigmatize him as a disabled invalid—not how he wanted to be seen.

Bill continued to live a very active life. He lost his legs, but he was still full of energy and drive. And there were practical reasons Bill preferred the wagon: he found the wheelchair too high—it prevented him from picking tools and other things off the floor—and there was no place on it to put anything. So Bill would sit on a cushion at the back of the wagon, and put his cigarettes and other items between what was left of his legs, toward the front of the cart. His granddaughter Marg Barnes remembers that all the door frames in the house were terribly chipped because when Bill went through the doors, he would hit the frames with the bent-nail cotter pins that held the wheels on the wagon.

Bill received $50 a month pension for the loss of his legs. When he lost his legs, he also lost his job, and he was supporting a family of seven—his wife Gladys, sons Patrick and Steve, daughters Elizabeth and Margie, and mother-in-law Louise Perry. His son Billy Joe was born after the accident. Consequently Bill needed more income, and he earned it in ways we might not expect of a man without legs. One of those ways was carpentry work. Bill could and did climb ladders and work on roofs, hooking what was left of his legs below the knees on the rungs of the ladder, and pulling himself up with his incredibly strong arms. He would also take over in building a house, telling others what to do and how to do it, getting around on his wagon and, when necessary, walking on what was left of his legs.

He also went fishing, getting his sons Pat and Steve to wheel him in his wagon from home to the boat, and telling them when to return for him and take him back home. When the ground was soft or rough, Pat says it was a hard pull for himself and his brother Steve, and sometimes they would pull so hard the front of the cart with the wheel set-up would come off. Bill had to get a welder to modify the front of his wagons so they could take the punishment.

He would fish lobsters and cod on a small scale. With his powerful arms it was no trouble to pull the lobster traps, or to land the cod, one of which Pat remembers weighing 40 pounds. His granddaughter Margie remembers that the clothesline in their yard was often full of salt cod drying in the sun. Pat says it was no small task for him and Steve to carry their father from the boat to the wagon. Since losing his legs, Bill had gone from 180 pounds to over 200 pounds. The boys would also drive him to his favourite hunting spot, carrying him from the car and setting him up and then coming back for him later—usually after he shot a deer.

Bill kept his sons busy, because he visited around

town, and when he had to go some distance to see a friend, he would get Pat and Steve to wheel him there in the wagon—a long haul, says Pat, when it was about a mile from the bottom of Hudson Street to the north end of Plummer Avenue where he wanted to go.

And go he did! His granddaughter Mary Gladys says she never thought of her grandfather as a cripple. He was a man who could do anything. He seemed so normal—nobody treated him as someone who couldn't do whatever he wanted to do.

Bill supplemented his meagre income any way he could. With a family of eight, and a $50-a-month pension, who would blame him for bootlegging booze, making moonshine, and running a card game in a little shack he had in the yard? No one was blaming him—as a matter of fact, a lot of guys were enjoying the "services" he was providing—and every weekend he had his regulars at the card game. One day the topic around the card table was the Devil. One fellow said that the Devil was always at a card game because gambling was sinful. Another of the guys joked about Bill having no legs, saying that if the Devil showed up here now, Bill couldn't run, so he would be left alone with Satan. And Bill said, "The hell I would. I would be on the back of the first guy out the door!"

The conversation would always be tavern-like, because Bill had his bootleg booze stashed under the little shack where they played cards. They would move a large toolbox, take out two loose floorboards, then reach underground for cool beer—another income supplement for Bill. Add to that that the card game would often go the full weekend, and Bill would chalk up a bit more income by providing lunches for the guys.

Bill himself was a pretty good card player, and Pat tells the story of the time when his father was in a five-card stud game. The stakes were high, and one guy threw his cards in, but instead of throwing them face down he threw them face up, allowing Bill to see a card that he thought his remaining opponent had—the only card that could beat him. So Bill knew that he had the guy beat. When his opponent raised the stakes, Bill bumped him an equal amount, and took the fat pot. More income!

Bill's moonshine enterprise was not as profitable, even though he made really good stuff. As usually happens, word got around about the moonshine, and somebody squealed to the Mounties, who in those days were more hell-bent against moonshine than they are now. Somehow, Pat got word that the Mounties were going to raid his father's moonshine operation. He told his father, but Bill did not take his son seriously. Perhaps Bill thought no one would bother a man without legs trying to make a living. For the most part, he was right. Many people would buy his moonshine just to help him out. However, he should have taken Pat's warning more seriously, because the Mounties were not in the least sympathetic to Bill, legs or no legs. One night they did raid him, seized the still as evidence, and dumped out the mash he had fermenting. Pat and his younger brother Steve were coming home from the midnight show, and as they walked towards home, Steve said he could smell the spilled-out mash. Steve told Pat that the Mounties had just raided their father's moonshine operation, and he was right! You could smell that stuff from a mile away.

Bill was never sick a day in his life, at least not with anything he knew about, or anything that slowed him down, but he died September 10, 1961, at the age of 59. Cigarettes were probably the primary cause, since he smoked three and four packages a day, but he was also diabetic. He died in a dory, fishing off Lingan. They had just landed a tuna when Bill started coughing and couldn't stop. His buddy asked him if he wanted something to drink, but Bill refused and kept on coughing. When the coughing continued, his buddy turned again to offer him something to drink, but Bill died without answering. His son Pat was living in California at the time, and says that when he was getting ready for work that day, a feeling came over him that made him think someone in his family was going to die. Before he left for work, a phone call came with the news that his father was gone.

What followed was a brutal disregard for Bill's widow by the pension and compensation boards. Bill's pension wasn't even continued to the end of the month of September; his widow received only half of that month's payment. As if that were not enough, the Compensation Board then asked that Bill's wooden legs be returned. Whatever they could use them for after they were fitted for Bill is a question, but in any case they would not be getting them back. Bill's son Steve was so angry that he took the legs out in the yard and chopped them up with the axe! Perhaps it is no wonder that the last president of the miners' union, the United Mine Workers (UMW), was Steve Drake Jr., Bill Drake's grandson.

Lawrence Farrell and Patrick Gaul

Lawrence and his wife, Margaret

METHANE GAS is composed of carbon and hydrogen. It is lighter than air, colorless and odorless; it is also poisonous and highly flammable. And it is found in coal. When it explodes, it kills brutally and violently, making the mine tunnels like the inside of a huge discharging shotgun, killing everyone in its path. When it is inhaled, it is a silent killer—invisible and gentle, but still it kills.

My own experience with methane was while driving diesel on 4 West level in 18 Colliery. Sitting on the diesel seat most of the shift, my butt was getting sore, so for a change in position I sat on the top of the backrest, putting one foot on the seat and letting my other leg stretch out to the floor about a foot and a half below the seat. This put my head much closer to the roof of the level. I was in this position, pushing the empty trip of coal cars off the spare road, onto the single road and under the coal chute.

Just as I was switching onto the single road, I felt my head fall uncontrollably backward—and no doubt the rest of me would have followed had I not driven out of the pocket of methane and back into fresh air. I have no way of knowing how many breaths of methane I had taken, but there was no doubt that I was on my way to passing out. The experience was perfectly painless, with no hint of choking or suffocation. Had I passed out, it would have been more peaceful than falling asleep. It was in this "gentle killer" role that methane claimed the lives of Lawrence Farrell and Pat Gaul.

It happened May 24, 1956, in 18 Colliery in New Victoria, just on the outskirts of New Waterford. Lawrence and Pat had been sent down on back shift to repair a leak in the compressed-air pipeline, and to extend the line closer to the coal face. Coal mining custom has it that one man is never to be sent down to do a job alone—he always has to have a "buddy." The "buddy" helps his partner get the work done but he's also there to go for help if either one gets into trouble. This system backfired this time. If there had only been one man working, only one life would have been lost.

Lawrence and Pat were buddied up to do a pipefitting job on the lonely back shift. They were on their way in the level at the top of 4 West wall. Part way in the level, there was a "cutoff"—an upward slanting tunnel driven into the coal seam at

90 degrees to the level. This cutoff was on the high side of the level—the side closest to the surface. Part way up this cutoff was a valve that they had to shut off in order to take the pressure off the pipeline, which would allow them to dismantle it near the coal face, about a quarter of a mile further in the level. They probably decided to go up the cutoff, turn off the valve, and have a lunch before they started their work, since they had carried their lunch cans up the cutoff with them instead of leaving them on the level. Word has it they never made it to the valve.

John MacLeod, now a member of the Men of the Deeps chorus, used to get a drive to and from work with Pat Gaul when both were on back shift. He drove to work with Pat on the night of May 23rd, but when the shift was over on May 24th, Pat had not come up. John figured that Pat simply had to stay down to finish his work, so he got home by other means, thinking nothing out of the ordinary. He was asleep at home when he was awakened to learn that Pat Gaul was dead.

Peter MacKinnon and Sylvester Saniga found Lawrence and Pat. Peter and Sylvester were going down on day shift to service the Dosco Miner on 4 West, and would also be walking in the top level of 4 West. They knew that Lawrence and Pat had not come up from back shift, and were to talk to them and find out what was keeping them late. They were on the way in the same level that Lawrence and Pat had travelled eight hours earlier, fully expecting to meet them in close to the coal face. They thought that perhaps Lawrence and Pat had encountered a hitch in the work they were doing, or perhaps they had finished their work, laid down for a sleep and slept too long, missing the rake to the surface. This often happens on back shift.

As they walked past the cutoff where Lawrence and Pat had entered to shut off the valve, they noticed lights a short way up the cutoff. It was obvious that these were Lawrence and Pat's lights. Their first impulse was to go up the cutoff and see what was keeping them so late, but they hesitated. Being operators on the coal cutting machine, they were equipped with specially polished lamp reflectors. With these lamps, they could see three or four times as far as with the regular miner's lamp. They shone their lamps up the cutoff and saw that Lawrence and Pat were lying down. The positions of both men made them suspicious. Lawrence was face down, and Pat was on his back. They did not look as if they had laid down for a nap. Peter and Sylvester immediately suspected methane, so they did not venture up the cutoff. That decision saved their lives.

They went back out the level to the phone and contacted the surface, telling them what they saw and suspected. Soon, the overman, George Muise, was there with his safety lamp testing for gas. To test for gas, George turned down the flame in the safety lamp until it was just a slight blue glimmer, then slowly lifted the lamp to the roof of the cutoff. If methane was present, it would very slowly enter the filters of the safety lamp, and make the flame burn brighter. In this case, the blue glimmer grew to a slightly brighter flame, and George slowly lowered the safety lamp. He found the cutoff was full of methane. They all knew then that Lawrence and Pat were dead, and had been for at least eight hours.

They had walked into a strong pocket of methane, perhaps continuing on for a few steps before they were overcome by the complete absence of oxygen, and peacefully collapsed. They had made it about 40 feet up the cutoff.

It is here that Peter and Sylvester remember the event differently, and we can understand, because it has been 47 years. Peter remembers that more miners gathered at the scene and formed a "life line" to reach Lawrence and Pat. A life line has a miner lying flat on his stomach, and squirming up to Lawrence and Pat, while another miner, also lying on his stomach, grasps the ankles of the first guy, then another grasps his ankles, and so on. Since methane is lighter than air and rises to the roof, the miners are able to breathe the fresh air that is close to the bottom of the cutoff. Peter remembers that this is the way they retrieved both bodies. Peter also remembers that there was a new guy there for his very first shift in the pit. When he saw what happened to Lawrence and Pat, he went home and never came back.

Sylvester remembers that they simply held their breath and went the short distance to the bodies without breathing at all, quickly pulling the dead men back down to the level.

Whatever the method, both bodies were successfully retrieved, and the pit knocked off as it usually does when there has been a fatality.

The old saying has it that "What you don't know won't hurt you." I don't know how this ever gained popularity, because it is precisely what we don't know that will usually hurt us. Lawrence and Pat did not know that there had been a huge fall of stone in the cutoff just a little above where they had gone to shut off that valve. No one would know about this, because no one before them had any reason to go up that cutoff. A "deputy" is supposed to travel every section of the mine every 24 hours, leaving his signature in chalk at certain stations, but the stone could have easily fallen after the deputy passed through the cutoff on his rounds through the rest of his section. This fall of stone had blocked the airflow into and through the cutoff, allowing a pocket of methane gas to collect below the fall. It was into this pocket of methane that Lawrence and Pat had walked.

Tommy Tighe, another member of the Men of the Deeps choir, was an official at the time. He was given the job of getting enough men down to clean up the fall. He remembers that he and the crew that were cleaning up the fall were not allowed to go down the mine on the riding rake, but had to walk down to the scene, constantly testing for methane on their way down. Once there, they set up "brattice"—a canvas-like fabric that directed fresh air up the cutoff. Then, after testing for methane at the site, they worked on the fall. Tommy said that they had to do this for two days before they could again ride the rake down in the usual manner. Lawrence and Pat died on a Thursday. It was Monday before the pit started producing again.

It takes courage to go down in the mine depending only upon a safety lamp to detect deadly methane gas, and much is made of coal miners' courage in facing dangers, but a word has to be said about the heroism of coal miners' wives. An argument can be made that it is easier to die than to live, when the death is as gentle and peaceful as it was for Lawrence and Pat. Margaret (MacDougall), was Lawrence's wife, and Rita (MacMullin), from New Aberdeen, was Pat's wife. After getting the shocking news of their husbands' deaths, and feeling their lives collapse around them, these women had to stagger to their feet and continue to live on, each with four small children. Margaret has since died, and Rita has moved west, but after losing their husbands they courageously carried on alone, facing financial and emotional hardship.

Helen Nearing, Pat's sister, remembers that day quite well. She now lives in Hudson House on Hudson Street in New Waterford. At the time of the accident, she was working at the town hall in Glace Bay. She knew nothing of her brother Pat's death before she went to work, but remembers that once at work, everyone was looking at her, making her uneasy without knowing why. Finally, Mary Hawley, who also worked at the town hall, came over to her. Helen asked, "Mary, is there something wrong?" Mary said: "I have bad news and it concerns you, Helen." Right away, Helen asked, "Pat! Is he badly hurt, Mary?" Mary said, "I'm afraid, Helen, he's dead." Helen said that she can't remember what happened after that. Bruce Sterns, who also worked at the office, drove her home. She remembers that she and her sister later went to New Waterford to visit Lawrence's wife Margaret. Helen said that Margaret was very sad.

Lawrence Farrell was a man of slight build, soft-spoken with a sense of humour. In the coal mine, he worked mostly around the levels, probably as a pipefitter. He and Margaret lived on Ellsworth Avenue in New Waterford across from the Anglican church. He was 33 when he died. Their four children have scattered throughout the country, no doubt remembering their coal mining roots in New Waterford, but no longer a part of it.

Pat Gaul's sister Helen said that Pat and Rita had a lovely home on Alexander Street in Glace Bay. Besides being a coal miner, Pat had a blossoming fish business. He would buy fish from central distributor P. J. Cadegan, and sell them to stores in Sydney, Glace Bay and New Waterford. She says that "there wasn't a mean bone in his body."

Both Lawrence and Pat died as unsuspecting victims of methane gas in 18 Colliery. Tragic as this double death was, this would not be the last time 18 Colliery methane gas claimed two lives at once. About ten years later, in August of 1966, after 18 Colliery was closed and sealed, it would be Diz and Buddy Bars Tighe. Once again methane would be silent, invisible and gentle, but once again it would kill.

Diz Tighe and Buddy Bars Tighe

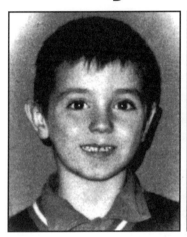 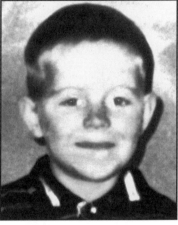

DIZ WAS SIX YEARS OLD, AND BUDDY BARS
WAS EIGHT. No, that is not a typo—their ages were
six and eight. They were not working in a coal mine:
they were playing in one.

Old 17 Colliery was started in 1865 and closed
in 1921, but in 1948 a slope was driven from inside
18 Colliery into 17 Colliery to retrieve what coal
was left there. The surface slopes of both collieries
were less than a mile apart as the crow flies, but
underground, the workings of both collieries were
much closer together. Once all the available coal
was taken from 17 Colliery, 18 Colliery went about
its own business, but the underground connection
between the two collieries remained. Started in

1937, 18 Colliery finished early in 1966. When it was finished, both of its slopes and the airway were sealed. This was a normal procedure, and nothing was thought about it.

However, the sealing of 18 Colliery prevented any gas from escaping, forcing it over into old 17 Colliery and up into its slope, which was also sealed. In 1966, the slope of old 17 Colliery had been sealed for over 40 years, but this seal was about 100 feet below the surface. After such a long time, its dependability was in question, so it was sealed again in the 1960s—this time right at the surface. As an added safety measure, earth was bulldozed over the slope entrance. What no one suspected was that under new pressure from the recently sealed 18 Colliery, gas had pushed past the 40-year-old seal in the slope of 17 Colliery, and had accumulated between that seal and the new one on the surface—a space of about 100 feet. Dangerous and deadly gas was now only a few feet below the bulldozed mound covering the opening of old 17 Colliery slope.

Seasoned miners and mining engineers had no reason to ever give this a second thought. How could six- and eight-year-old Diz and Buddy Bars ever know about it? For them, the business of sealing off 18 Colliery would be no more than a few days of entertainment as the children watched the men and machines seal the slopes and airway. Then they would return to play around old 17 Colliery slope as they and kids in the neighbourhood had for years, oblivious now to any new underground changes made by the sealing of 18 Colliery.

Diz and Buddy Bars were first cousins, and inseparable friends. Diz's given name was John, and Buddy Bars' name was Danny. They had both lived at the settlement at New Waterford Lake, but Diz's parents, Dempsey and Lila Tighe, bought a new home on the New Waterford-Sydney highway, a few hundred feet on the Sydney side of old 17 Colliery shaft, and on the opposite side of the road. Buddy Bars stayed with his parents, Wallace and Joyce Tighe, at the Lake. Even though the homes were now about a mile apart, the two boys remained inseparable, travelling back and forth between the two homes, eating and sleeping at whichever one was most convenient at the time.

The two kids were a common sight in the neighbourhood. They would "make their rounds," looking for whatever would fuel their interest and excitement. Buddy Bars was a youngster who was extra smart for his age. He was friendly with grownups, and grownups were friendly with him. Everybody loved him. Even the police would stop to talk to Buddy Bars, sometimes driving him and Diz home from town—a distance of about three miles. Diz and Buddy Bars, like most youngsters, were both looking for adventure, and if the circus was in town, no one would have to wonder where Diz and Buddy Bars were. They would be right in the middle of everything, enjoying it all.

It was August 12, 1966, when Diz and Buddy Bars started what should have been a routine day. It turned out to be as far from routine as any day could possibly get. Diz left his home on the highway and walked out to the Lake to meet Buddy Bars, then the two of them came back out to Diz's highway neighbourhood. They tried to pressure the milkman to let them ride with him on the milk run, probably offering to help deliver the milk, but that didn't work, since the milk company had a "no riders" policy for all its drivers. To ease their disappointment a little, the milkman gave them some money to go buy candy at Brown's store. Buddy Bars would probably have bought the source of his nickname, a Neilson's Buddy Bar—a chocolate candy with two small crispy crunch bars in the package.

No one knows for sure where they went after they left the candy store. One place they did visit was the dam across the road from the old 17 Colliery slope, where they picked some cattails from the bullrushes there. Certainly they would have explored anything else around that caught their interest. Eventually they found themselves at the slope area of old 17 Colliery, a popular spot with all the kids of the neighbourhood. No one feared for the kids' safety here, because the actual entrance to the shaft had been sealed; ironically, the job had been done by their own granduncle, Jack Tighe, councillor for the area. Jack had the shaft bulldozed in at the surface. But time and weather had opened a small hole at the crest of the mound of earth that sealed the slope. That small hole, and the curious and adventuresome spirit of the two young boys, were a bad mix. They saw that they could squirm through and have a look at a real coal mine, just like the one where their fathers worked.

They yielded to that temptation and crawled in, venturing down the old slope that was dimly lit by the daylight coming through the small hole they had crawled through. They went down about 25 or 30 feet, far enough so that they entered a pocket of gas pushed close to the surface by the sealing of 18 Colliery. They died quickly.

The front page of the *Cape Breton Post* suggests that it was methane that killed them, but others think it could have been hydrogen sulfide. It really doesn't matter. The lives of two young boys were snuffed out that day by whatever gas it was. They died so gently that they were still holding the treasured cattails they had picked from the bullrushes across the road.

No one was alarmed in the least when Diz did not return home for supper, since they took it for granted that he was having supper at Buddy Bars' house. Buddy Bars' family was not concerned either, since they thought that he was having supper at Diz's house. It wasn't until later that evening when Diz's older sister Brenda called Buddy Bars' place that they realized the boys had not been at either house.

The boys went missing on Thursday, and very serious searching began on Friday morning. There was no sign of them anywhere. By Saturday morning the families were alarmed. They called and looked everywhere they could think of, and notified the police. Hope was kept alive by reports that people saw the boys in town or the surrounding areas. Finally, on Saturday night, Jack Tighe, and a man they called "Pink" (George McNeil), Dempsey Tighe's brother-in-law, came to Diz's home. Diz's sister Brenda remembers them saying: "There is only one more place to look: in the old mine slope." Armed with flashlights, Jack, Pink, and Diz's father Dempsey walked over to the old 17 Colliery. They found the small opening at the crest of the mound of earth that sealed off the slope, and shone their flashlights into the darkness. What they saw made their hearts break. There, about 25 or 30 feet below the surface, were the bodies of Diz and Buddy Bars. They knew at once that they were too late. Indeed, if they had come within two or three minutes after the boys went into the slope, they would still have been too late. If it had been anyone else but coal miners that found them, the first impulse would have been to rush to the boys and try to help them, but brokenhearted as they were, these men knew better. Their first suspicion was gas. Had they hurried to the boys, it would have done no good—the boys had been dead since Thursday afternoon some time—and rushing in would only cost more lives. Even so, Jack and Pink had a hard time to keep Dempsey from going down the slope after his son.

News spread quickly that the boys had been found in the old mine slope. Late that night, or early Sunday morning, a priest came to Tommy Tighe's door and awakened him and his wife Polly with the bad news. Tommy is a first cousin to Dempsey, Diz's father. Tommy dressed quickly and went to the old mine slope. It was a very busy place by the time he got there. The RCMP, the town police, the firemen, and concerned neighbours were all there. The police had to control the traffic to keep it moving. Tommy remembers joining the others in restraining Dempsey; he still wanted to go into the slope after his son.

Tommy's first thought was to go a little way up the highway toward Sydney to get Mickey Baker's scuba gear and to try and go down with that, but that was too risky, since they were unfamiliar with scuba-diving equipment. Tommy reasoned that since it was a coal mine, and it was too late to save the boys now anyway, they would wait and use coal mining equipment. He called Johnny O'Brien, then the manager of 12 Colliery, and asked him to summon some draegermen to come and get the boys. There was no sense taking chances with anyone else's life. Two crews of draegermen soon arrived—five men to each crew. A backhoe enlarged the hole the boys had crawled through. Some of the draegermen geared up properly and went down the slope and brought the boys to the surface. It was about 4 o'clock Sunday morning.

The frantic search for Diz and Buddy Bars was over. Now the families and the community began to mourn. Diz and Buddy Bars were waked together at Diz's home, and their funeral was held at St. Joseph's Church on Tuesday. The tragedy happened 37 years ago, but every time a family member, relative or close friend drives by the old 17 Colliery slope, they remember: Diz and Buddy Bars ride with them in their memories at least part of the way to Sydney.

The same equipment used to reach dead or trapped miners was used to reach two young boys who were not working in the coal mine, but playing in it. The boys probably wanted to see what it would be like to work in the pit, looking forward to the day when they would be hired on as real, grownup coal miners. It was the dream of a lot of coal miners' sons.

Bobby Roper

IT WAS FEBRUARY 8, 1952—a cool, cloudy day
with a bit of snow on the ground, but Bobby Roper
did not have to worry about snow—he had no car.
Very few 18-year-old guys had a car in those days,
at least guys he knew. As a matter of fact, in the
coal mining town of New Waterford, not all that
many families had a car. If they did, chances are
that it would be secondhand, and would take all of
somebody's skill to keep it on the road. Money was
scarce and a family was fortunate if they had a son
or two who could also work in the coal mine and
help the coal miner father meet the bills.

Bobby had been working in 12 Colliery for about
a year now, and because of that his family was enjoying some extra income. Indeed, with a job now,
Bobby could look ahead to an independent life of

his own, because as soon as he found a girl that he liked, they could get married and start their own home.

As it was, however, Bobby had no steady girl friend just yet, and as he climbed aboard the 2 p.m. Scotchtown-to-New Waterford bus from his Daley Road home, he was thinking only that this was Friday, night shift, the last one of the week. The ever-welcome weekend was just around the corner. No doubt he was thinking of how best to spend Saturday and Sunday before he started work again on Monday day shift. Whatever plans he had, however, would be brutally cancelled. Another kind of future was already planned for him, waiting in the pit.

Bobby got off the bus and started the one-minute walk from Ellsworth Avenue to the 12 Colliery wash house. Over 200 other sons and fathers were arriving at the wash house around the same time, each with the "Thank God it's Friday" attitude. This made the Friday fellowship of miners much brighter. Talk was easy and happy, with plenty of play.

Bobby lowered his pit clothes by rope and pulley from the ceiling rafters where every miner's pit clothes were hung, and began to change from his street clothes to his dusty, dry, stiff and smelly working clothes. Once changed, he hoisted his street clothes to the rafters where his pit clothes used to be. Now he looked around for his buddy Hughie Gillis, or someone else he would spend a few minutes with before going down. If it were a warm summer day, they would put in a chew and go outside until the last rake went down at 3:45 p.m., chewing, spitting and talking. Now, however, in the February cold, they sat together in a not-too-busy spot in the wash house, talking the minutes away before boarding the last rake down.

Bobby and his buddy Hughie Gillis worked in the gob. They had the bottom 50-foot section on 21 West wall. The gob is the place in a coal mine where the coal used to be. Now, however, the coal had been replaced by man-made wooden chucks that helped hold up the roof. Chucks were two-and-one-half-foot-square, five-foot-high pillars built with hardwood blocks. Each section also had a ten-by-twenty-foot dummy wall, built with fallen stone. It also had six to ten timber scattered throughout the gob. Like the chucks, the dummy wall was placed there in an effort to hold up the roof while the supporting coal was being taken away. Once a section was mined out, the job of the gob worker—like Bobby and Hughie—was to take some of the roof-supporting chucks out, and build new ones closer to the coal face. In the space where these supports were removed, the roof was *supposed* to cave in—a method of controlling the fall of the roof, relieving the pressure from the coal face where the loaders would be working. This controlled cave-in was by far the most dangerous and dramatic aspect of coal mining. It was called "cutting the gob."

Bobby and his buddy Hughie had "drawn," or taken out, all the back line of chucks and built a row of new ones closer to the coal face. They were almost finished, and the shift was nearly over. All there was to do now was to cut the gob—that is, cut the five or six remaining timber in the empty gob, and let the roof cave in. Since Hughie was a big man and could not move easily in the limited space between the chucks, Bobby was the one who was to chop out these last timber and nimbly keep out of the way of the fall. He had all but one of them chopped so that they were bent—not really holding much weight. Now for the last remaining timber.

I should add here that I have personally worked with Bobby Roper. He is my brother-in-law. I have always said, and still say, that anyone who worked with Bobby had an easy shift, because Bobby did most of the work. He bulled at his work, not really stopping to check things out as carefully as he might, vigorously going at it and getting the job done. Perhaps an extra degree of caution could have saved the day for Bobby this February 8, 1952, at approximately 9 p.m., but no one can say for sure. The fact is that this last timber had to be cut, and Bobby attacked it in his usual manner: Get this job done!

Reaching out with one arm as far as he dared, Bobby took his first swing at the last timber and sank the axe into it. Unfortunately, and unusually, all it took this time was that one solid chop. The gob was just waiting to come in, and it did! With Bobby's head and shoulders still too far in the gob, the roof caved in with a violent and quick cave-in— so quick that Bobby could not get all the way back to the safety of the newly-built chucks. The roof caved in on his head. His feet, legs, and most of his body made it, but he could not get his head out in time. Tons of stone crushed his head. Bobby is alive today only because there was some "duff"—just a few deep inches of fine coal cuttings left by the mining machine that undercut the wall face—under Bobby's head. This duff served as a meagre cushion for his head. Bobby remembers the violent down-pounding power of the falling stone, and knew he was in a terrible accident. Then he lost consciousness.

His buddy Hughie saw the whole thing happen, and rushed to get the stone off Bobby's head. Panic-stricken, he tore at the stone with his bare hands. Hughie's size and strength were in Bobby's favour now, because he was able to move enough of the massive pieces of stone to free Bobby's head and shoulders. Once he pulled Bobby free, he hurried down the wall and out the level, frantically looking for somebody to help get Bobby out. This was the right thing to do, but that left Bobby completely alone, and completely in the dark, since his lamp and helmet were smashed, and still beneath the stone. Worse: it was so close to the end of the shift that everyone else had gone home—including the overman.

Out from under the stone now, Bobby regained consciousness, and tried to spit his chewing tobacco out of his mouth, but he could not spit. In order to spit, he had to partially close his lips and expel air between them. He couldn't partially close his bottom lip, however, because it wasn't there. It was folded down on one side of his chin like the corner of a handkerchief. He had to hang his head and let the chew fall, pushing it out with his tongue, along with most of his teeth and a full mouthful of blood and coal particles. Then he started to crawl down the wall, fading in and out of consciousness.

Not many people know the complete blackness of total darkness. There is absolutely nothing to give a hint of any surroundings no matter how close to the eye they may be. It was in this absolute, total darkness that Bobby crawled down the wall toward the level. Going by memory and feel, and with a terribly mangled and broken head, he crawled the 50 to 70 feet down the wall, feeling his way between the chucks. He made it to the level, and crawled onto the conveyor belt on the inside end of the Sydney Mines Loader. He remembers wanting to lie on the smooth conveyor belt, thinking that the rats would not get him so easily there.

It felt like Hughie was gone for a very long time. He was, and for good reason. He found the inside end of the level deserted, so he kept going out the mile-long 21 West level to the outside end, desperately looking for someone to help. Here the facts get foggy. Since Hughie is dead now, no one knows for sure what he did at the outside end of 21 West level. Most likely, he went to the phone and called for help. Whether he went in the above, and parallel, 20 West level looking for help, we will never know. The fact is, however, that loaders from 20 West wall, who were still down because they had taken on an extra section of coal, somehow got the news.

I spoke with Tom Hurley, one of those loaders. He said that they got the news that "some guys were buried on 21 West wall." Two, three or four of them went to 21 West wall, Tom Hurley being one of them. Max Baldwin was another, but he, too, is dead now, and neither Tom nor Bobby can remember who the others were.

They found Bobby at the inside of the Sydney Mines Loader where he had miraculously crawled. They put him on a stretcher, and started carrying him out. Tom remembers this as being one of the most tiring times he had in the pit. Already mostly spent from loading extra coal, he and another man stretcher-carried Bobby out the mile-long level. They had to walk bent over most of the way, since the level was not high enough to stand upright, and many times they would strike the sides (the ribs) of the level hurrying through the narrow spots. Finally, they got Bobby on the auxiliary deep rake. When that rake got to the top, they carried him through the transfer to the main deep that went to the surface. It is uncertain whether it was a trip—that is, a string of 15, three-ton coal-carrying boxcars on rails—or a man rake that took them to the surface. By the time they got him to the surface, it was between one and a half and two hours since Bobby was buried. He doesn't remember, but an ambulance was waiting, and he was whisked to the hospital.

Word spread quickly that Bobby Roper was buried in the gob, and that he was in very bad shape. His father Art and his younger brother Harry were summoned to the hospital, along with his aunt Liz Singer, and her husband Tom. Agnes, Bobby's first cousin and a nurse, was also called to the hospital. His sister Norma was at a dance at the Strand, but word got quickly to her there. When it did, many of her friends went with her to the hospital, offering to give blood.

Bobby remembers seeing them all there—but that's not all he saw. Bobby remembers seeing them all from an out-of-body experience. He can remember seeing himself on the operating table. Out in the hall, Dr. Chisholm was talking to his parents and relatives, telling them that he was dead, but that he was going back to check for sure. His sister Norma remembers the same incident, her father saying in response to Dr. Chisholm: "No, he is not dead. Go back in there and check." About this time, Bobby remembers his elevating body as close to the operating room ceiling. His out-of-body "shoulder" touching the ceiling, and then he returned to his body. They would not take Beck, his mother, to see him until a day or so later when they were more hopeful that he was going to live. When she did see him, Beck remembers that his head looked like a "black and blue football." She doesn't say much else about the accident; she did not know whether her son was going to live or die. When her husband did not want her to see their son, she knew it was serious.

For eleven days and nights, Bobby had special nurses attending him. Thirteen days after the accident, he left the hospital for home. Once he was able to travel, he went to Halifax for reconstructive surgery on his head. He had seven skull fractures, nine teeth gone, his upper jaw was broken, his left tear duct torn away, and his nose was like jelly. His face would be permanently disfigured because of the severely broken jaw. Over 40 years later, a dentist jokingly asked him: "Are you sure you can breathe?"

Bobby received $52 every two weeks while he was off on compensation. He received not a cent of pension for his damaged and disfigured head. He figures that the company didn't give a damn about him. He is right.

Eleven and one half months later, Bobby went back to work in the same place in 12 Colliery, the same job. He says he was terrified to cut the gob again, but he gradually got used to it. He spent three more years in the gob, then transferred to 18 Colliery, where he continued to work at the coal face. A few months before 18 Colliery closed in January of 1966, he went back to 12 Colliery, then to 26, then to Lingan, then back to 26 where he finished his mining days.

Bobby is retired now. He turned 70 on May 18 of 2003. He is still very active, and spends a lot of his time as an original member and soloist of the famous Men of the Deeps choir. Most people who talk to Bobby now don't know why he looks the way he does. Those of us who do know have long since taken his slightly disjointed head and scarred face for granted. He has since grown a beard and a belly, and is affectionately referred to as the "leprechaun" by his friends in the choir. It is a lighthearted joke, but there is irony in relating him to a character of spiritual folklore. Bobby really should have been dead in 1952.

Joe Kispal

JOE KISPAL WORKED IN ONTARIO for Massey Ferguson for about three years, but he didn't like it there, so he decided to come back home to live in New Waterford, Cape Breton. Since he had no education beyond high school, he figured there were only two worthwhile options for employment for a guy from New Waterford: the military or the coal mines. Joe planned to enlist in the Navy, but things did not go as planned. He was engaged at the time, and when he told his girl friend Donna that he was going to join the Navy, Donna took off her engagement ring and said, "Here, take this with you." Joe quickly reconsidered the Navy. Now there was only one option!

He put his name in the pit. This meant going to

12 Colliery office in New Waterford and telling Frank
Robertson, Superintendent Davey Morrison's secretary, that he was looking for work. In those days,
the coal mines were a going concern, so it wasn't
very long before Joe was leaving from 12 Colliery on
a bus with 30 or 40 others for the required medical
exam at the Sydney steel plant office.

He remembers feeling embarrassed on being told
to strip naked in a crowd of strangers, but he would
have to get used to that, since if he got hired on, he
would be doing this every day in the showers with a
hundred or more miners. For now, he and other naked bodies were processed by two doctors, not unlike a herd of sheep lined up for shearing. Joe was
in good shape. About two weeks later he was told to
start work in 16 Colliery, New Waterford. That was
August 1, 1950. Joe was 21.

Actually working in a mine was a totally new
experience. He had grown up in a coal mining society, but he had never been in a coal mine. He and a
few other new miners were put to work "cleaning
off" a wall. That is, they loaded what coal was left
in sections that had had no loaders that day. It was
hard pan-shovel work.

After a very short break-in period, Joe was put
in the gob with seasoned miner Eugene Roach. Their
job was to take out hardwood-block pillars and timber that had been erected after the coal was removed, and build them again closer to the coal face.
At first, Joe was put to work digging out the front,
bottom block of each of the block pillars, or "chucks"
that supported the roof. There could be 20 to 22 of
them. He wasn't allowed to knock the chucks down.
That was left to his more experienced buddy, Eu-

gene. It wasn't long, however, before Joe caught on and was permitted to "draw," or take down, the chucks himself. Rudy Olszoeviec, Joe's overman, praises Joe as being a very good worker. The gob, however, does not distinguish between good workers and bad ones. When it is ready to fall in, the roof falls.

It was April 16, 1956, on day shift. Joe and Eugene were well into their shift, building a dummy wall. That is a wall of stone from pavement to roof, about ten feet wide, and running at a 90-degree angle from the coal face. The dummy wall was started when coal extraction began in any section, so it would be as long as the level through which the coal was hauled—in this case, about three quarters of a mile. As each cut of coal was taken from the coal face, the gob workers would build another section onto this dummy wall. If you could look down from the surface, and could see through to the uncovered coal mine, it would look like a huge "E" with ten fingers on the "E" instead of three—a three-quarters-of-a-mile "finger" for each of the ten, 50-foot gob sections along the wall.

Eugene and Joe had the third gob section from the bottom. Both of them were recognized as good gob workers. The gob had not come in for three days now, leaving a highly dangerous amount of unsupported roof beside which they had to work. This made even a small fall of stone more likely now because of the increased weight on the roof close to their working area.

Rudy Olszoeviec, the overman for the wall on which Eugene and Joe were working, remembers mentioning to them to be extra careful, because the gob could come in at any time now—then he continued on up the wall. Rudy says that he was no farther than three sections above Eugene and Joe's section when word came to him that he was wanted below—a man was hurt. It was Joe.

Joe had been busy trying to fill in the dummy wall, and since their gob had not come in for three shifts now, he was busier than usual, because there was very little loose stone to shovel into the dummy wall to fill it to the roof. Joe was not foolish enough to go in under the unsupported gob back to where the loose stone was, so he was looking for anything he could find to throw into the dummy wall. He eyed an extra long cap piece on top of a supporting timber. When a timber is put up to support the roof, a cap piece is put on top of it to increase its support. The timber and cap piece look like the letter "T." The cap piece is usually about two and a half feet long, but this cap piece Joe had his eye on was about the length of a full six-foot timber. The pressure of the timber against the center of the cap piece had the cap piece bent in the shape of an inverted "V." Like a small, dry branch which we have stomped on would bend up at both ends, so this cap piece had its ends bent down from the center of it where the timber "stomped" on it. The bent cap piece therefore was not touching the roof, so it was not supporting anything.

Also, the cap piece was badly broken right at the top of the timber, because the timber had it very narrow where it was squeezing it to the roof. Joe yanked down on one end of the cap piece, breaking it more. All that was needed now was a chop with the axe, and Joe would have half of the cap piece as more fill for the dummy wall. He swung the axe to cut the last few splinters off. He didn't have to swing the axe again.

It wasn't the whole gob, but one brutally big piece of stone fell, snapping the cap piece off right next to the timber where Joe had hit it with the axe. The stone drove Joe's head down onto the pavement, crushing his skull. The overman Rudy says that the only thing that saved Joe from instant death was a smaller piece of stone, about seven inches thick, that was already on the pavement. Joe's head was driven beside this stone. This smaller stone stopped the stone that hit Joe, supporting it and preventing it from completely crushing Joe's head.

Joe does not remember anything about the accident. Indeed, he doesn't even remember going to work that day.

Joe's buddy Eugene, and Lenny Ryan, a pipefitter who happened to be right there, moved the killer stone off of Joe's head. Miraculously, Joe stood up, but there was blood coming from his ears, nose and mouth. Lenny tried to bend Joe over his knee, lowering his head so the blood would clot, but Joe began choking, so they straightened him up again, applying pressure to the bleeding. The overman Rudy was there now, telling Joe to spit the chew of tobacco out of his mouth, but there was no chew of tobacco, it was all blood that was choking him. Later, it was found out that Joe was also bleeding spinal fluid. When the bleeding stopped, Joe passed out. Working in Joe's favour was the fact that they had got a stretcher to him right away, and he was quickly on his way to the surface.

However, he was very seriously injured.

Spike Gillis knocked on the door of Joe's home on lower Emerald Street. Donna answered the knock with eight-month-old Debbie in her arms. Spike said, "Donna, Joe has been hurt in the pit. You had better come to the hospital"—but it did not really sink in for Donna. Her first thought was that it was an arm or leg injury, and she would wait until they sent Joe home, so she told Spike she couldn't go right then because she was busy with the baby. Spike said, "Oh no, Donna, Joe has very serious head injuries, you had better come now." Donna left Debbie with her mother-in-law, and went with Spike to the hospital.

When she saw Joe, she realized that the stakes were high. Joe's head was horribly swollen and discoloured. They did not expect him to live. They respectfully left Donna alone with Joe for a few minutes, telling her not to give him anything to drink, but Joe was hallucinating for the orange pop they had home in the fridge, and begging for a drink. When the nurses left, he told Donna, "They won't give me any, but I know you will." Donna couldn't refuse him, so she gave him two spoonfuls of water. When she did, Joe started throwing up and bleeding again from his nose and ears. The nurses rushed back in and gave Donna a bit of hell for giving Joe water.

Joe was in the New Waterford hospital only for a few hours. Dr. MacMaster told Donna they were flying him to Halifax, but he said: "I might as well tell you, there is not a hope in hell that he will make it to the Sydney airport"—about 15 miles away. Dr. MacMaster went with him to Halifax, and Joe made it all the way.

In Halifax, Joe regained consciousness briefly.

He remembers a priest putting oil on his forehead, anointing him for death. The priest said: "You are going to be all right, my son." Joe was barely conscious, but he noticed a dead body beside him. Even injured as badly as he was, that made him uneasy. The dead body was beside him for a good reason. There were a lot of dead bodies there. After the Halifax medical staff had checked him out, they had decided that there was no hope for him, so they had put him in the morgue! The priest must have reported some sign of life to the medical staff, because when Joe regained consciousness again, he was in a regular hospital room.

Joe's father had gone with him to Halifax, and stayed a few days. When he came back home, Donna and Joe's sister Mary went up to see Joe. When Donna saw him, she despaired, feeling that Joe "was such a mess" that he could not possibly live. She could not recognize him. His head "was three times its normal size," and was "black, blue, orange and yellow." Donna and Mary stayed for a few days, but saw no change in Joe. After Donna went home, she received daily telephone calls from a friend in Halifax telling her about Joe. He was still not very good, but there was a " slight improvement" day by day.

Joe beat the odds! After three months in Halifax, he returned home. One shoulder was lower than the other, he had no hearing in his right ear, his left eye was out of alignment, and he had lost his sense of balance, walking like a man who was drunk. He still has those symptoms to this day, almost 50 years later. Joe and Donna had two more children, so he jokes, "Something was still working."

The accident did not kill Joe, but it took a lot of

life and happiness away from both him and Donna. Donna found that life with Joe was never the same after the accident. A lot of the time, she says, Joe is okay, but then he will have a "mood swing," and completely ignore Donna, as if he were semi-sedated and introspective. Dr. Roach says that there is nothing more that can be done for Joe. It is a problem with blood flow to his head. He told her, "You are going to have to live with this." There were times when Donna herself has asked for medical aid to help her cope.

Joe was on compensation for one and one half years. Then he was given a pension of $17.50 a month.

Tommy Tighe and Alan Tighe

TOMMY TIGHE SPENT 47 YEARS in the coal mine. He started at the New Waterford Lake power plant in 1942. When it closed two years later, he went to 18 Colliery, about half a mile from where he lived. His first job was on a "tugger"—a small winching machine, about twice the size of what we see on the front bumpers of 4 x 4 trucks today. He jokes that this made him an "engineer."

This was the beginning of a long career. Tommy immediately started studying to be an official in the coal mine—that is, a shotfirer, overman, underground manager, or manager of the mine. He had made it to overman in about a year, and was sup-

posed to go to the annual Mining Society confer-
ence held in Ingonish on July 7, 1954, because he
had won a prize for making the highest marks in
Nova Scotia on his exam for mine manager. An accident put those plans on hold.

It happened on his very first day as overman on
3 East wall in 18 Colliery. All the walls then were
using what were called shaker pans to convey the
coal from the wall face to the level below. Each pan
was seven feet long and about three feet wide. It
looked like a huge bread pan with sides but no ends,
the sides tilted outward, and made with a tapered
"step" in them for strength. About 20 to 25 of these
pans were bolted together to make one pan line.
There were three of these pan lines, in line, along
roughly 500 feet of wall. Engines, one to each pan
line, run by compressed air, would pull each pan
line up the wall about two feet, then push it down,
and jerk it quickly up again. The coal shoveled onto
the pan line would slide down the pan line, and kept
going down each time the pan line was jerked
quickly up. This moved the coal along.

As the coal was moved from the wall face, these
pan lines had to be dismantled and set up again
close to the face. This meant that the bolts that held
the pans together had to be removed, and the pans
"shifted" one at a time and bolted back together.
Work on this particular pan line on Tommy's first
day as overman was going well, until the bolt boy,
Corky (John) Barton, got to the drive pan—the one
to which the engine was connected. He could not
get the gob side bolt out. The gob side is the side
farthest from the coal face. Just then new overman
Tommy Tighe came along. Part of his job was to

make sure this pan line was shifted and ready for the coal shift.

He pitched right in to help Corky with the bolt problem. Since this was the drive pan, it was higher off the pavement than the rest of the pan line, so Tommy could crawl under it. He tried to reach the bolt from underneath. No doubt they would eventually have got the bolt out—but the bolt was no problem compared to the unsettled roof and wall problems where they were working.

The wall had already been undercut with the Sampson machine. This left a four-inch-high, five-foot-wide opening under the entire 500-foot length of the coal face. The roof was flaky right where Tommy was, so the coal face was not secured to it at all. Consequently, that portion of the wall detached from the roof, tipped into the four-inch opening under it, and rolled outward onto the drive pan under which Tommy had just crawled. This would be at least 20 tons of coal. The coal went right over the pan line and hurt the guys on the other side who were also working at the stubborn bolt—but it buried the pan line and Tommy.

The only thing that saved his life was the protection of the drive pan over him. His head and shoulders were under the pan, but the rest of him was exposed to the roll-out of coal. He suffered a double fractured pelvis, four fractured ribs, and a paralyzed bowel.

Tommy said that there was no real problem getting him out from under the coal—the problem was getting him out the level on the stretcher. They had to go over several coal boxes, since they had no room to walk beside them. Bad enough—but the stretcher would not stay locked, and kept collapsing! Its sides would go in and out like an accordion. He says he will never forget the pain.

Tommy survived. They offered him a choice of payment for his injuries: $2500 settlement, or $25 a month plus $300 retroactive. He took the $25-a-month pension with the $300. He speaks fondly of a beautiful secondhand Ford car over at Reserve costing exactly $300. He says that he couldn't get there fast enough. He and Polly bought it, and settled in with the $25-a-month pension.

Tommy describes the "cure" for his double fractured pelvis. He was on crutches, and off work for three months with his injury. During that time, he and some friends went to Prince Edward Island, and stopped on the way at a liquor store in New Glasgow. Tommy went in using his crutches, and remembers that he had to carefully lift each leg over a six-inch step to get inside. Apparently, this stepping exercise had a miraculous effect. He doesn't remember what liquor he bought, but he says he never used the crutches on the way out, or since. He says that the liquor store was like a shrine—like Ste. Anne de Beaupré in Quebec!

The accident happened in 18 Colliery, but that was only the beginning of Tommy's mining career. When 18 closed in 1965, he went to 20 Colliery until it closed in 1970. Then he went to 12 Colliery until the fire in 1973, when he started working in Lingan Colliery. Tommy spent most of his years since the accident as an overman, but after one year in Lingan, in 1974, he became underground manager on night shift—a welcome and well-deserved promotion.

He loved his work as underground manager, even though one of the frustrating things any manager had to deal with was the fact that the men would "run away"—that is, go home before the eighthour shift was up. If any man ran away, that man would have to make sure no one in upper management saw him. If Tommy happened to bump into a guy who had left his work early, Tommy was expected by higher management to "dock" that guy—take away part of his pay. "If the work was done," Tommy says, "I used to close one eye." And Tommy would always check with the overmen to be sure the work *was* done. He may have had one eye closed, but the other one was definitely open. No one was going to goof off and get away with it. For the most part, Tommy was well respected, and loved for his sense of humour. He got along well with the men.

After 40 years in the pit, Tommy went to get checked for silicosis. As could be expected, the report said: No. There was no silicosis. But Tommy knew better. Many a night when he went to sleep, his daughter and his wife Polly would have to sleep somewhere away from him because of the noise of his wheezing. Tommy went to a compensation lawyer, and the lawyer sent him to a Dr. Lundrigan, a doctor who, Tommy noted, "had 13 letters after his name." Tommy says that the doctor told him, "They tell you in Glace Bay that there is nothing wrong with your lungs? They will hear from me, and you will hear from me too." Tommy heard, all right—he got $3000 back-time compensation for silicosis, and a monthly pension. Tommy still wheezes a lot, and is supposed to spend at least 19 hours a day with oxygen piped to his nostrils from a machine he has in the house. He also has cartridges of oxygen to take with him when he travels.

His coal mining career left its marks on Tommy. He takes all this in stride, and still maintains his sense of humour.

There is another accident, however, from which Tommy never fully recovered, and never will. That is the accident that killed their son Alan on July 9, 1979, in Lingan pit.

They were at home on July 9—just another day. Tommy was underground manager on night shift at Lingan Colliery, so it was expected that he would be informed about happenings there, even when he was not on duty. It was day shift, but someone did call Tommy at home, telling him that a man had been killed at Lingan. Their son Alan worked at Lingan, so Tommy immediately began to check it out. He called the watchman at Lingan and asked him what he knew about it. The watchman said, "Where are you, Tommy?" Tommy said, "I'm home." The watchman said, "Oh yeah, okay." Then, he hung up. Tommy didn't like that. Something was wrong.

Shortly after that, John Williams called and asked, "Tommy, what's going on out at the mine? There's women crying and a lot of confusion." Tommy said, "I don't know, but hang up, and I'll call the lamp cabin." He called the lamp cabin, and his wife Polly heard him say, "Yes, this is Tommy—it's me— it's Tommy!" The voice on the other end of the phone said only, "You had better come out. There has been an accident, and you probably have to tour the mine."

Until now, nothing was said about Alan, but Polly

says that she "took the shakes, and got that sick that I didn't know what to do." Polly told Tommy to go, and to call her from the pit and "tell me it is not Alan."

As Tommy started on his way to the mine, Bernie Corbett met him and said: "Tommy, you had better not go." Then Tommy's sister Victoria came in the front door. When Polly saw the look on her face, she knew—it was Alan who was killed. Victoria cried out the dreaded news, hugged Polly, and they both cried. Then Fr. McNeil, Fr. Everett, and Dr. Lynk came to the house.

Alan, a mine electrician, was part of a crew that was having trouble with the Python Coal Conveyor that day. The Python could be as long as 500 feet, roughly three feet wide. It is a stationary conveyor, moving the coal by means of two parallel steel chains with steel crossbars between the chains every three or four feet. This conveyor chain drags the coal down the top of the Python, goes around the circular drive sprockets, and returns empty on the bottom of the Python. The Python would occasionally stick when it was filled to capacity. When that happened on this day, they had to send Alan up to the bank of Wallace Town Switches on the deep to set the power so that the Python could be reversed. They would run the Python in reverse for a while, and then Alan would have to reset the power to start the Python going the right way again. He had to repeat this power change several times that day, walking up the deep and back down again.

While Alan and his buddies were occupied with the Python, another couple of men were taking a material trip out of 2 East level, about 1000 feet above Alan. A material trip is a string of ten or more coal boxes filled with hardwood blocks and timber, instead of coal. This trip derailed while being pulled out of 2 East level and up the deep. They got it back on the road, but it is believed that the jolting from this derailment "popped a pin" partially out of the last full box of five-foot hardwood blocks. The boxes are connected by one-and-a-half-inch-round, foot-long steel pins, one through each hole in a strong "figure 8" coupling.

The sad part of it is that this pin was supposed to have a locking cotter pin in it, so that the pin could not accidentally be jolted out of the coupling. This time, through carelessness, the pin had no such cotter pin. The partially lifted pin went unnoticed until the trip was pulled up on the straight road and pointed down the deep—then it let go completely. Some say it was one box, and some say it was two or three. Some say it was a tram—a box with no sides on it—but it really doesn't matter. The box or tram, loaded with five-foot hardwood blocks, went by the run, hurling down the deep.

Precisely at this moment, and well below the runaway box, Alan had again reset the power to the Python, and was walking back down the deep. Due to the deafening noise of a circulating fan close to Alan, he was unable to hear anything behind him. By the time the box reached him, it was going at a terrific speed. It hit Alan and killed him instantly. Two other men below Alan were luckier, because they were not on the road, but they were close enough to get grazed by the wildly speeding box.

Carmen Hughes was hit on the hip and driven

to the roof, falling down in the middle of the road. He said the box was just a blur. His buddy, David Gardiner, was slightly grazed on the knees. Carmen needed stitches to close his hip wound, but David was just bruised. Some other guys escaped because they dove underneath the belt—another conveyor line that was parallel to, and beside, the road.

Some time after the accident, Alan's close buddy, another electrician, came to see Tommy and Polly. He said to them, "I am going to tell you something. You can believe it, or do what you want with it." He told them that the day Alan was killed, he was alone in his bedroom, sleeping in later than usual. He was off work with an injured foot. Sleeping soundly, he was awakened by someone touching him on the toe, and saying, "Get up, you have to get ready for work," or something like that. He lifted his head off the pillow and saw a person there, but he could not see the face. With his hands, the person was beckoning him to come, but at that moment he couldn't move.

After that unusual experience, he went downstairs and told his mother. She said not to tell anyone, because they would think he was crazy. Later on, he and his mother went to Sydney to get a pair of sandals for his injured foot. When they returned home, he got the news of Alan's death—and he realized that he had been wakened at exactly the same time as Alan had died!

To this day, when Tommy speaks of Alan, he will often say, "God love him—God love him."

Arch booming with wooden logs. Number 12 Colliery, 1952.

Danny MacDougall

BACK IN THE 1950s in New Waterford, the Strand—on the corner of Plummer Avenue and King Street—could truly be called a community centre. Along with bingos, meetings, and other social events, there was a dance at the Strand every Saturday night. It was at these dances that Danny MacDougall and Lillian MacDonald of Sydney Mines first became an item. Apparently, the distance between New Waterford and Sydney Mines—about a half hour drive one way—was not a problem for Danny and Lil. They spent enough time together to know that they wanted to stay together. They decided to get married.

Danny had spent a little while working with his father as a plumber. Then he got hired on at the Sydney steel plant in the plate mill. As hopeful as that was, it didn't last. The steel plant was having hard times; Danny got laid off. Not one to be idle for long, Danny applied for work in the coal mines in New Waterford, at either 16 Colliery, 18 Colliery, or 12 Colliery. The call came for him to start at 12 Colliery. It could have been in 1949 or 1950, because Danny and Lil bought a house on King Street, not far from the Strand, and on July 31, 1951, they got married. Danny was well established in the pit by then.

Danny's breaking-in period in the coal mine was spent working on the deeps and in the levels—greasing rollers, replacing them, cleaning road switches, fixing the signal wires, trying to keep the trips running smoothly. After a few weeks of that, he was promoted to the production shift on 17 West wall as general mechanic. Now, if anything went wrong with any of the three pan lines on the wall, or with the Sydney Mines Loader on the level, Danny would be called. He handled his new job well. But while working as mechanic in 17 West, Danny broke his ankle, shutting him down for about two months.

Shortly after his return to work Danny's mining career—and my own—went along the same path for a couple weeks. Two diesel mine locomotives had arrived at 12 Colliery machine shop, and four young miners were chosen to be broken in on their operation: Danny MacDougall, Hank Martin, Earl Watts, and me. One day the underground manager told us to stay on the surface. We all went over to the shop to see the new diesel mine locomotive. A representative from R. J. Logue, who sponsored the locomotives, was there to introduce us to the machines. What a welcome change from working underground!

It was like a vacation—even better, because we were getting paid to learn. We had two exciting and informative weeks on the surface, even travelling to Sydney for a few days to learn about diesel engines.

The "diesels," as they were soon called, were fifteen feet long, four feet five inches high, and four feet wide. They weighed fifteen tons and were powered by a five-cylinder, four-stroke Crossley diesel engine. Danny already loved his job in the coal mine but he reveled in this new adventure with the diesel locomotives, and eagerly learned every mechanical detail he could. A poet once looked lovingly at a tiny mole, and wrote words to the effect that "The creature has a purpose, and its eyes are bright with it." This would be a good way to describe Danny. He was ambitious, he was going to get ahead in life, and his eyes were bright with purpose. Looking back, I strongly suspect that Danny really appreciated this whole new movement in mine mechanization. The Dosco Miners were just on the horizon for 12 Colliery, and Danny was positioning himself for a job as operator on one of them.

I remember the day of his promotion to the Dosco Miner. I was on the diesel in 19 East, waiting to drive the men in to start the shift. Unknown to me, someone else had been appointed to my job, and I was sent to 17 West to take over Danny's job running the diesel there. Danny had already started his last shift on the diesel, and waited for me so he could haul a few trips with me on the front with him, and I could get the feel of that level. We had two trips together, Danny pointing out the bad joints, the grades, and the approach to the slant, an upgrade that turned a bit to the right, then hard to the left, and switched onto the main 17 West level. After the two trips, Danny went up the wall to begin his new job as one of the operators of the Dosco Miner. He held that job until October 26, 1956.

On that day, Danny was in town proudly showing off his two-year-old daughter Paula. She was a real charmer, and Danny loved her as much as any parent could. During this time with Paula, Danny met his younger brother Ray, and they talked about their plans to go rabbit hunting the next morning. Tommy (Tank) MacDonald was going with them, and they were looking forward to the trip. Then Danny took Paula home and got ready for work on the night shift.

About 2:30 that afternoon, he and Lil got in the car and drove to 12 Colliery. Danny went to the wash house to change into his pit clothes. Lil took the car back home so she could use it to go to night school sewing classes.

For some reason, the pit was shut down that day from regular production, and management planned to use the shutdown to "brush" 16½ East level, meaning that they would be taking out stone to make the level wider and higher. They were having a hard time getting coal boxes out that level, and empty boxes back in, because the levels in a coal mine just naturally try to squeeze back to solid stone like they were before the level was driven.

Steel arch rails were used to hold the roof and sides of the level in place, and they did that for a few months. However, these steel rails were no match for the relentless and powerful pressure exerted by the mass of stone around them. Consequently, a lot of the arch rails had been squeezed too close to the haulage road, and were being hit by the coal boxes and the diesels on their way in and out the level. These rails had to be removed. They had just this weekend to do it, so they "put a drive on" to get all the protruding arch rails out of the way. Usually, that meant taking a diesel to the problem arch rail, hooking one end of a steel cable to the rail, the other end to the diesel, and using the diesel to yank the rail out. With the pit down, more diesels than usual were free to attack the job. The steel rope, rail and diesel operation was the same, but instead of just one diesel, they had three or four diesels—each one pulling rails out at different spots along the level. Time was limited, and they had to get out as many rails as possible. Danny happened to be on the outside diesel, with two or three diesels working inside of him.

Danny and the men working with him had already yanked out a few bent arch rails. His buddies Henry Copan, Nooks Villa, and Melvin Quinn tied the steel cable to another bent rail, and hooked it to the diesel. On a flashing signal from the guys in front of the diesel—an up-and-down wave of a light—Danny started the diesel out to take up the slack, preparing for a strong, steady pull on the rail.

Some say that Danny was not paying enough attention, but it is more likely that the opposite is true—he was paying too much attention. He was intensely focused on what the guys were doing in front of his diesel, but his view of them was extremely limited. The level opening was almost the same width as the diesel. Consequently, he stood from his sitting position to try to see over the top of the diesel. From what he knew of the level, that was safe, since ninety percent of the level was arch railed and, although those rails were bent, there was still a bit of an arch at their peak. Danny used this space to try to peer over the diesel. What he did not know—and did not suspect—was that arch rails had previously been removed from this spot and a boom had been installed to take their place. A boom is a huge timber about 20 feet long and at least eight inches in diameter. This was propped across the top of the level to support the roof but, instead of being arched, the boom was flat across, which meant that there was very, very little room between the straight boom and the top of the diesel.

It was too late when Danny realized that it was not an arched rail behind him, but a boom, and that he did not have the clearance over the diesel that he thought he had. Much worse, he was half standing, trying to see over the top of his moving diesel. In this stooped, standing position, his head got caught between the boom and the diesel.

Henry Copan saw him first—Danny squeezed between the diesel and the boom. Thankfully, Henry knew the basics of how to operate a diesel; he leaped aboard and shifted the transmission into forward, opened the throttle, and moved the diesel in the level—but it was too late. Released, Danny fell back into the seat, fatally injured.

Word was sent in the level to overman Eddy Durdle, who hurried to the scene. There was not a thing that Eddy could do, except direct and oversee Danny's removal from the diesel, onto a stretcher, and on his way to the surface as quickly as possible. A priest, Fr. Hector McNeil, was summoned to come to the pit. Fr. McNeil went down the main deep, and speculation has it that he met Danny while he was being carried from the auxiliary deep across the transfer to the main deep, and there gave Danny the last rites. Those at the scene of the accident were sure that Danny died instantly, but the doctor told Danny's brother Ray that Danny died in the hospital. The priest had been in time.

Danny was 29 when he was killed.

It was around 8 p.m., and Lil had just returned home from night school with no hint that her peaceful, routine life was about to be shattered. Apparently, Fr. McNeil had come from the pit to Danny's parents' home, and alerted them to the accident. Danny's dad phoned Ray with the news, and Ray went immediately to the hospital. Fr. McNeil and Danny's mother went to see Lil, planning to take her to the hospital to see Danny. Lil immediately got ready to go to the hospital with them, but just then Danny's brother Ray came in telling them tearfully that there was no need to hurry. Ray said that Danny did not appear to be broken up that bad, but the doctor told him that Danny had died.

Lil did not see him until just before the wake at the funeral parlor. It just would not sink in to her that Danny was not coming home from his shift. It seemed like a terrible nightmare from which she was waiting to awaken. When she thought of going on alone without Danny, a terrible fear gripped her, but their little daughter Paula needed her and she would not let her down. Lil says that her parents in Sydney Mines, and Danny's large family, helped her a lot. As for Paula, her uncle Ray took over for

Danny, never replacing Danny, but filling in as much as he could. Paula has since grown up and married, and has two grown boys of her own, Steven Daniel and Robert Paul.

A lot of people hate the coal mine because of the injuries and death that it caused, but this hate would not be a proper memorial to men like Danny. He loved the coal mine and the job he was doing. It is no idle speculation to suggest that Danny would have been in high management office had he not been killed. Back in 1956, his brother Ray says that Danny had been approached, or was about to be approached, to accept the job as overman. Danny was on his way up, and his "eyes were bright" with his purpose.

Albert Chiasson

ALBERT CHIASSON and his wife Evelyn Maillet grew up in two of the most beautiful places in Cape Breton Island—Albert in Margaree and Evelyn in Cheticamp—about a 20-minute drive apart, but they didn't meet until they were both working in New Waterford. They were quickly bonded by their common country backgrounds, and began a lasting relationship.

Although the scenery was beautiful in young Albert's Margaree, the economic scene was not so bright. Jobs were scarce. He managed to find work in Baddeck, about an hour's drive from Margaree. He worked at milking cows for Fownes brothers' farm for a year or so—22 cows every morning and every evening. Then in 1943, his family moved from

Margaree to New Victoria, a small community just west of New Waterford, about one half mile from 18 Colliery.

Albert's uncle, J. J. Chiasson, had lived in the Glace Bay area (a section called Number 11), and then he moved to the New Waterford area and started a grocery store. Back in Margaree, Albert's dad Arsene heard from his brother J. J. that there was a good chance of employment in the coal mines in New Waterford, so Albert's dad decided to go for a piece of the action.

Albert was about 17 years old at the time—ready to stop milking cows and start work in the coal mine. Shortly after arriving in New Victoria, Albert and his dad went to 18 Colliery to see the manager, James R. MacNeil—better known simply as Jimmy R.—to check out the possibility of getting a job for Albert. Things turned out much easier than either of them expected. Jimmy R. asked who the young fellow was, and Arsene told him that this was his son Albert. Jimmy R. asked, "Does he want to work?" Arsene said, "Yes sir, that is why we are here." Jimmy R. said, "He can start tomorrow morning if he wants to." And that was the beginning of Albert's career as a coal miner.

Although he was big and strong, Albert was not assigned to any of the backbreaking labour that coal mining can be. He began as a chain runner on 2 West level. A chain runner is the person who hooks haulage ropes to the full and empty trips—in 18 Colliery that would be 11 three-ton boxes linked together. He then signals the haulage operator to move the trip in or out the level. When the boxes are filled and hauled to the outer end of the level, the chain runner takes the steel cable off the inside of the trip and puts another steel cable on the outside of the trip. This outside steel haulage rope will then take the full trip out to the deep and on its way to the surface.

Albert did this chain runner job for a while, and his luck with easier jobs held. Instead of being put on the coal face after his break-in period, he was given a job on the haulage itself—operating a "donkey." A donkey is a large drum with a half mile or so of steel rope coiled on it, the other end of the rope being hooked to the trip. The drum is driven by compressed air. The donkey pulls the empty trip in close to the coal face. There, another "spotter donkey" positions the trip under the loading chute where the boxes are filled with coal. Then the spotter donkey hauls the full trip back to the spare road (a siding) and leaves it there. Now the rope from the bigger haulage donkey is hooked to the full trip, and lets it run downgrade out the level to the landing. All the donkey runner has to do is to pull one lever to open a compressed-air valve and pull another one to operate the brake. Running donkey was considered an easy job! That is the second job that Albert Chiasson had. It sure beat milking 22 cows twice a day.

Albert was beginning to settle down to this life, but a general strike in 1947 put an end to his budding coal mining career. All the Cape Breton mines were shut down. Once again unemployed, Albert tried for relief payments, but did not qualify. They were giving relief payments only to the married men. It was back to the rural life again for Albert. He and some of his buddies went to work cutting in the Mira woods for a Joe MacDonald. Life must have been good there, because Albert stayed for quite a while. As a matter of fact, he stayed too long. The strike ended, and the mines were back in production, but Albert did not report to work soon enough. When he did report for work someone else had his job as donkey runner in 18 Colliery, and all the other jobs as well. There was no work available.

Once again, he tried to take up life in Margaree. On October 26, 1947, he and Evelyn went to Margaree and got married. Then he went to work in the woods again, and for a short while on the power line, but he got laid off again. He applied for unemployment insurance. Instead of receiving benefits, they told him that they were hiring on at the mines again, and that he should go there and apply. He did. Even though Albert had worked in 18 Colliery, he had to start all over again from the very beginning. This time it was not a matter of simply asking the manager for a job; instead, Albert went with a group of hopefuls to the Sydney steel plant office for the basic physical exam to see if he was fit to work underground.

Albert remembers a big guy from Main-a-Dieu, who desperately wanted a job in the mine, and wondered aloud to Albert if he would pass the exam. Albert spoke to him on his way out of the exam and asked how he did. The big guy was despondent, saying that they would not hire him. Albert was surprised, because the guy was so big and strong. He asked what happened, and the big guy said that they told him he had a cold in his back. Albert began to worry about his own chances after hearing that. He also remembers talking to a little guy who was afraid he was not heavy enough to get hired on, so he did what countless lighter guys had done before—put on big boots, and put in as much lead in them as would fit. The doctors, however, had long since caught on to this trick, so they made the little guy take off his boots before they weighed him. Albert didn't get the chance to see the little guy again, so he never found out whether he got hired or not.

Albert was the last guy examined that day. Apparently, things went well. About a month and a half later, he was called to start work again in 18 Colliery. As it turned out, however, it would have been much better if he had been turned down.

This time when he started working in the coal mine, Albert was given a job as "mucker" behind the Dosco Miner, or as the miners dubbed it, "the pig." Mucking was one of the hardest jobs in the pit, and it was also one of the lowest paid. As it cut a five-foot slice of coal off the 500-foot-long wall, the Dosco Miner left behind about a foot of duff (fine coal particles). That duff had to be shoveled off the pavement (bottom) and onto the pan line. Bad enough if it was only the dry, dusty duff that had to be shoveled. Making it far worse—this duff was soaked with the dust-depressing water sprayed on the coal as the Miner ripped it out. That made the duff more than twice as heavy, and sticky, sloppy— not unlike the difference between dry snow and wet snow. Worse yet: the duffers—two men—had to rush to keep up with the Dosco Miner. When that cutting machine was going good, duffing behind it was very hard work. It was this mess that earned the Dosco Miner the nickname "the pig." And Albert worked at this job until Friday, October 8, 1954.

Albert, Evelyn, and family had planned to spend that weekend back in their old neighbourhood in Cheticamp—a beautiful place on the Cabot Trail that they loved dearly. That happy weekend, however, would be a long time coming.

Albert was working his last shift on 2 West wall. The Dosco Miner had made its cut down the wall and, for whatever reason, Albert, Duncan MacKinnon, and Jamesie Tighe were walking beside the "drive" on the top of the wall. The drive was simply a huge drum roller turned by an electric motor. It powered the 500-foot belt line that conveyed the coal to the bottom of the wall. The empty belt came up the wall under the pans on which the belt rolled, turned around this drive drum, and went down the wall again—carrying coal with it when the Dosco Miner was cutting. The whole thing was not unlike a simple belt sander, only thousands of times larger. At this point in the shift, the Miner was through cutting coal, but the men were still using the belt line to convey material down the wall.

For some reason, the drive had lost a lot of oil, or someone had spilled oil when they filled the drive with it. Albert and Jamesie walked past the drive, stooped over. Albert stepped into the oil, slipped, and fell. No big deal if that were all there was to it. But there was an inspection plate about four inches wide and fifteen inches long, on the side of the drive. Someone had taken it off, and left it off! When Albert fell, he put his arm out to break his fall, and his outstretched hand went right into the opening left by the missing inspection plate. His hand went inside the drive, on top of the belt that was moving up the wall just at the point where it was going under and around the roller. Albert's hand went between the speeding roller and the belt, and was drawn with the belt around the roller. Albert was yanked into that mechanism, and stopped only when his body hit the inspection plate opening. He could not be yanked through that small opening—but his arm could. In an instant, Albert's arm was ripped from his shoulder and went around the roller.

The miners were horrified. For an instant, most of them didn't know what to do. But Malcolm (Malcie) McNeil immediately took off his shirt and stuffed it into the opening in Albert's shoulder. Then the men laid Albert down, made him as comfortable as possible, and sent for a doctor and a priest. No one thought Albert was going to live.

Albert did not pass out. He remembers when the doctor came. The doctor gave him a shot to "take him out of his misery," as he heard him telling the manager, Johnny (Moose) MacKenzie, who was quickly on the scene. Albert also remembers the doctor saying to someone that "he hasn't got much of a chance." Blood was everywhere. Albert's buddies were surprised to later find out that he could remember so much of what had gone on. When they got Albert to the surface, the ambulance was waiting, and he was taken quickly to the hospital. It was now about three o'clock in the afternoon.

Albert's brother Gus and his brother-in-law Louis Pat Bourgeois were supposed to take the bad news to Evelyn, but that plan was short-circuited by a neighbour who lived close by. Albert and Evelyn were now living on 12th Street, New Waterford, and had been since 1952. When the neighbour was on her way home, she noticed the ambulance at the hospital, and asked some questions. She was told that Albert had been in an accident. She was also told not to mention it to Evelyn, but she couldn't wait for word to get to Evelyn as officially planned. Evelyn had no close family around her for support when the neighbour went right to her house and told her the news. Evelyn said, "She came in and told me right there"—nodding her head to a spot in the kitchen.

Apparently, the woman gave her unofficial version to a lot of other people as well. The house soon filled with people. They all thought that Albert was dead, or soon would be. Evelyn huddled close to her three small children and worried about Albert, still not really knowing what had happened. Gus and Louis came with the official news, and arranged to take Evelyn to the hospital. By then, however, Albert had passed out. When she finally saw him, unconscious, full of coal dust and blood, she says she "almost fainted." She was told that Albert was not dead, but that he had a 50-50 chance to live. Evelyn signed the necessary papers to allow the doctors to operate, and waited.

Albert did live, and is alive and well to this day. There was some muscle left hanging where his arm was, and the doctors used that to fill the hole left by his missing arm. He suffered a lot of pain, but he began healing quickly. Every two weeks, he was paid $36 compensation, and he had to report regularly to Dr. Lynch, the company's compensation doctor. In 1955, two weeks short of a year since the accident, Dr. Lynch told Albert that he had been on compensation too long, and he would have to return to work.

Albert reported for work to Danny Murray, then manager of 18 Colliery. Danny told him he could not yet go back to work. He first had to go to Halifax to be fitted with a shoulder that would help restore his balance. Albert asked, "Why did Dr. Lynch tell me to go back to work?" He was told that Dr. Lynch was a company doctor, and a "hard man to get along with." Following the manager's instructions, Albert went to Halifax and was fitted with a shoulder. He was told not to return to work until he was sure the shoulder was fitting okay.

Just about a year after losing his arm, Albert went back to work in the coal mine. After his compensation stopped, they offered Albert a lump sum of $10,000 for his arm, or $119-a-month pension. Dr. Lynch suggested that Albert take the $10,000 and start a business for himself. Albert asked, "What if the business fails?" Dr. Lynch told him, "Well, that would be your own hard luck." Albert took the pension—and went back to the pit.

They gave him jobs he could easily do with one arm, like his old job on the donkey. Albert tells a story about the time he was on the "spotting" donkey—a donkey that moves the boxes under the coal chute half a box at a time until each box is filled, then moves to the first half of the next box, and so on. Albert would be busy starting and stopping the donkey about 35 or 40 times while the entire trip was being loaded. His one arm had all it could do. During this time, the phone was ringing beside him, but he could not pick it up because he needed his arm to work the donkey. After the trip was loaded and Albert had hauled it to the spare road, he stopped the donkey, just as the brand new underground manager stood scowling beside him. Apparently, the manager had been trying to get Albert on the phone, but could not, so, mad as hell, he had to walk in to get the information he wanted. The underground manager asked, "Is that phone working—does it ring?" Albert said, "Yes, sir." "Then why don't you answer the damn thing!?" Albert, knowing that this fellow did not know his situation, stood up, stretched out his one arm, and asked, "What do you want me to do, sir, answer the phone or run the donkey?" At that, the underground manager shut up and kept on going, angrier than ever.

They retrieved Albert's arm from the scene of the accident, and buried it in the Mount Carmel graveyard. Albert said that he felt very sad about his arm, that it was a lot like losing a loved one. For a while after the accident he felt "down," but he says that the staff at Camp Hill Hospital in Halifax helped him through that. He has long since accepted his loss, but says that he can still feel his arm. "On some rainy days," he says, "I can actually feel blood running from my fingertips." He is speaking of his left arm—the one that he lost fifty years ago. He still feels it there, with his hand resting on his stomach.

Albert proudly showed me how he can still roll up his shirt sleeve with his one arm, and also how he cuts his own fingernails! I will leave it to the reader to figure that out.

James (Jamie) Proctor

JAMIE PROCTOR WAS BORN March 3, 1944. He grew up in Glace Bay in a family of 12 children—six boys and six girls. His father was a coal miner for 47 years—more than long enough to get "black lung," and eventually die from it. Most of his family moved away when they were old enough, but Jamie wanted to stay home and work in the pit. He remembers his father telling him not to go in the pit because "it will tear you apart, and you will be an old man before your time." Jamie's response was, "You work in the pit, and you are still here, why can't I do the same?" His father realized there would be no way he would be able to talk Jamie out of it, so he gave up, telling Jamie to do whatever he wanted.

Jamie's pit plans, however, would have to wait, because they were not hiring on at the mines. He followed other family members and went to Ontario, looking for work. He was hired on at a factory and stayed there for a while, but he didn't like it and he came back home. There were no jobs at the pits, so he went to Prince Edward Island and worked on a farm. When that was over he came back to Glace Bay, and this time they *were* hiring on. Jamie says, "I jumped in the mine."

He started in 26 Colliery in 1966, and he says that he loved it. He was supposed to start on a Monday, but he was so anxious to start that he went out on "spec" the preceding Saturday.

In those days, getting a "shift" was different in 26 Colliery from what it was in the New Waterford collieries. In New Waterford, miners went into the wash house before the shift they wanted to be on and, if they had no steady place, they asked an overman for a "shift." Once they got the okay from the overman that they had work, *then* they changed into their pit clothes and went down to the place of work assigned by the overman. In 26 Colliery, however, the miners changed into their pit clothes as soon as they came into the wash house, then they went down a 700-foot shaft to a Waiting Head area at the bottom of the shaft. Here they waited for the overmen, and each overman would pick the men he wanted. The men selected would travel the motor road to their assigned workplace. Any man not picked for a shift would have to go back up, shower, change into street clothes, and go home.

Jamie got picked for work on his very first day. Probably the fact that it was Saturday helped, since there would be less men out on the weekend. His job that day was to help move the Sydney Mines Loader in the level to a new spillage point closer to the wall face. The Sydney Mines Loader was a 100- to 150-foot conveyor belt mounted on small rails. Each time the coal was taken off the wall face, it got farther from the Sydney Mines Loader, so 15 or 20 feet of new rails would be laid in front of the Loader, and it would be pulled in the level on these rails, closer to the coal. The rails behind the Loader would be taken up then, and used again in front of it the next time it was pulled in closer. This was a good and easy break-in shift for Jamie.

He had other, more labour-intensive jobs later on, like in the gob, or mucking at the face, and he must have been a good worker at these jobs, because he was only in the pit three months when he was put with the brushers at the inside end of the level. When he started with them, he wasn't yet a brusher, but he did the same work as they did and, what is more important, he was in line to fill in as a brusher when one of them was off.

Jamie was on what was called the "overthrow." The brushers were responsible for removing the overhead stone at the very end of the level after the coal had been removed from under it. They shot this stone down, and used it to build a roof-supporting "pack" at the side of the level and part way down the wall. This pack would be about six feet wide, reaching 17 feet down the wall. Once this pack was filled with the stone that had been shot down, there would be some stone left over. This was the "overthrow," and it was Jamie's job to get rid of this by shoveling it down the wall beyond the 17-foot point.

Aside from putting up the arch rails, Jamie worked just as hard as the brushers, but he could not go home when his work was done because he was not on contract like they were. When the amount of stone contracted to them was loaded, and the rails were put up, the brushers went home. Jamie had to stay for his eight hours, even though his work was also finished. This "overthrow" position did not last long, because one of the brushers retired and Jamie took his place. Jamie was now a brusher, and stayed as one for 26 years.

Although he could go home when the brushing was finished, he stayed down for extra shifts on straight time. He didn't have to wait at the bottom of the shaft to get picked by an overman. He was such an energetic worker that the overmen were glad to have him, and assigned him his extra shift without even seeing him. Jamie worked 13 and 14 shifts every week, and says that he once worked four straight shifts without coming to the surface: two shifts mucking behind the continuous miner, and two shifts timbering behind it—by no means easy shifts! Even yet, at 59 and with only one arm, Jamie is in exceptionally good shape. He did some boxing at one time, and worked two shifts in the mine before going into the ring that same day. He did not do as well as he wanted, getting pounded by a boxer who is now in the Hall of Fame—but what he did gives an idea of the good shape he was in.

Jamie was a brusher when he lost his right arm, but that was not the job he was doing. Jamie was part of a crew that was driving a new level. As a brusher, he had helped drive a new level in 200 feet or so, but had to stop when they needed to extend the conveyor closer to the inside end of the new level. They were getting ready to drive a new wall off this level, but they could not continue because they had run out of pans—they could not extend the Python chain conveyor any further in. Consequently, they had to remove this Python conveyor, and set up a belt conveyor, one they could extend in as far as they wanted. This meant that there would be no more driving the level by the brushers until this longer conveyor was installed. So Jamie, instead of brushing, was part of the crew that was installing the belt conveyor.

The drive for this belt conveyor had been partially set up at the outside end of the level—next to the deep. There was no cover, no brake, and no switch on the thing yet. It was just hanging from the arch rails by four chains, and the belt had been threaded through it, but was still very slack—so slack that the drive wasn't touching it with enough friction to move the belt. That really didn't matter to Jamie and his crew. They were not there to take up slack in the belt, but to install a straight road rail vertically from the pavement to the arch rails above, so that the partially installed belt drive could be solidly anchored. This is what they were doing, and getting along quite well. When they stopped for lunch, someone who was concerned with the slack in the belt came to check things out. They wondered which way the drive was turning—reverse or forward— and decided to put the power on the drive to see.

At that point, there was no on/off switch hooked up to the drive. The drive was wired, and the power to it was shut off at the main switch about 50 feet away. Someone went to the main switch and turned the power on, starting the drive; but they still could not see which way the belt was moving, because there was too much slack in it for the drive to move it at all. Jamie's buddies were standing there looking at it, and Jamie was sitting a few feet away eating an orange. Since nobody was doing anything, Jamie decided to get up and see if he could do something to help. He never finished the orange.

Jamie saw a loop of slack on the top side of the belt and thought that if he just pushed down on that, it would touch the roller and the belt would move. He was absolutely right! It moved—and moved so fast that it took his hand into the feed roller and lifted him right off the pavement. With his left arm, he grabbed one of the chains that were holding up the drive and tried to pull his right arm out of the drive. It came out some, but the drive took it back in again. He pulled it out a bit again, but the drive took it back. Jamie fell off the belt, but never touched the pavement—his mangled arm held him from falling. To make matters worse, the slack belt fed itself into the drive, doubling itself on the drive rollers, and chewing up Jamie's arm. The third time he pulled his arm out, the drive did not pull it back, because there was no arm there to pull—he had lost it. All he could see was a white cord that had been part of his arm.

A lot of people would have passed out, but Jamie did not. When his arm no longer held him on the belt, Jamie stood up. He knew what had happened and what he had to do. He had a first aid package on him, and with his left arm, quickly took out a roll of cloth to make a tourniquet. He put the tourniquet around one side of the stump still attached to his right shoulder, and went to wrap it all the way around, but it fell to the pavement. He was afraid to bend over to pick it up because he thought he would faint. He grabbed one of his buddies with his left arm, and shouted to him to pick up the tourniquet and tie it around his arm, but his buddy was panicking, saying to Jamie, "Go away—go away!" Jamie would not let him go, pleading, coaxing, trying to convince him that he had to pick up the tourniquet and tie it around the stump of his arm, or Jamie would bleed to death. Finally, the miner did that, and started to walk Jamie the 30 or 40 feet out the level to the deep. His other two buddies had also panicked and run away, but one of them recovered and came running back to Jamie, bumping into him. Jamie got him to press his hands where he was bleeding the most, so some of the bleeding could be stopped. Then they started to take Jamie to the surface.

By now the underground manager had arrived at the scene with the first aid guy. They were looking for a stretcher, but Jamie said, "Just get me out of here as fast as you can. Never mind the stretcher—I'll get in a box." Jamie asked for something to kill the pain, but the first aid guy just gave him a roll of bandage to bite on. Jamie bit right through it and spat half of it out. Jamie remembers being confused by the fact that the hand on his missing arm was paining terribly!

Jamie met the doctor halfway out of the coal mine on the motor road. He pressed the doctor with two requests. One: "Am I going to live?" The doctor checked him a bit and said, "Yes, you are going to make it." Then Jamie asked for something to knock him out, because the pain was so hard to bear. The doctor gave him a needle, but would not knock him out, because Jamie had lost so much blood. It was 2:35 a.m. on back shift when Jamie lost his arm—it was 4:35 a.m. when he was admitted to St. Joseph's Hospital in Glace Bay.

At 6:30 a.m., the hospital called Jamie's wife Barbara to tell her that Jamie was there with serious injury. From what she was told, she didn't know if Jamie was going to live or die. She went to the hospital immediately, and when she saw Jamie he was in such a state that she still didn't know if he would live or die. She held a cool, wet cloth on Jamie's brow, hoping desperately that he was going to be all right. The doctor told her the same thing that he had told Jamie—that Jamie was going to make it. She took some comfort from this, but stuck right with Jamie, tearfully voicing her urgent wishes that Jamie get the best medical help possible. He did, and he did make it. That was April 26, 1980.

Very early that same morning, before day shift was to begin, my brother-in-law Bobby Roper received a phone call from the pit, saying that he was wanted out to work. Bobby had been one of the mechanics setting up that belt drive, and they wanted him out now to retrieve Jamie's arm. Bobby can't remember who it was, but one other guy was sent with him. When they got down to the drive, it was jammed solid with the slack belt that had fed itself into the rollers, and they had to cut the belt at least nine times and pull it out piece by piece. It took the two of them over four hours to get to Jamie's arm, and when they did, it was still in the sleeve of his jacket. But Bobby said it was more like a grease spot than an arm. They put the arm in a clean stone dust bag, and took it to the surface.

When Jamie lost his arm, the company was going to give him the "world"—easy job, no worries—it seemed that they couldn't do enough for him. A year or so later they told him that he had to go back to work, because he could not stay on compensation forever. That suited Jamie fine, but when he reported for work, they had no light-duty job for him. Financially, things started to get serious. On compensation, he was receiving 75 percent of his wages, but they stopped that, and replaced it with a $400-a-month pension for the loss of his arm. His house payment was $500 a month! Jamie had to get work somewhere, so he went temporarily with the Town of Glace Bay on a garbage truck. When that work ran out, the unemployment payments were far below what they would have been for an unemployed coal miner. Jamie was an unemployed miner, not an unemployed civic worker, so he wanted the same income as any other unemployed miner—no more, no less.

Finally, Jamie ran out of patience, went to the appropriate Devco official, tore off his shirt so that his missing arm could be clearly seen, and blew his anger at the official. He told him, among other things, that it would have been better for family if he had died at the accident, rather than live the way they were treating him. Whether his outburst did it or not, the company found a light-duty job for

Jamie at the Prince Mine at Point Aconi, where he got his 20 weeks needed to qualify him for unemployment insurance. Ironically, he didn't draw even one unemployment check before they hired him on at Phalen Colliery in New Waterford. He was given jobs he could do with one arm, then he filled in as an overman, and finally went back with the brushers, the job he knew best, doing everything with them except shoveling. He may have one arm, but his ambition was still very much intact.

Jamie is proud of his career as a coal miner, and loved working in the pit. He is extra proud of the fact that he was a draegerman before he lost his arm. A draegerman is a miner who goes down in the mine after a fire or explosion to help injured miners, and take any fatalities to the surface. Jamie trained to be a draegerman and was active in the 26 Colliery explosion, as well as several other fires, one of which singed his eyebrows.

Oddly enough, of Jamie's family of six brothers, four had accidents which resulted in amputations. Jamie lost his arm at the shoulder; Jamie's older brother Joey lost his arm below the elbow to a payloader accident; another brother lost most of his hand; and another lost several fingers.

Jamie retired in 1996 from Phalen Colliery, spending about 30 years as a coal miner, 16 of those years with his right arm missing.

When I went to interview Jamie on October 1, 2003, he was just returning from playing golf. He says he can drive the ball about 200 yards with his one-arm swing.

Donnie Turnbull

DONNIE TURNBULL AND I used to be in the same gang of about a dozen teens that coasted down the hill on the road going to 18 Colliery. That would be around 1948. Donnie grew up with six brothers and five sisters in New Victoria. We crossed paths, but we never hung out together. Donnie went to school in New Victoria, while I went to Central School in New Waterford. It was much later in life that we met again.

Donnie didn't waste any time getting started in the mine. In June of 1951, a few short years after our coasting parties, he was working in 18 Colliery. He must have had a few strings pulled, or hood-winked someone, because he was only 16 years old. About six months later, Donnie married Olive

Gardiner from New Waterford. He was still only 16. On his first day in the pit they took him right to the coal face. It was a very busy spot, sparking Donnie's excitement with this whole new underground scene. At the coal face, a half dozen or so miners' lamps battled the darkness, flashing back and forth as the men worked. Donnie remembers that his own lamp was a problem: its weight would make his pit cap fall forward when he bent over, and the cord attached to it would tug it backwards when he stood straight. He had to learn to get it balanced just right. He was surprised and a bit worried by the amount of coal dust in the air, and by the white smoke from the Monobel blasting powder that came intermittently from the wall below. He wondered if he could get used to breathing air like that.

During his first few days in the pit, Donnie fell prey to the usual fun the older miners have with a new guy. They knew he was impressed with chewing tobacco—a real symbol of a working miner—and wanted to try it, so they gave him a chew—a big one—too big for his untrained jaws. As expected, Donnie swallowed some tobacco juice, and the older miners enjoyed the violent spitting and hacking reaction they knew would come. Donnie went back to chewing gum.

Donnie was also a victim of the old "stayhole" gag. A stayhole is a hole about four inches square, dug three or four inches deep into the side of the coal face where it meets the roof. One end of a timber is stuck into this hole, laid across the roof, while a second timber is put under the other end to make what is called a "strap." Of course, there is no such thing as a stayhole aside from the ones that miners dig with a miner's pick. New guys do not know that, so the older miners sometimes give them an empty bucket, and send the poor souls up the wall for a bucket of stayholes. Bad enough for a beginner to crawl up the wall, but it is worse when you are carrying a bucket. When the new guy gets to the fellow he is supposed to ask for stayholes, he is told that "there are none here"—and that he would have to go see another guy out the top level. When they thought the greenhorn had searched and stumbled long enough, someone would mercifully tell him that there is no such thing as a stayhole you can put in a bucket—but not before they all got a good laugh.

Donnie did not remain working on the wall, because they thought he was too young to be at the coal face, so they put him on the level. Here, he had to carry material: six-foot timber, two-and-a-half-foot hardwood blocks six by six inches thick, and booms—booms being the same as timber, only much longer and bigger. Donnie would have to lug the blocks and timber out of the coal boxes—often with only a foot or so clearance over the boxes—and carry them in to the wall. The booms would come on trams—boxes with no sides on them. He would have help with the booms.

Donnie did this work for about a year, then went with the road makers, repairing and laying new narrow-gauge tracks for the coal boxes to roll on. Then he went with the pipefitters for a while, still working on the level. He did different jobs around the levels for about two years; and then for some reason or other, management gave him a choice of continuing the lighter work but all on night shift, or loading coal. There was no way he was going to work all night shift, so Donnie chose to load coal. The party was over.

Donnie said that his first section of coal was "Awful!" He had to crawl up the wall on the pan line, carrying a big water can, a big powder can, a lunch can, a pick and shovel, and a duffer—a duffer being a flat shovel that went under the wall of coal and cleaned out the duff so the coal, when shot, could fall. Donnie said that he really needed a mule. Once he got to his section, he said there was no room. It was "first cut," which meant that the pans were tight to the coal face and the chuck-block pillars supporting the roof were tight against the other side of the pan line. There was only about five feet between the pavement and the roof. It was work just getting to the work.

When he did get going, Donnie said he found that the coal was hard. The next day was not that much better. It was "second cut," which meant there was more room—about five feet between the coal face and the pan line—but this also meant that he had to shovel the coal twice as far!

Difficult as it was, Donnie prevailed, loading coal for about two years in 18 Colliery, then transferring to 16 Colliery in New Waterford in 1955, where he continued to load coal. He says that he found the coal much softer in 16 Colliery. Sometimes, he says, when you shot just one hole, the whole section rolled out, and now and then it rolled out just by cutting and duffing under the whole section. It could come too easily. You had to be careful.

In 1962, when 16 Colliery was closing, Donnie transferred again—this time to 12 Colliery, also in

New Waterford. In 12 Colliery, Donnie was put behind the Dosco Miner. Sometimes he would be timbering behind the Miner—putting up straps—and sometimes he would be "mucking"—loading powdery coal duff that was soaked with water, which made it quite heavy. Donnie says that mucking behind the Miner was harder than loading coal, and the coal dust in the air was so thick that sometimes you could not see your buddy standing right beside you. It was no picnic, but it was Donnie's steady job now.

Donnie was never officially broken in for running diesel, nor did running diesel replace his steady job of timbering and mucking. But somewhere along the line, he learned the basics of how to operate the diesels. Management saw this, and when a diesel runner was off, Donnie would be asked to fill in. Quite often, when Donnie thought he could be on a diesel on day shift, he would go out for an extra shift, then stay down on his regular job on night shift. He says that this was a good arrangement since the shift on the diesel was easy, and he could save his energy for the much harder shift behind the Miner. Of course, the extra shift earned him extra money. But it was this extra-shift combination that cost Donnie his right leg.

It was April 28, 1965. Donnie had gone down for an extra day shift, intending to stay down on night shift. Donnie remembers that on that day there were three trips on 21 East level: a full one and an empty one on the landing, and another empty between the doors, just a little way inside the landing. There were also two diesels, each with an empty trip in front. This was because the wall had not "cleaned off" on the last production shift—there were still 50 or 60 feet of coal left to cut, a common occurrence—so they put enough empties in the level to hold that coal. That way, they would not have to compete with other walls, and wait for empties. Donnie's was the maintenance shift; they had to finish cleaning off the wall, then maintain it. They had no time to lose.

With the two empty trips in front of the diesels, there was no way they could get the diesels where they were supposed to be—in front of those trips. A trip was never supposed to be *pushed* in the level—the diesel and its operator were always supposed to be at the front end of the trip. On this day, however, that was impossible, and the trips had to be pushed in. Donnie was to drive the men in by pushing the trip in that was between the doors. He started the diesel and proceeded to do just that. Gussie MacDonald who was operating the other diesel, was to wait until he was sure Donnie was all the way in, then he would push the second trip in. Had things gone as planned, it would have been just another day. But things did not go as planned.

Donnie started in with the first diesel. He got halfway in when the diesel caught a piece of stone that overnight side pressure had pushed a little too close to the road on the low side of the level. The boxes all passed the stone, because they are rounded on the bottom corners; but the lower, squared corners on the bottom of the diesel caught on the stone, and Donnie's diesel stopped. He got off the diesel and peered in beside it, seeing the stone that had stopped him. He backed the diesel out a bit, got off again and tried to remove stone from between the front of the diesel and the first box. He tried this several times. After five or ten minutes, and as many times on and off the diesel, Donnie stepped off the diesel once again to assess his progress. Preoccupied with the stone obstruction, Donnie forgot that the other diesel runner was going to give him only enough time to get in, then start in himself. Gussie did give Donnie plenty of time to get in—but not enough time to get out of unexpected trouble.

With the diesel engine running in front of him, Donnie did not hear the other trip coming. He was still working at the stone problem. When he stepped off the diesel again to walk to the front of it, he was in the middle of the road with his knees only an inch or so from the diesel's bumper. One step would have saved him, but before he could take that step the first box on the incoming trip slammed into the back of his knees and crushed his legs against the diesel in front of him. In the very narrow and low level, there was no way Gussie could see what was in front of his trip, so he was going at normal speed when he hit Donnie. Donnie says now that the only thing that prevented his legs from being completely severed was the fact that the bumper on the box was about ten inches wide, crushing his legs instead of cutting through. Louie Ruelland was with Gussie, standing on the club link in the diesel bumper behind Gussie. When their trip hit Donnie, it stopped so fast that Louie nearly hurled over Gussie.

Donnie's pain was excruciating, and it continued, because Gussie and Louie did not know what they hit. They were afraid to move the trip any more for fear of further damage. Louie said that they "thought the level came in." After a few minutes, trying to figure what happened, they decided to move the diesel back out about half a box length. In other words, while they discussed the situation, Donnie was pinned there, unable to move. He was screaming to the men at the front of his trip, but no one could hear him. With his legs still pinned, Donnie painfully reached to the diesel controls immediately in front of him, and shut off the engine. Then he picked up his pit cap with the light still on, and slowly waved it to the men inside. Before they got to him, Gussie had moved his diesel out half a box length, and Donnie fell. When men came out to see what happened, they found Donnie crumpled to the pavement with his legs horribly mutilated. Leno Bresolyn, the overman, wanted to put tourniquets on Donnie's legs to stop the bleeding, but Donnie would not let him. The pain was that severe. Then Donnie passed out.

When he came to, he was in a coal box on the way out the level, heading to the surface. Gussie and Louie went with him. They did their best to stop the bleeding, applying pressure on Donnie's legs, but he lost a lot of blood. When they got to the surface, doctors and an ambulance were waiting.

It was the hospital that called Olive. They told her that Donnie had had a little accident. When she got to the hospital, he was in the Operating Room. All she could do was wait. Finally, a nun told Olive that the doctors had done all they could, that it was up to God now. A little while later, one of the doctors told Olive much the same. Donnie had lost a lot of blood. They gave him 17 pints. Olive remembers with gratitude that many of Donnie's buddies called the hospital offering to donate more blood if it was needed.

Donnie made it. At first no one knew whether his legs would. He had casts on both legs up to his hips, but they had to remove them after ten days because of circulation problems. Donnie says that his legs "were playing games." Circulation would stop in one leg, start in the other—then the opposite. They were ready to remove the left leg when its circulation started up again. Eventually, it stopped in the right leg—just stopped—and that leg had to be amputated about four inches above the knee.

On his road to recovery, Donnie spent a lot of time in Halifax. From the stories he tells, the Compensation Board was not ready to support those trips. Friends would drive him to the train station, but he was left to travel on his own. He remembers falling into a snowbank while on crutches, trying to get onto the train from the little boarding stool. No one met him in Halifax. He called the Compensation Board, and they sent a taxi for him; but Donnie's "good" leg was so sore that he couldn't follow the taxi driver to the cab. That driver called another one, and the two of them got Donnie into the taxi. After a meeting with the compensation doctors, they sent him to a boarding house—where his room was up a flight of stairs! Not trusting himself to climb stairs, Donnie sat on each step, going up backwards a step at a time, lifting himself up with his arms.

After about six months in Halifax, the artificial leg proved unsuitable. Then he spent some time in Fredericton, New Brunswick, where he was finally fitted with an artificial leg that fit and worked.

Donnie was off work for two years and two months. He was offered a pension, but he knew that he and his family—Olive and three boys—could not live on that amount. However, with the pension plus a weekly pay, they could probably do okay. So in 1967 Donnie went back to work at 12 Colliery. They wanted Donnie to go back underground, but he flatly refused. William (Bull) Marsh, president of the miners' local, got Donnie a job on the surface, but the job was impossible for a man with an artificial leg. There were times he was expected to climb on top of a timber pile and load boxes with pit props! Once again, through Bull Marsh, Donnie was able to get a job in the "shop" repairing broken coal boxes. The floor in the shop was nice and even, and Donnie worked there until he retired in 1990. He had worked over 40 years in and around the coal mine.

Donnie continued to suffer. He underwent surgeries for multiple hernias, a problem he felt started when they put in a plastic vein to improve circulation to his leg. Other hernias continued to give him problems. The doctors refused to connect his problems with his accident. Without that connection, compensation would not pay for his medication.

Donnie Turnbull died October 16, 2003.

Cyril Eldridge

IT IS A PLEASURE TALKING to Cyril Eldridge, because he remembers a lot of the same things that I remember, especially Jack Beaton's pool room in New Waterford, where I hid out when I didn't want to go to Central School. Cyril didn't want to go to school either, quitting St. Agnes School in Grade 6. I made it to Grade 11. But it didn't make much difference back then, because we both ended up in the same place—12 Colliery in New Waterford. Cyril started a year before me.

Like his brothers John and Roddie, Cyril delivered groceries for Ouellette's and "Whistling" Benny Gaum, two of the several grocery stores in New Waterford at that time. He was only making $12 a week, just enough to keep him in pool money. In fact, those days he would be looked upon with envy by guys in the pool room—myself included.

One fine boring day, however, Cyril and his first cousin were hanging around town with nothing to do, probably broke, and Cyril was thinking, "There must be something better than this." His cousin suggested to Cyril that they both go to 16 Colliery office to see if they could get hired on at the pit. Manager Mickey Mullins didn't promise anything, but he took their names. They left, and continued roaming around town.

"The first thing I know," Cyril says, "I get a call to go in Sydney to see Dr. Lynch for a medical." Very good news—but Cyril was worried about his weight. So the day he was to go for the medical, he put lead into his shoes. His normal weight was 130 pounds, just enough to get hired on, but with the lead for insurance he weighed 135 pounds. Other coal miner hopefuls often filled up on bananas and water just before the examination.

A week or so later Cyril got a call to go to 12 Colliery. He signed papers to allow the office staff to take so much off each pay for doctor, hospital, union dues, unemployment insurance and whatever else that had to be paid. This was called the "check-off." Then he went to the warehouse for a pit hat, pit boots and gloves. The manager, Adam Forsyth, told him to come out the next morning. That was Thursday, May 4, 1950. Cyril was 18 when he started in 12 Colliery.

Cyril was hired on, but he had no work until he found it on his own. He had to go to the wash house in the morning and, from about 200 or 300 men, find out who the overmen were; then approach each one of them asking for a job that a new guy could do. As it turned out, Cyril could not find any work that first morning, so he went home and came out again on night shift. This time he landed a job with overman Billie Saxon in 19 West—a job carrying timber at the top of the wall—a job that nobody really wants. It is heavy work at the lowest pay, but it is relatively safe for a new guy. When he thinks back on it now, Cyril shakes his head and says: "What a place, b'y!" It wasn't the best job in the pit, but Cyril stayed at it for about two years. Billie Saxon treated him well, often asking him to stay down for extra time, since the wall was usually late "cleaning off." On one of these extra shifts, Otto White, a production overman, asked him to go loading coal for him. Cyril said he would "give it a crack." He loaded coal for a while, then went to various places and jobs throughout the pit, even getting a chance at some big money, working at brushing when a brusher was off.

When Cyril had his accident, he was working in the gob for Donald MacLeod on 16½ East wall. It was day shift, Thursday, May 5, 1955, and his buddy Richie Woodland was off. Cyril was already working alone on his gob section when a new guy came to Cyril and told him that he was sent to work with him. He wasn't really "new"; he was one of the guys transferred to the New Waterford collieries when Caledonia closed down in Glace Bay. He was new to 12 Colliery and 16 East wall, but he and Cyril got along quite well. They were almost done for the day, except for "legging the face."

When the Dosco Miner cut the coal on the way down the wall, timbermen would put straps against the roof behind the Miner where the coal used to be. A strap is simply a six-foot timber laid across the roof from the gob to the face. It was held up at the face end by sticking it into a "stayhole"—a small hole dug into the solid coal. They braced it at the gob end of the strap with another upright timber. After the Dosco Miner was "fleeted" back up the wall, the gob workers had to put another timber under the coal face end of the strap, because the stayhole which supported the strap would be mined away on the next cutting shift. With a timber under it, however, the strap would continue to support the roof even when the stayhole was gone. Putting these timber under the face side of the straps was called "legging the face."

Cyril and his new buddy were short two timber to finish legging the face, so Cyril sent him up the wall to the level for the timber. The fellow came back, saying that there was no timber there. Actually, he was not familiar with the place; he did not go out the level far enough. Cyril knew there would be some timber farther out, so he went for them himself. This errand cost him the toes on his left foot, and eventually his leg up to four and a half inches below the knee.

Cyril lost his toes in a "bullwheel," a spoked steel wheel about three feet in diameter, part of what is called an "endless haulage."

It is called an endless haulage, but it could be called a booby trap. The horizontal bullwheels at either end of the haulage are positioned between and under the rails upon which the coal boxes roll— and where miners walk! There is *supposed* to be heavy rubber belt covering these wheels, so that no one can step on them; but the wheel under the rails where Cyril was walking had no rubber belt over it. Miners just had to be careful when this wheel was turning. Most of the time, the wheel was stopped. But a miner at this inside bullwheel had no way of knowing just when the wheel would turn. He could not hear the bell signals at the outer end of the endless haulage, where the engine operator was—about four or five hundred yards out the level.

The roof was low and the level narrow beside the Sydney Mines Loader where Cyril was stooped over, walking for timber. When he got to the bullwheel—when he walked by the wheel—he would have to put one foot right in front of the other, because he simply did not have the room for an open stride. This made it easy to lose his balance—which is exactly what happened. Instead of stepping beside the wheel, Cyril stepped in front of it, just where the steel rope started around it.

And as luck would have it, the operator at the engine started the haulage at that same instant. Cyril's foot went between the steel rope and the bullwheel. Cyril almost went down, but recovered his balance and continued walking. However, sensing something different, he shone his light on his pit boot, and stared in disbelief. He shouted: "Holy geezus!—the toe of me boot is gone!" Cyril says today that he couldn't have done a better job if he had used a huge pair of scissors.

As it happened, his brother John was only a few feet away, outside the loading point. He heard Cyril and came running. When he saw Cyril's foot, he got the chute runner to rap the haulage "holt," helped Cyril outside the loading point, and sat him down.

John cut Cyril's pit boot down through the laces and tongue, and took the boot off. Cyril said that he could see small, white bones, and his little toe was turned upside down. He said that there was no pain, nor was there any blood, but he still could not walk on what was left of his foot. They had to carry him out the level on a stretcher.

He doesn't remember why there was no trip available to drive him out the level, but does remember that it was "one son of a bitch" of a long walk, at least a mile, and those carrying him had to walk bent over most of the way because of the low roof.

At the auxiliary deep at the outside of the level, there was an empty trip waiting for him. They put him in one of the boxes, and went up to the top of the auxiliary deep where they had to carry him again through a "manway" that went to the rake on the main back deep. This rake went to the surface, and was used only for transporting men.

They put Cyril in the bottom-most carrier, which was the ambulance box. No sooner did the rake start up when someone "rapped 'er holt," because one more guy was running for the rake. When he got to where Cyril was, he threw his heavy army coat on ahead of him, and jumped in the ambulance box with Cyril. Men routinely got in the ambulance box when the rake was full, and likely this guy did not realize that Cyril had been injured. Cyril said that there had been no pain in his foot until now, but when that coat landed on it—"Geezus, I could have gone right clean through the roof!"

The ambulance was waiting on the surface, and quickly took him to the old New Waterford General Hospital. Dr. Allan "cleaned up the mess" of Cyril's foot. No attempt was made to find Cyril's toes. By now, the rats in the pit were feeding on them and, hopefully, this was the last feed the rats would have from this bullwheel, because the next day miners put the piece of rubber belt over it that should have been there in the first place. That is the way it always worked in the pit: someone got hurt, *then* they fixed the safety problem.

Cyril was just after buying a brand-new motorcycle, and had 29 miles on it when he lost part of his foot. Four other guys and Cyril had planned to go to Wisconsin to watch motorcycle races. Just before the others left, however, the guys came to see Cyril in the hospital, and when they said good-bye, Cyril jokingly said: "Go, you bastards, go!" They all laughed, but really wished that Cyril could go with them.

After Cyril was out for a week or so, he fired up the bike and went for a ride, taking a friend to Baddeck and back. He dropped his friend off in Glace Bay, and started for New Waterford. Cyril remembers crossing the "new bridge," but the next thing he remembers he was wiped out at the top of Carpenter's Hill, about a mile away. His bike was halfway up a guywire on a telephone pole, on the opposite side of the road. Cyril had passed out. A blood clot from his amputation had moved, shutting him down. He got twelve stitches in his forehead and two big shiners, but they fixed the bike for two dollars. He never rode the bike after that.

Soon after, two of his toes were turning black. In a Halifax hospital, a Dr. Currie told Cyril that he was going to take him upstairs tomorrow and "have a look" at his foot. Cyril says that he never mentioned taking it off, but when he woke up in the recovery room, his foot was completely gone—cut off at the ankle.

That was not the end of it! Cyril said his leg hurt terribly. They had not got all the gangrene, and they had to operate again. This time Dr. Nathanson from New Waterford assisted. They cut the leg off four and one half inches below the knee. This time the gangrene was gone, and so was the pain.

As in most cases, the compensation and pension packages for Cyril were less than satisfactory. He actually lost his leg three times. The first time was May 5, 1955, but more leg had to be amputated twice after that. Cyril says that they took him off compensation before he went back to work. He had been receiving $132 a month. He went back in 1958, after they put him on a pension of $58.93 a month—less than half!

Cyril had a problem getting light-duty work. When he asked for a job on the surface, the answer was an emphatic "No!" However, due to his own belligerence with an overman, he got a soft job on a "tugger" above 21 East when they were driving that level. A tugger is a small compressed-air-driven haulage machine about twice as big as those on the front of many 4-wheel drives. In the pit, a tugger hauls one coal box at a time.

From the tugger, Cyril went as "chain runner" on the auxiliary back deep where they transport men only, and then he went as chain runner on the main back deep that went to the surface—a real "piece of cake"—and he retired from this job. A chain runner is the fellow who signals the hoist operator to move the hoist up or down, and signals at what speed to do it.

In the early 1970s, when they were setting up Lingan Colliery, a lot of guys from 12 went to Lingan, but Cyril went on PRL—pre-retirement leave. He could be called back to work from PRL, but who is going to call a guy with one leg? Cyril stayed retired.

There are accidents and accidents. When I asked Cyril what his impressions were of his first day underground, he said that he hadn't minded it a bit. What he *did* mind was the day—about a year before he retired—when he had to go and check out why the hoist engineer was "rapped holt" at a spot in the deep where no one was supposed to be. The hoist operator thought that a piece of lagging might have fallen and hit the rapping wire, but wanted to be sure. When Cyril checked it out, it was not a piece of lagging. He saw a "streak of blood," and a guy's head on the pavement. The guy had been riding up on a full trip—against the rules—and must have stood up a little too high to turn around between the boxes he was riding. There are arch rails most of the way up the deep which provide ample clearance above the boxes, but in a few places they had taken out bent arch rails and replaced them with straight rails, only a few feet above the boxes. When the guy stood at one of these places with very little clearance, the straight rails tore his head off.

The electrician picked the head up by the hair, placed it in the centre of a blanket, gathered it up by the four corners of the blanket, and took it to the surface. The rest of the guy was also retrieved.

Hand loading coal at the pit bottom in the old room-and-pillar
mining method that was replaced by longwall mining.
Number 20 Colliery, 1949

Tom Hurley

TOM HURLEY'S FATHER Michael (Ikie) and his uncle Joe worked at 12 Colliery, New Waterford, the same time I was there. They traveled the mine with the deputies before each day shift to check for gas, roof collapses, water or anything unusual. Then they filled in at the lamp cabin to finish their shift, handling check numbers and lamps for miners coming up or going down. Everyone in 12 Colliery knew these two guys, but not as Joe and Ike Hurley. We all thought their last name was "Poles." Long before we came on the scene, the miners at 12 Colliery had re-christened Joe and Ike, calling them "Poles" instead of "Hurley."

Tom is not sure whether it was his father or uncle who made the innocent slip of the tongue, but that is all it took for the name change. "Timber" was the term for the six-foot softwood props that were used for underground roof support. Sometimes they were called "pit props," but they were never called "poles." That is, until Joe or Ike finished his first shift in the pit, and someone asked what he was doing for that shift. The answer was: "Carrying poles." The other miners thought this word for "timber" was such a joke that they never let him live it down. It doesn't matter if it was Joe or Ike who used the term, because the name stuck; and through time all their family members, including the women, were called "Poles" instead of "Hurley." Nicknames happened often in New Waterford. "Baloney," "Punkin," and "Wooden Horse"" are three more examples. Tom Hurley says that the name "Poles" has almost faded now, being mentioned only by a few of the older people, but he really does not mind this little story being told.

Tom could have done any number of things in life, but his destiny definitely leaned towards coal mining. His grandfather was a coal miner, his father Ike started in the pit when he was 13, his uncles and brothers were coal miners, and Tom grew up sandwiched in between 16 and 12 Collieries in an area called the "Dam." The two collieries were hardly a thousand feet apart, with 21 families on the street running in between. Today, that whole area is known as "Colliery Lands Park."

Tom's first job, however, was not in the coal mine. He quit St. Agnes School in Grade 8, and worked as back-shift dispatcher for Midway Taxi for a few months, earning $12 a week and giving $5 of that for board at home. The back-shift hours and $7-a-week pay were not all that attractive to a teenage boy, so he sought greener pastures picking potatoes on Prince Edward Island. This was hard work but twice the money. He came back home after six weeks, still hoping to get hired on at one of the collieries.

His father Ike asked Hugh Forsyth, manager at 12 Colliery, to hire Tom on. Hugh said yes, and it looked as if all Tom had to do now was wait a little while and he would have a job. A few weeks later, Hugh Forsyth asked Ike how his young fellow liked the pit. Ike said that it was not his young fellow, but Ike's brother Wilfred, that Hugh had hired! Hugh was sorry about the mistake, and promised that Tom would get hired on the next time.

Not long after, Tom got word to go for a medical exam. He was happy about that, but he worried about his weight. He was a small man and the weight requirement was 130 pounds. We have often heard someone tell a slow-moving person to "get the lead out of your arse"—well, Tom put the lead *in*! He took some stitching out of his pants from the seam around the belt and inserted flat pieces of lead. He cut an extra piece to put in his wallet. He was still under 130 pounds, so he was a bit worried the day of his medical. When the doctor told him to drop his pants, they dropped! When the doctor asked what the "clunk" was, Tom told him it was his pocket watch. The doctor smiled and continued with the examination. They accepted Tom at 129 pounds. Tom jokes that he needed help to pull his pants back up.

Tom got hired on at 12 Colliery in New Waterford, February 24, 1958. On his first shift he carried timber for overman Murdoch Johnson, and he was hell-bent to prove himself, because he was a little guy. Carrying timber is hard, brutal work, especially in the winter, because the timber are still snow-covered and icy when they first come down, and the roof is always low where they have to get the timber out of the boxes. Some of the fatter timber would easily weigh 40 pounds, but that did not slow Tom. He was determined to go timber for timber with the best of his buddies. He remembers the huge pile of stone the brushers had to shovel off the level, and how they were ticked off when they had to stop shoveling to let the timber carriers walk over the pile on their way to the wall face. They had all the timber in by 10:30 a.m.

Tom spent most of his time until 1968 carrying timber, but he was also preparing himself for better things by studying for shotfirer's and underground manager's papers. After he got his shotfirer's papers, Tom's coal mining career began to move; he was often asked to fill in as shotfirer. A shotfirer is the one who puts explosives into the drilled holes, makes sure there is no gas present, then shoots down the coal or stone. Tom now had his foot on the bottom rung of the ladder to becoming an official. He was sometimes more than a shotfirer, because they asked him to take the check numbers of the men he was working with, and to mark their time—which meant that he was also filling in as supervisor, known as "overman" in those days. He was still on shift work, but he was definitely an official.

Before fire closed 12 Colliery in 1973, Tom went operating a diesel locomotive, still filling in as shotfirer and supervisor. After 12 closed he went to

26 Colliery in Glace Bay, which was right up his alley: he had married Gloria Wareham from Glace Bay in 1963 and moved to the Glace Bay area. Number 26 Colliery was closer to home. Speaking about his move to 26 Colliery, however, Tom says, "Guess what?"—when he started in 26 Colliery, they put him back on the timber—the job he had had in 12 Colliery for ten years!

Then Tom was put with a crew that was driving an airway, looking after the timber and arch rails. With their help, he quickly loaded a couple of boxes with 30 timber and two sets of arch rails. When they got the material to the place of work, Tom asked, "What do I do now?" The brusher told him, "Nothing. You're finished. You are on task work." Tom could hardly believe what he was hearing, because task work meant that Tom could go home when he was finished. He gladly accepted his good fortune and headed for the surface—shortly after 9 a.m. He met the manager at the pit bottom and told him the story. The manager said, "You have a better job than I have!" Tom was going up when the manager was just coming down.

Things continued to improve for Tom in 26 Colliery. When they finished driving the airway, he was put on a "drive." That meant he had to watch a Python conveyor spill point. If stone built up at the spill point it could back up under the Python and jam it. This was a soft, boring job, not at all to Tom's liking, but it didn't last long. Someone who was driving a new wall face got hurt, and Tom gladly took his place. They drove the wall face and started putting rails up on the bottom level.

About this time, management was looking for

supervisors to go from 26 Colliery to Lingan Colliery in New Waterford. It was a good move for the supervisors from New Waterford, closer to home. That left openings for supervisors in 26 Colliery. Tom was moved to one of these positions, making him a full-time supervisor. No doubt he was happy with this appointment, but this was as far up the official's ladder as Tom would go.

At the time of his accident, Tom was supervising the transfer of coal at the bottom of a wall. He was responsible for the smooth operation of the Python, the stage loader, and the level belt conveyors, as well as for securing the roof where the wall and level meet. He had three men working for him at this section. The coal came down the wall on the Python conveyor and spilled onto the stage loader, which took it at a right angle from the wall and started it out the level. From there it spilled onto the level conveyor belt, on its way out to the deep.

Sometimes a huge slab of coal would fall off the coal face immediately in front of the Anderton Shearer, come down the Python, and jam at this spill point, causing the coal to pile to the roof and jam the Python. For this reason, the guys always had a maul close by, and were quick to smash any big lumps before the coal started to pile up. Tom speaks well of the three men he had working for him: Wilfred MacDonald, Charlie Wadden and Sammy Kane.

Tom had the habit of going in to the bottom of the wall around home time to make his report, and to see that everything was going smoothly. This day, the three guys had finished "building on"—that is, they had built chuck pillars under the roof on both sides of the level, while keeping an eye on the Python spill point. Everything was going well, so they asked Tom if he would watch the spill point while they went out the level a short way for lunch. Tom didn't mind in the least. He enjoyed watching the coal on its way out.

Perhaps it hadn't happened that whole shift, but it happened now—a slab of coal about seven feet long came down the Python, jammed at the spill point, and started a build-up of coal. Tom grabbed the maul, leaned over the stage loader, and hit the slab. The slab broke—but it broke more easily than Tom thought it would. The momentum of the maul caused him to lose his balance. He fell on the moving stage loader conveyor chain and his light went out. He actually remembers thinking, "O my God, I'm on the stage loader and my light is out!"

Tom says he was on the running stage loader for what seemed like a long time, but it was only seconds.

Tom's left leg was caught between the lump of coal and a hydraulic jack that was set close beside the platform loader. The conveyor chain carried Tom and the big lump of coal out the level—but his leg stayed behind. He heard a "crunch" but felt no pain—only numbness as he tried desperately to get off the stage loader. He fell off on the high side of the loader—the side closest to the surface. He managed to get his light back on and signaled his men to shut everything down. In the light he could see that his leg was gone!

In the hospital, guys told Tom that he was pretty tough to go through an accident like that, and while there is a lot of truth to that comment, Tom does not remember himself as being so tough. Even in the confusion of the accident, he knew that it was serious; and it was then that he had an experience he will never forget. He "heard" himself being asked, "Tom, are you ready to die?—Are you ready?" Tom's answer was a frightened "No!" He was more scared than tough, and he began to pray fast and furious. He says that it is surprising how many prayers you can say in such a short time. Although things went as smoothly as they could immediately after the accident, Tom does not claim that it was entirely due to his prayers, but he does say, "After I prayed, it helped *me*!"—he felt more peaceful and not so frightened.

In that confusion, Tom wrapped both hands around the stump of his leg, trying to stop the bleeding, and shouted to his men: "Come help me, I'm bleeding to death!" Charlie Wadden was first on the scene. Tom told him to take off his belt and make a lasso to put around what was left of his leg. As soon as word went up the wall, everybody on the wall and top level came running. Mechanical supervisor Sandy White and "Wishie" Donovan arrived and took over, replacing Charlie's belt with a proper tourniquet, winding it on Tom's upper leg.

Tom told them to call his doctor, J. B. Tompkins, and tell him that his leg was off. When they put Tom on the stretcher, he told them to put his leg on with him. He knew that no one wanted to touch his amputated leg, or to tell him it was off. Tom praises "Curly" MacNeil who was shift boss at the time, because everything was ready and clear for Tom's trip to the surface. When they got Tom to the pit bottom, Dr. Tompkins was there with nurse Rita Butts, and asked Tom how he was doing. Tom said okay, and felt better that he was in good hands now. Dr. Tompkins assured him that the Operating Room at the General Hospital was ready, and that they might be able to save Tom's knee. They tried, but the knee was so mangled that they had to cut it off. Tom's accident happened July 7, 1976, at 9:20 p.m., and at 10:25 p.m. he was at the Glace Bay General Hospital.

Tom thanked the guys who got him to the hospital, and asked someone to call his wife Gloria and tell her what happened and that he was okay. They were all afraid to do that because Gloria was six months pregnant with their third child, Karen. So, before Gloria heard anything official, a neighbour called her and asked if she heard about a Hurley man who lost his leg in a mine accident on night shift. Gloria said no, and asked the neighbour which Hurley it was, thinking: "Oh my God, Tom is working night shift!" The neighbour dodged Gloria's question, and said she thought it was Jim Hurley from Steel's Hill. Gloria had just finished making a night lunch for her girls, Barbara and Gail, aged 12 and 9, and was telling them about Jim Hurley, when the phone rang again. It was Dr. Tompkins. Gloria's heart sank. She knew it was about Tom. After the phone call, Gloria ran into the girls' room; they knew by the look of their mother that something was terribly wrong. "It's Da, isn't it?" Tearfully, Gloria said, "Yes," and they comforted each other.

Tom's brother Mike was on his way to work when production manager Reggie MacIntyre gave him the news. Mike took Gloria to the hospital. Tom was a hard-looking sight, still full of coal dust, but he told Gloria that she looked worse than he did. He said, "Take it easy, it's only a leg." He did not know what he would have to put up with for the rest of his life.

After two days, the hospital called Tom's brother, asking him to come and get Tom's pit clothes, because they were getting a smell from them. Tom's leg was still in the pit clothes! Mike said, "There's no way I am touching that." So Tom got the doctor to take care of it. Tom doesn't know what they did with his leg—he never asked—but most likely it was burned in the hospital incinerator.

Home from the hospital, Tom had a visit from Joe Boutilier, President of the Amputees Association. Joe told him how to strengthen the leg stump to get it ready for fitting the artificial leg. Tom was faithful in doing what Joe told him, and when the time came to be fitted, they found him more than ready.

Up until now, Tom had been very upbeat, accepting the loss of his leg as something that was going to slow him down for a little while—but he says, "When they put that artificial leg on, I realized then what I had lost."

Tom sank into depression, and did not want to do anything but lie down on the couch and stay there. He did just that for quite a while. But the time came when they told him that they were going to take him off compensation and put him on pension. That meant Tom would be getting only half of the $341 every two weeks that compensation was paying. On pension, he would get that amount once a month. With a wife and three children, there was no way they could live on that, so Tom had no choice but to pull himself together and look for some kind of work.

He went to the office at 26 Colliery, looking for a light-duty job, but they had nothing available. They sent him to the company doctor to see what he was capable of doing. Work around the wall face was out of the question, and so was anything where he had to walk up the deep, because he had to go sideways up any incline. Tom was afraid of turning down any job; he felt they might not offer him any work at all. He told the doctor that he would take whatever they had for a man with a leg off above the knee. The company offered Tom a job supervising the bunker—a large, underground storage room for coal. Empty boxes are not always immediately available to take the amount of coal that is being produced. Instead of having miners waiting for "empties," the coal is put in this bunker and taken from there as boxes become available. In 26 Colliery, all the coal was taken to the bunker by conveyor belts, from the bunker into boxes, in the boxes to the pit bottom, then to the surface, two boxes at a time.

After Tom was on the bunker operation for about six months, he was called into the office and asked if he was interested in a new computer operation soon to be set up on the surface. Tom accepted, and eventually found himself in an air-conditioned room holding a huge book of instructions. The book was threatening at first, but as Tom read it over and over he began to understand the process. When the computer was set up, he was the first one to have the job.

After 26 Colliery closed in 1984, Tom was offered

an early pension package, but he turned it down. He wanted to keep on working. Tom kept his official status, but as an instructor. The company used his talents at Phalen and Lingan Collieries, having him instruct miners on various subjects, including the details of compensation and pensions, the use of toxic materials, and roof bolting. Tom worked at this job for about six years.

In 1992 Tom was asked again if he was interested in an early pension package. This time he took the offer seriously, and accepted it, even though he lost about $1000 a month. After 34 years working for the coal company, Tom retired.

He says, "To all the men I met and worked with, the pleasure was mine." And like so many other mining people, there are always a few accidents that the miner remembers, and worries that others may forget—like that of Tom's uncle, Joseph Campbell, who was killed in 16 Colliery on November 22, 1961.

Wilfred Attwood

WORD HAS IT that Wilfred's father, Tom Attwood, and my father, Grant MacKenzie, were close friends—they were the first two people in the New Waterford area to have a radio. That meant parties around the radio, and some skill at repairing this form of entertainment. Both families have kept old radio components as mementoes of those days. They drifted apart as they began families of their own, abandoning possible radio careers for employment in the coal mines.

Wilfred was born on March 5, 1932, almost a year before me. We never became close friends, but we did know each other, both of us going to Central

School in New Waterford. Wilfred finished Grade 10, but I flunked it; then we went our separate ways, Wilfred starting almost immediately in 12 Colliery, while I took another run at Grade 10.

I don't know how they managed it, but Wilfred and his father Tom must have had "connections," because Wilfred was only 15 years old when he got hired on—much too young.

No doubt Wilfred was given a job such as timber carrier, valve tender on the wall, or some safe and relatively easy work during his break-in period. It wasn't all that long before Wilfred was on the wall, loading coal—one of the hardest jobs in the pit. He took it all in stride, because this was not just a job to him. He loved working in the coal mine, and enjoyed making it his career.

Beyond coal mining per se, he was one of those rare men who volunteered to train for one of the most dangerous jobs in mining—draegerman. A draegerman is a fellow who puts on special breathing equipment and goes down into the coal mine after a fire, explosion, or serious accident, to retrieve bodies and to rescue survivors. He's the first one to go in.

Wilfred saw action as a draegerman during the Springhill "bump" of 1958. The floor in Number 2 had lurched up and smacked the ceiling, crushing equipment and men, leaving behind bodies and injured miners, and the mangled lives of their families and friends. Wilfred was proud to be part of the rescue, helping where he could.

Back in 12 Colliery, Wilfred had an eye on the future, setting his sights on advanced mining techniques. For a coal miner in those days, his Grade

10 was fairly impressive to management. Mechanization was just around the corner, beginning in 12 Colliery late in1951. The Dosco Miner, or "continuous miner," was already in 18 Colliery. It was coming to Number 12, and Wilfred was one of the miners who began training on it as mechanic. It wasn't long before he was cutting coal with this new machine, loading 500 tons a day now instead of the 20 tons he used to load by hand with a pan shovel.

The Dosco Miner was a machine that began at the top of the long wall, and moved along the wall on caterpillar tracks, like that on a bulldozer, cutting the coal beside the pan line with a 600- to 700-pick rotating gib that pushed into the coal. The gib was something like seven brutally huge chain saws side by side in a single unit. The coal was ripped from the coal face and spilled 90 degrees onto the conveyor pan line by a small conveyor belt on the machine. It was high technology at the time, but it was limited. The Dosco Miner could cut coal only one direction—down the wall. Once the coal was taken from the wall, and the Dosco Miner was at the bottom, it then had to be "flitted" back up the wall, and the pan line moved over close to the coal face once again.

During the "flitting"—or "fleeting" as the miners called it—and the shifting of the pan line against the coal face, there was no coal produced. Once it was back up at the top of the wall, the Dosco Miner had to be maneuvered into a "stall"—a room hand dug for it into the flat coal face. Now it would be facing the coal ahead of it, and production could begin once more as the machine cut its way down the wall again. As advanced as this machinery was at that time, it soon became obsolete. But Wilfred was part of that system for about two years. He made good money for a coal miner, but he ate a lot of dust. The coal dust behind the Dosco Miner was unbelievable. Not only did you see it, you could feel it against your face. The operator could not see the cutting gib only 15 feet away—he had to rely on a light signal from his buddy on the gob side of the machine.

The Dosco Miner was eventually replaced with the Anderton Shearer, a machine that travelled on top of the pan line instead of beside it. Also, it pulled itself along the pan line and, with a side-mounted gib, cut the coal as it went. A corkscrew rotation of the gib pushed the coal sideways onto the pan line. And: using hydraulic jacks, or "walking jacks" that held up the roof, the pan line was pushed close to the face as the coal was being cut. No more "flitting," and no separate shifting of the pan line. It was a single operation. When the Shearer got to the bottom of the wall, its cutting gib was rotated to the top end of the Shearer, and was ready to cut coal on the way back up the wall. Every shift was now a producing shift. Compared to the Dosco Miner, itself a revolution in coal mining, this was an amazing advance in coal mining technology. And Wilfred Attwood was part of it all, now one of the operators on the Anderton Shearer.

It was Tuesday, January 7, 1969, on 28 West wall in 12 Colliery. They had finished cutting coal on back shift, and the Shearer was at the bottom of the wall. The cutting crew could have gone home, but management asked them if they would stay down a little while to get things ready for the next cut on day shift. Wilfred and his buddies agreed to do this, since there wasn't much to be done. All they had left to do was move the very bottom end of the pan line against the coal face, and put the cutting gib of the Shearer into the coal again so it could cut on the way up the wall.

Their work was briefly interrupted by a piece of stone that fell between the pan line and the coal face, just a little on the low side of where the Shearer was mounted. This stone prevented them from moving the pan line as close as it should be to the face. So Wilfred got between the pan line and the face, preparing to roll the stone out of the way and onto the pan line. This would have been uneventful, had it not been for a simple makeshift "improvement" the miners had made to the Anderton Shearer.

Like the old Dosco Miner, it is extremely dusty behind the Anderton Shearer—so dusty you could hardly see a person standing beside you. Consequently, the miners rigged a small wire to the start and stop switch of the machine so that they could control it from the gob side where there was much less dust. It was this improvement that claimed Wilfred's life.

Wilfred was between the pan line and the coal face, close to the rotor on the Shearer—too close. Just as Wilfred bent to lift the stone onto the pan line, a small piece of roof coal fell and hit the wire that was hooked to the start switch, starting the cutting gib's rotation. The teeth on the rotating gib caught in Wilfred's belt, pulling him under and around the gib to its other side, between the cowl and the gib—a space of about three inches.

One of his buddies saw what happened, and ran

panic-stricken down the wall and out the level, looking for help. But there was no help possible for Wilfred. He died instantly.

Wilfred and June McPhee were married July 31, 1955. They had four children: Wilfred—who is mostly called Tom—was 12; Richard (Rick) was 10; Linda was 6; and Robert was almost 4. June overslept that morning, because Wilfred did not awaken her when he came home from back shift. June suspected nothing, because he often came home late, staying down to do exactly what they were doing this morning—get the wall ready for the cut on day shift. When she did wake up, she was more preoccupied than usual with getting the children ready for school, because she did not want them to be late. Still in her nightclothes, she had Tom and Rick out the door on their way to school and was now dressing Linda. Just as she was putting a beloved "red fur" coat on Linda, a knock came to the door. June was a bit irritated with the interruption. She told the man to wait in the kitchen for a few minutes until Wilfred came home, thinking he was a car salesman from the dealership she and Wilfred had recently visited. She also noticed her brother Bernie outside in the yard, walking back and forth. She wondered why he did not come in for a cup of tea, but still suspected nothing.

After sending Linda off to school, she went into the bedroom to change. She had just finished dressing when the "car salesman" tapped on the bedroom door, and pushed it open. June, in a raised voice, asked him what he thought he was doing. It was then that he opened his coat, revealing the clergyman's collar, and said, "I have come to tell you about Wilfred."

June began to panic. She asked if Wilfred was hurt and in the hospital. The clergyman just shook his head. When June asked where Wilfred was, the clergyman told her there had been a terrible accident, and Wilfred had been killed. It didn't sink in. It seemed like a nightmare. She began to feel her life collapsing. The thought of going on alone filled her with fear. She had trouble believing that Wilfred would not be coming home. It was not fair. June was shocked, confused. She remembers the house filling with people.

Their oldest son Tom got the news in school. Tom was in the school yard when one of his buddies asked him if everything was all right. Tom said, "Yes," thinking nothing of the question. When he was seated in school, the principal came to the classroom door with a note for the teacher. The teacher then came to Tom and told him that he had better go home, since something was wrong.

When Tom got home, he saw a lot of people there, crying. This scared him and, instead of going in the house, he went over to Warren Avenue to his first cousin's place. They were just getting up, and as they were talking to Tom, the phone rang. It was news of the accident, but Tom didn't want to hear anything. Instead, he "ran and ran" to his maternal uncle's place in Scotchtown.

Uncle Wilfred McPhee has since died, but his wife Regina remembers that day. She said that the little guy came in sobbing, "Daddy's gone, Daddy's gone!" She tried to comfort him by telling him that his daddy was fishing. When she called June and got the real news, she confirmed Tommy's worst fears, and kept him for the rest of the day. Neighbours kept Richard and Linda, while June's sister took the baby Robert.

Regina's story to Tommy that his daddy was fishing *should* have been true. That is where he had expected to be after back shift, on Lingan Bay with Wilfred McPhee and Tom Hutchinson. Tom Hutchinson was already there with a hole cut in the ice, but around eight o'clock that morning Wilfred McPhee went out and told Tom what had happened. The news shattered the world around them. Those fellows hunted and fished together all year round. They had shared the fresh smell of early morning mist rising from the water, heard the bird's first chirp, and listened to a solitary crow squawk over the awakening timber line. Now it was over. It would never be the same without Wilfred. The two men packed the ice fishing gear in the car and went home.

That was May 3, 1970. June had the wake for Wilfred in their home. Family and friends kept coming to the house with enough food to feed an army. The funeral was held at the Anglican church on Ellsworth Avenue in New Waterford. June says that the church was packed and more people stood in the yard. The Men of the Deeps choir sang "The Battle Hymn of the Republic."

June said, "It was a great tribute to a fine miner, draegerman, fishing buddy, hunting buddy and friend."

Russell Marsh and Donald MacInnis

FIFTY YEARS AFTER AN ACCIDENT—when it wasn't one of the "big" ones we call history—it's hard to find someone who was at the scene. As I searched for stories, I was usually lucky enough to get eyewitness details from miners. And my luck held out when I looked for memories of the accident that claimed the lives of Russell Marsh and Donald MacInnis. It was 44 years ago, and most of the miners who were there have died. But Eddy Durdle was alive and well—aside from troublesome joints worn down by 46 years of crawling around underground. Eddy was the overman the day Russell and Donald were killed, and he remembered it well.

Russell Marsh and Donald (Bullneck) MacInnis were killed by the same fall of stone. It was on 16½ East wall in 12 Colliery, Friday, November 6, 1959. Russell died instantly. Donald died two days later in Halifax. Russell had started in the coal mine—there only a few weeks—while Donald was a seasoned miner. The accident happened in the "40 foot" at the bottom of the wall.

The "40 foot" is simply a continuation of the long wall face to the other side of the level at the bottom of the wall. Whether it was by hand loading or by machine, the coal had to be removed from the inside, butt end of the level, and then a little bit below it on the other side of the level. This was done so that the level tunnel could be extended in close to the coal face, and also to make a place to shovel the stone that was removed to make the level higher. When the brushers shot the stone down from the roof of the level, they needed a place to put it. The "40 foot" provided this place. With the coal removed, they could then shovel the stone into this "40 foot" section on the low side of the level where the coal used to be. Not only was the "40 foot" a place to shovel stone when the level was brushed to make it higher, but—according to Hugh Morrison, a retired underground manager—if the coal was not removed from the low side of the level, the roof would crack and become very unstable over the level. This section might not have been exactly 40 feet all the time—it could be anywhere from 30 to 40 feet—but it was always called the "40 foot."

The approximately 500-foot main coal conveyor on the wall ended at the high side of the level, dumping its coal into the "Sydney Mines Loader" that took it out the level. Another very short conveyor had to be used to convey the coal up from the "40 foot" on the low side of the level to the same Sydney Mines Loader. This very short conveyor that dumped the low-side coal into the Sydney Mines Loader was *also* called the "40 foot." Its sides and main body were made of plate steel, and it used a single chain with cross bars to drag the coal up to the level. It was much smaller than the main conveyor, but it did the job. The setting now is that we have a section of the wall below the level called the "40 foot," and a conveyor in that section that is also called a "40 foot."

Hand loading had been a thing of the past for five or six years, and the Dosco Miner was in use here in the "Half." The cutting crew would cut the wall face to the level, past the level, and into the "40 foot" on the other side of the level. They would leave the machine there in the "40 foot," and go home. However, this day, someone from the maintenance shift had gone to the manager lamenting that the Dosco Miner was supposed to be taken back out of the "40 foot" and the roof of the "40 foot" secured before the production shift went home. The manager agreed. He got in touch with production shift overman Eddy Durdle, and ordered him to have the machine taken out of the "40 foot," and to have the roof secured before the shift was finished.

Eddy, of course, did what he was told, even though he and his crew did not like the fact that they would have to stay down an extra half hour or so. Russell Marsh and Donald MacInnis were there. The rule now was to get the Dosco Miner out of the "40 foot" to the high side of the level. This is what they were working at on November 6, 1959.

They had just taken the machine to the high side of the level, and were preparing to secure the roof in the "40 foot." Russell and Donald climbed over the 40-foot conveyor to do that job, but they never got the chance. A huge and brutal piece of stone—a rare, single, massive piece—crashed down on both of them. Eddy says that it was about 20 feet long, two feet thick, and six feet wide. It was so sudden and furious that when the cutting crew saw what happened, some of them panicked, adding to the confusion and shock. Eddy had to get the panic-stricken guys out of the way before the rescue could be attempted.

Alcorn MacNevin was the first man there with a road jack. He started to lift the stone. Eddy and others put pieces of timber and chuck blocks under the stone as it came up, preventing it from falling back down. It took only about five minutes to raise the stone a foot or so, but it didn't really matter—the damage had been done in an instant.

As soon as he could reach under the now slanted piece of stone, Eddy stretched under it to see if he could get hold of Russell. He was pushing what he thought was a piece of coal out of the way, but realized that it was not coal—it was Russell's head. It moved so easily that Eddy knew Russell was dead. He left him and started with the others to help Donald.

Donald was not completely under the stone. He might have been better off if he had been killed with Russell. Donald had been crushed against the "40 foot" conveyor. His midriff was torn open. His head and shoulders were on the conveyor, but the rest of him was under the stone. When they got him out, his legs were like twisted rope. They had to tie them together to keep them on the stretcher.

It was a heartbreaking effort getting both of them out. The men worked furiously but they knew there was little hope—no hope for Russell, and very little for Donald. Halfway up to the top of the auxiliary deep, they were met by a doctor and a priest. Eddy remembers the priest getting in the box with Donald, and asking him, "How long was it since you were at confession, son?" Donald, still conscious, replied: "Father, I am a Protestant."

No one expected Donald to reach the surface alive. He lived until they got him to the Victoria General Hospital in Halifax—250 miles from home. He died two days later.

Russell's death was especially troubling to Eddy. He had seen miners die before, but this was different. Russell lived right next door to him—the Marsh and Durdle families were close neighbours! Eddy had taken Russell into the pit on Russell's first day. Russell's father had asked Eddy to "look after" Russell, leaning a bit on the fact that Eddy was an overman. Eddy told him that he couldn't make any promises because he was all over the place, and couldn't always watch the son. Instead, Eddy put Russell loading spillage, an easy and reasonably safe job. This kept Russell away from the "action" of the coal face, busy cleaning up coal that spilled from conveyor belts and loading points. It wasn't long, however, before Russell became bored with that job and looked for work mucking on the wall behind the Dosco Miner, a much harder job but also more exciting and more money. Eddy was reluctant to put him mucking because he was still quite new in the pit. Russell persisted, so Eddy took the matter to Russell's father, telling him that he felt Russell should wait a little while. Russell's father told Eddy to go ahead and let Russell work on the wall face if that is what he wanted. It definitely was not his inexperience that killed Russell, although he was crushed while he was working on the wall face.

After the accident, Eddy hated to go home, knowing that he would have to face Russell's grief-stricken parents—not something he wanted to do after a day like this. He needed some time to himself before he met the parents. But that was not to be.

As soon as he was in his house, Russell's father came to see him, but not to lay blame or lament about losing his son. Fortunately, Russell's father's intention was just the opposite of what Eddy feared. He had received the news of his son's death, and had come to tell Eddy that he knew it was not Eddy's fault, that he did not blame Eddy in the least. He spoke the truth: there was no way Eddy or anyone else could be held responsible for this tragic accident. Eddy says that "we lost two fine young men, and that was it." Hard to accept, but it had to be chalked up to the dangers of the coal mine.

Adding to the tragedy is the fact that Russell was only 17 when he was killed, and had been in the coal mine only six weeks. Brian, Russell's brother, says that their 92-year-old mother still will not talk about Russell's death, and will change the subject if someone brings it up. However, she did mention something quite interesting. She said when Russell left for night shift, on the night he was killed, she watched him walking away on his way to work.

She saw Russell walk out the yard and start down 8th Street toward Plummer Avenue—but then he stopped and came back. He walked into the yard again, and she thought he was coming back for something he forgot, but he never came in the house. When she went to see where he was, there was no one there.

Russell was in the pit for six weeks, but Donald MacInnis was in it for six years. He started in 1B in Glace Bay when he was 18, but transferred to 12 Colliery in New Waterford when 1B closed in 1955. He was 24 when he was killed, and left behind his wife Ginger (MacKenzie) and three small children: Weldon, Wayne, and six-month-old Luana.

His brother Joe was on security at 16 Colliery in New Waterford that day, but heard nothing about Donald's accident until he got home. It was then that prizefighter and friend Red MacPherson called him from New Waterford, pretending to be interested in who won a boxing match—but it was really to tell Joe about Donald as gently as he could. After the phone call from Red, Joe called their brother Norman. And together they broke the news to Ginger.

Joe went to Halifax with Donald, but with little hope. They flew Donald to Halifax on a Saturday, and on Sunday he died with severe bowel injuries. It was Joe who phoned the sad news to New Waterford. Shortly after the accident, Ginger and the children moved to Ontario.

Eddy never got used to the dangers of the coal mine, although he had plenty of experience. He was introduced to a fatality on his first day, even before he got underground. June 25, 1946, Number 12

Colliery. He went to the wash house, changed into his pit clothes, and went to the back deep to get on the rake. He was sitting there when news came that the pit was "knocked off." It always shuts down for 24 hours when a miner gets killed. Joseph Gallant had been killed by a roof fall. Eddy changed back into his street clothes and went home.

By June 7, 1949, Eddy was well established in the pit. He went down to begin loading coal in the top section of a wall when he got word that he was to replace a brusher who was off. Lawrence McDonald came to take Eddy's place at the coal face and Eddy gladly handed him the pan shovel to load the section of coal. Brushing was harder work, but it was more money. Eddy climbed over the pan line to head down the wall to where he was to go brushing. Lawrence climbed over the same pan line toward the coal face to load coal. It was not five seconds later that the roof came in on Lawrence, killing him instantly.

Eddy was in the pit when fire broke out in 12 Colliery, resulting in the deaths of Earl Leadbeater and Donald MacFadgen. That was on the back shift of March 2, 1973. A trip got loose and went by the run down the auxiliary deep, jumping the road around 15 East, cutting the 500-volt armoured cable and starting the fire. All the men had got out except Earl Leadbeater. By the following day shift, management called its officials to formulate a plan of action. They were going to send officials down to evaluate the situation, see what they could do about the fire and about Earl. Eddy and Donald MacFadgen were among those officials. Donald was an engineer disciplined in mine ventilation. They traveled the pit and stopped just above the fire. The ventilating air went downwards in 12 Colliery, exhausting through old 14 Colliery and a shaft at Low Point. This made the smoke curl at the fire point and then go down farther into the pit. Eddy says that the smoke was red, green, blue—all colours. No flames could be seen through the smoke, but they could hear the lagging and timber crackling. It was a scary situation. The safety committee, draegermen, and officials were contemplating going through a cutoff above the fire, hoping to reach Earl Leadbeater by another route.

At this point, Donald MacFadgen had sent the chain runner for a diagram of the ventilating plans for this area of the coal mine. When he got the ventilation diagram, Donald just had time to open it and begin to study it when, Eddy says, "He just went down—dead." They sent for Dr. Nathanson, who came into the pit even though it was on fire. It was a heart attack, caused by the extreme anxiety and tension. Nothing could be done for Donald.

Earl Leadbeater was trapped below the fire and the draegermen could not get to him. He suffered the fate most coal miners dread the most—that of being left in the coal mine. Number 12 Colliery is his grave.

Eddy thought that they might have been able to save the mine by flooding the area with water, but he was not the one to decide. Higher management decided to seal off the mine. That was the end of 12 Colliery.

Eddy Durdle lived another 30 years. He died on the morning of August 3, 2003.

Top brushing. A posed photograph. If the machinery were running, all that would be seen would be dust.
Number 20 Colliery, 1949

Freddy Bishop

MOST MINE INJURIES are traumatic, violent and obvious. Usually, the seriously injured miners cannot make it to the surface on their own, so their buddies carry them up on a stretcher. We are inclined to see these unfortunate souls with their broken bones and bloody wounds as the only injured miners. Such is far from the truth. There have been hundreds of other injured miners, many of whom don't realize that they've been hurt until it is too late, because their tragedy happened so slowly and gradually. To lose part of your body—fingers, foot, an arm or a leg—is an obvious injury. The loss of lung capacity is a less obvious handicap. But black lung and silicosis can destroy a man just as surely as a fall of stone.

Freddy Bishop is one of the hundreds of victims

of silicosis. And Freddy's injury is worse than most because he was a brusher—a miner who works mostly with stone instead of coal. Most miners agree that brushing is the hardest work in the pit, and they also agree that because of the huge amounts of stone dust, brushers have a much higher risk of developing silicosis.

Freddy grew up in a family of eight, close beside 16 Colliery in New Waterford. He was already making "big money" before he started in the pit. As many of us did back then, Freddy went picking coal on the Scotchtown stone dump right beside a place we called "The Summit." This is where the S & L railway took "hoppers" full of stone from the pits. The hoppers had much lower sides than the regular railway coal carriers; they were designed to tip sideways, pitching their cargo of stone beside the tracks and down the slope. Once the stone was dumped, there was a scramble by Freddy and others to retrieve the precious chunks of coal mixed with the stone. The treasure hunt was slowed down a little by Mr. Roach, who had the contract to pick over the stone. Once the Roach workers were finished, then Freddy would join the other scavengers foraging for the lumps of coal that were left. Freddy did well, making more money at picking coal than he would have made if he had been employed in the pit, which Freddy says was $3.10 a day back then. Little did he suspect then that someday he would be working underground as a brusher, sending up the stone and coal mix for a new generation of kids to scramble over.

Freddy started in 12 Colliery on September 28, 1943, working day shift. His first job was carrying timber, as it was for most guys starting in the pit. It was break-in time for Freddy. He and a buddy took six-foot timber from the coal boxes as they came in, carried them to the wall face and put them on the shaker pan line, which carried them down the wall to the loaders. Once broken in, Freddy did anything they gave him. He says that he did just about every job in the pit, and that could very well be true, because he worked in three coal mines: 12 Colliery in New Waterford, Prince Colliery over in Sydney Mines, and Lingan Colliery back in New Waterford—a total of 45 years underground. Perhaps Freddy actually did do *all* the underground jobs, because most miners never get the chance to go brushing. Freddy did.

The opportunity to go brushing on a level was given to the men who began driving that level in the first place—right from the deep—the deep being the sloped tunnel that follows the coal seam down, and which keeps going well below the spot where the level is started. The deep and level connection would look much like a branch growing from a maple tree. The level begins at a slight angle to the deep; that angle increases steadily until it is at 90 degrees to the deep. Then it follows across the coal seam horizontally, being driven ever farther away from the deep, which continues on at a downward angle. When the level is in about 600 feet from the deep, a tunnel, or "wall," is driven into the coal seam on each side of the level, making a "T" shape— the level being the stem of the "T," and the walls being parallel to the deep.

The coal seam is roughly six feet thick, but when the level is being driven an additional seven feet of stone is taken out above the coal, to make the level about 12 feet high. This is where the stone-and-coal mix comes from that is taken to the dump. It is too much trouble at this point to separate the stone from the coal.

Without going into confusing details, Freddy's job can now be described: when the walls begin working, the coal is taken out from under the stone and sent to the surface. The stone that is over the coal on the walls is left to cave in, into what is called the gob — the gob being the place where the coal used to be. On the level, however, the stone has to be more systematically removed and shoveled to the side of the level, so that the level will be high enough and clear enough for the coal to be shipped out and for material to come in. Removing this stone is the brusher's job.

When Freddy and his buddies began their shift, they were looking at the very inside end of the level—there is no more level in beyond this point. The brushers have to extend the level in about six feet each shift to keep up with the removal of coal from under the stone. Looking from the roof down, they are faced with a section of solid stone about 13 feet wide and 7 feet high, with a six-foot opening below it. The opening is there because the coal has been removed from under the stone.

Now, this stone on the level has to be shot down and loaded. Working on the wall, those men loading coal do not have enough room to stand up straight. But now that the coal is gone from under the stone on the level, the roof is so high that Freddy and his buddies have to build staging six feet high — the height of the coal seam that was there—and stand on that to work at the stone.

Once up on the staging, the brushers start boring holes into the stone. They have a jackhammer run by compressed air. Two men push on the jackhammer, boring about eight holes six feet long. Dust from the drilling is blown in their faces, into their mouths.

They put blasting powder in the holes, remove their staging, and blast the stone down. Stone that does not fall has to be "barred" down with a six-foot-long steel chisel. Freddy says that they had to keep prying until no more stone could be removed from the roof. Sometimes they had to go ten feet up to get to solid stone.

Now the brutal work starts in earnest. The volume of stone would be close to that of a section of coal, but the *weight* of that stone is two or three times as heavy as coal. There are four men in the crew—and they start shoveling the stone into the low side gob beside the level, the side farthest from the surface. Most of the stone has fallen too far away from the gob for one man to shovel it where it belongs, so they have to relay the stone from one man to the other, passing it to where they want it.

It is the weight of this stone that makes brushing the hardest job in the pit. There are special shovels for shoveling stone—smaller than the pan shovels, or "banjos," used to load coal. However, Freddy says that he and his buddies did not use these smaller shovels. Instead, they chose to use the pan shovels. This made their work faster, but it also made it grueling. Each shovelful was heavier. I asked Freddy if this made him overtired. He said no, that "You got used to it." He said that the extra punishment was borne gladly, because brushers worked on contract and could go home when they were finished instead of staying down for the full eight-hour shift. Freddy said that they hardly talked to one another during the shift. They concentrated on what they had to do, and did it efficiently so that they could go home as early as possible.

Once all the stone was cleared from the level, Freddy and his buddies had to put up booms to secure the roof. Booms resembled timber; except that where timber were six feet long and could be carried by one man, the booms were 16 feet long, much thicker, and needed two or three men to lift them and lay them across the roof. They were held in place by "stayholes" laboriously picked into the solid stone on each side of the level. Once the booms were in place, the men were free to go home. The level was now about 13 feet high—plenty of room to stand up under the brushing they had done.

However, the level started to close in almost immediately. It closed in to the extent that a month or so later, the booms were bent, broken, and only about five feet above the level bottom. The level had to be brushed again to keep it open. A pair of "backbrushers" had this job. They took down a little less stone this time, but instead of wooden booms they installed steel arched rails—making their work more permanent.

In 1969, management discontinued the backbrusher's position. They put the two backbrushers with Freddy and his crew at the very inside of the level. The six of them installed only steel arched rails, preventing the level from closing in so quickly. This was an improvement in the brushing technique, but there was just as much dust—maybe more.

During their shifts as brushers, Freddy and his buddies had no serious accidents. No stone fell on them—no broken bones or serious wounds—but they were being seriously injured! Boring holes, blasting and shoveling produced copious amounts of stone dust. Hard work and heavy breathing drew this dust deep into their lungs. Bad enough if it had been pure coal dust. Coal dust becomes imbedded in the lungs, and causes them to harden, a condition known as black lung. Stone dust is worse because it contains silica.

When Freddy and his buddies worked in the stone dust, small particles of silica were getting stuck in the tiny sacs in their lungs—sacs that extract oxygen from the air and pass it on to the blood. When that happens, white blood cells come to the spot where the silica is trapped, eat up the silica, and die. This causes inflammation at that spot, which in turn attracts more white blood cells. These cells also die, expanding the area of inflammation. Then the body's immune system seals off the area by encasing the inflamed spot and forming a small, round nodule. Scar tissue forms on the lungs, further preventing the flow of oxygen from the lungs into the bloodstream, putting extra strain on the heart by making it work harder.

By 1971 a doctor in Halifax told Freddy that 20 percent of his lung function was gone. Was this an accident? No, but it sure as hell was an injury! Now Freddy had a higher chance of suffering from heart disease, lung cancer and arthritis. And just as an arm or a leg will not grow back, so Freddy's lungs will not heal.

There is no cure for silicosis. The only "cure"

would have been prevention, and in the days when Freddy's lungs were injured no one thought about protective breathing masks. Indeed, no one seemed to care. When a miner complained about shortness of breath, compensation doctors dismissed the complaint, probably wanting to protect the company. X-rays and other testing devices could not prove conclusively that the miner's shortness of breath was due to silicosis. So the miners continued to sacrifice lung capacity to the industry, unless they could afford to hire a lawyer and fight their case.

There is also this complicating factor: When a miner loses fingers, toes, etc., that is usually the extent of the accident. The wounds heal and the miner adjusts to his loss. Lung injury can continue to worsen even after the miner is no longer exposed to silica. If the miner has difficulty making a successful compensation claim for silicosis, what hope does he have of claiming compensation for continuing loss of lung function? What hope does he have to be compensated for diseases caused by silicosis, such as heart disease, lung cancer, tuberculosis, or connective tissue diseases like rheumatoid arthritis? The ordinary miner could never afford to fight his case. The industry won by default.

Freddy Bishop is just one of the hundreds who suffered from silicosis. When I started this story on silicosis, I found it difficult to find an old-time brusher, because most of the old-time brushers are dead.

Freddy retired from Lingan Colliery in 1989. He was 75 years old when we talked. He suffers from shortness of breath, and always will.

Ernie Bishop

ERNIE IS FREDDY BISHOP'S younger brother. Ernie followed his father John (Jack) and his older brothers Freddy and John Jr. into the pit, making his first day in the coal mine less dramatic than it was for most fellows. He says that it just felt like a family matter, the next right step in his life. His father and brothers seemed happy with what they were doing, so Ernie simply took applying at the pit all in stride. His strong, coal miner father, as well as his brothers, were like pioneers who led the way.

The only thing Ernie did not like about the pit was back shift. He says that he almost drew his time when back shift became a production shift. He had to go to work when "even the animals knew enough to go to sleep."

Ernie was born and grew up on May Street in Scotchtown—about one half mile from Daley Road where I grew up. Daley Road was actually an extension of May Street. In 1947, when Ernie was 15, he went to work for Kroliche's grocery store across from Horyl's on Union Highway—better known to the locals as "Crow's." This was the only job he had before he started in 12 Colliery on October 15, 1950.

He went through the same routine to get a job as most of us in those days—called to the steel plant office in Sydney for a medical exam. However, Ernie was turned down the first time he tried because of high blood pressure. Who knows why? The excitement? The pressure not to fail where his relatives had succeeded? Maybe it was the shock of a small-town boy stripped naked among 20 or 30 other guys, and having his testicles squeezed during the examination. Whatever it was, he was re-examined and accepted as fit enough to work in the New Waterford coal mine.

Ernie's first shift was cleaning around the Sydney Mines Loader in preparation for moving it in the level, closer to the coal face. This was a safe, easy, break-in job. Sydney Mines Loader was a 100-to150-foot conveyor unit; a lot of spillage had to be cleaned from around it before it could be rolled in on the rails on which it moved. From this job Ernie was "promoted" to working in the gob with another Scotchtowner, Frankie Selvet. Now the work got dangerous, and more brutal, but Ernie handled it well, doing the same "gob job" on several different walls—removing the many roof supports, rebuilding them closer to the coal face, letting the roof cave in over the mined-out area from which the supports had been removed. He worked in the gob for about four months, then went loading coal in 17 West for overman Frank Shema.

This was a short wall, about 200 feet long, with only 11 loaders; but it was a top wall, which meant that the velocity of the ventilating air through there was vicious. The air had to be forced down to 21 West, about 2000 feet below. When the men in the pit got to the wash house at the end of the shift, everyone could tell the fellows who worked on 17 West because of their wind-reddened eyes. To this day, remembering that wall and the work involved in loading coal on it makes the 71-year-old Ernie shake his head, wondering how he did it. He concludes that he had more "determination" then, and agrees that this is all any of us knew, so we saw nothing extraordinary about it.

Ernie loaded coal on this and other walls for a year or so, and he must have been a good worker, because when mechanization came in he was recommended for a job on one of the Dosco Miners, the first "continuous miners," that came into 12 Colliery. The company was looking for a special breed of man to operate these things. Management would meet and the overmen would be asked for the names of their most dependable men. At that time, Ernie was loading coal in 18 West for overman Albert Penny, and Albert recommended Ernie for the new training. Management put Ernie on 19 East, "fleeting" the Dosco Miner.

"Fleeting" was what the miners called it, but the technical name was "flitting." It meant that Ernie's job was to take the Dosco Miner back up the wall after it had made a cut of coal the length of the wall. He had to ready the Miner for its next five-foot-wide cut down the longwall on the next production shift. Ernie did the same work on 18 East for a while, and then he advanced from "fleeting" the Dosco Miner to actually cutting coal with it. He operated the Dosco Miner on the same walls on which he had been fleeting. Ernie was finally moved to 22 East, and settled down cutting coal there for eight years. It was on this wall that he had his accident.

The Dosco Miner measured close to five feet wide, four feet high, and about twenty feet long, and it weighed around ten tons. It had a cutting "gib" on the front—something like seven giant chain saws all in a row. Hydraulically, the front end of this gib chewed its way 18 inches into the coal; then the gib was lifted as it cut upwards, continuing to tear into the coal. Then it was returned to the bottom of the coal seam, pushed 18 inches into the coal again, raised up as it cut another five-foot wide swath through the coal—and so on down the wall, 18 inches at a time.

The dust behind the Dosco Miner was unimaginable. It was so thick that the operator could not see where the gib was at any given time, so he and his buddy took turns as the "spotter." The spotter would situate himself just down the wall, slightly below the Miner, out of the dust so he could see the cutting gib. He would flash light signals to his cutting buddy, telling him when to stop the gib from going too high or too low.

It was February 7, 1964, on a Friday night shift

on 22 East wall in 12 Colliery. Ernie was cutting and his buddy Malcie MacNeil was spotting for him. It was about 7 p.m., and they were about halfway down the wall. Steel "German jacks" were in use at the time and as the Dosco Miner cut its way down the wall, steel "rails" were laid across the roof every six feet or so, and a jack was put under the face side of the rails.

Ernie had just cut the coal past where there should have been a rail put up across the roof. At this point, they were unable to put one there because they could not connect it to its companion gobside rail. No big deal, since that meant only about 12 feet of unsupported roof—and the roof looked good. They kept cutting, planning to put up a steel strap and jack at the next place for one.

Sloppy maintenance, however, caused a problem at this next place. There was a jack there that was supposed to have been removed on the maintenance shift.

Once Ernie had cut a little bit past this neglected jack, one of the guys putting up the rails and jacks behind the Dosco Miner tapped him on the shoulder, signaling him to stop cutting so they could support the roof. First, however, the forgotten jack had to be removed by Ernie's cutting shift, so that a steel rail could be laid across the roof and that same jack put under the face end of that steel rail. Ernie stopped cutting, stepped a few feet up the wall from the machine, and leaned his back against the wall with his feet slightly out in front of him. There was not enough space to stand up straight. Ernie left the Miner running, because the guys could do this steel-and-jack set-up in two or three minutes. As coal mining would have it, however, it was almost an eternity for Ernie.

The roof-supporting crew started to remove the jack. One of them gave its locking pin a tap or two to let it down as gently as possible, but this time it was like trying to gently defuse a bomb, and failing. The roof "exploded" behind the Dosco Miner, right where Ernie was leaning against the wall. The weight of the collapsing stone drove Ernie's chin hard into his chest, pressing down on him so that his feet slid out from under him and he was driven into a sitting position. The falling stone continued to crush him into a doubled-up position so that his face was pushed hard between his legs and hammered solidly into the duff on the pavement. So completely and violently was Ernie doubled up that his bladder emptied into his own face.

Ernie struggled desperately against the weight of the falling stone, but it overpowered him, pinning him to the pavement. He was horribly doubled up, helpless now, and certain that he was being killed by this fall of stone. He began to lose consciousness.

In the midst of the surprise, violence and pain— in his semi-conscious state—a mysterious peace descended upon Ernie. As he was slipping away, he felt thankful that he was the only one under the fall of stone. Most of all, he remembers "the brightest light you ever want to see in your life." He felt very peaceful, and knew that "this was it"—he was going to die.

But his buddies on the other side of the stone were not about to let that happen.

Clinically, Ernie was right. It took them ten minutes to get him out from under the stone. When they did, they could not get a pulse. Then he started to come around, and Ernie says that he never felt so sick in all his life. He was so sick that he just wanted to be left alone. He resented his buddies pulling on him to move him out of harm's way. He must have told his buddies to just leave him alone, but they overruled him, telling him that they had to move him because the place was "still working." They had to get him to a safer spot.

George Kearney was one of Ernie's buddies on that shift, and was himself buried to the waist by the same fall. He remembers seeing the fall of stone moving a bit as Ernie struggled to lift himself from under it. George, Malcie MacNeil, Kenny Pastuck, Derek Tatlock, and others got a bait-and-pry, hoping to lift the heaviest stone from off Ernie's head. When they pried it up, the stone split, easing the pressure on Ernie while they kept digging frantically with their hands.

Ernie's brother Freddy was also there, working on the same wall. He came to the scene when he heard of the accident. When they got Ernie out, he was semi-conscious, and George says that he would not give the proverbial "two cents" for him. Malcie also thought that Ernie was "finished," because he looked "terrible," and was "squashed up" and scarcely breathing.

They straightened Ernie out and laid him on a stretcher. There was still hard going ahead. Both George and Malcie said that they had a terrible time getting Ernie down the wall on a stretcher because of the extremely cramped space through which they had to carry him. George thinks it could have taken about an hour to get Ernie down the wall and into an empty coal box—a box still left on the trip that was being loaded—and on the way out. When they did get him to the landing on the outside of the level, Ernie's father Jack was there, on his way down for back shift. He stopped at 22 East when he heard of the accident. Ernie was able to tell his very concerned father that he was "okay."

Word came to the surface that it was Ernie's brother Freddy that had been in the accident, and that he had been killed. That is the first word that got to their mother, but when she heard it, she said, "No, it is not Freddy, but Ernie." She was about a mile away from 12 Colliery, and about another two miles away from the underground scene of the accident, but she knew that it was Ernie. There is something about the reach of love that we will never be able to understand on this side of the grave.

As the facts filtered through during the night, Ernie's mother called Alma, Ernie's wife, and told her that Ernie had been in a serious accident. Alma went over to her mother-in-law's house, and was there only for a short time when her sister-in-law phoned and said that Ernie was dead. It was grapevine news, but Alma accepted it as the real thing, leaving for the hospital to see her dead husband. When she got there she saw that Ernie was still alive, but from the look of him Alma was not sure how long he would live. Ernie's face was covered with a mess of tiny blood blisters from when he had been rammed so violently into the duff. His eyes were bulging out as if he was still being choked; and he was suffering a lot of pain. X-rays later showed that there was significant damage to Ernie's vertebrae.

George Kearney says that when he went in the day after the accident, Ernie's head was twice its normal size. But the worst was over for Ernie, and he was beginning to recover. Today, Ernie proudly displays a Turtle Club certificate awarded to him on April 30, 1964. This award is given to those whose safety helmet is credited with helping to save their lives. After five days in the hospital, Ernie still didn't feel well, but he asked the doctor if he could go home, since they could do nothing more for him there. He figured that he could lie down at home as well as in the hospital. So, in the middle of a snowstorm, Ernie and Alma called a taxi and went home.

Ernie felt like going back to work after about four weeks, but his nerves were bad. When he did go back, he asked the manager for an easier job to give him a little break from cutting coal. The manager put him back on his old job of "fleeting" for three weeks. Then he went back to cutting coal on 22 East again, settled in at operating the Dosco Miner, and stayed with it four more years.

Like most injured coal miners, Ernie was not satisfied with how he was treated by the Compensation Board, saying that he "fought tooth and nail for years and years," but all he got was an "insultingly small" pension. One doctor recommended compensation for 20% disability, but the Compensation Board would not even accept that low amount. Ernie says that if his accident had caused an amputation, it may have been easier, since that would be visible, but he couldn't show them his pain—all he could do was tell them about it. And they would not accept his claim. On one occasion, he was off work 16 weeks with back pain, and there were times when he would go to work bent and twisted, hoping the kinks would work themselves out during the day. His buddies would tell him that he was crazy to come to work in that condition, but what else could he do to provide income for his family? Eventually, guys like Ernie must have made some impact, because in recent years changes are being made in the Workers' Compensation Act, changes that support workers with chronic pain—40 years after Ernie's accident.

Albert Young

ALBERT SAYS THAT HIS FATHER was "sore as
hell" when Albert decided to go into the coal mine
and—from his father's point of view—for good reason. Albert had graduated with Grade 12 from St.
Ann's High School, Glace Bay, in 1947. At that time
even Grade 11 was a big deal. Anyone with Grade
12 was seen as college material. Some colleges at
that time even accepted Grade 12 as a first year of
college. But Albert hated school. He only finished
Grade 12 because his mother's "belt" drove him. She
tried to persuade him to go into the Air Force. Both
parents tried to steer him away from the coal mine,
but Albert was hell-bent to go his own way when he
got out of school.

He graduated in June and went to work in

Toronto at what he soon found out to be "cheap factory jobs," not a bit to his liking. Still, he stayed at it for about two years. Albert wrote home to his older brother John, asking him to watch for a chance to get hired on at one of the coal mines. Albert had decided that he was going back home, even though his father's sister in Hamilton wanted him to stay with her until she could get him hired on at Westinghouse.

A letter arrived from John telling Albert that they were hiring on at the mines. Albert was on his way home.

His father's attitude had not changed. Albert says he nearly ate him when he came back to go into the pit. In those days, the coal mine manager required a note from a young boy's father or guardian, telling the manager that he agreed with his boy going into the pit, and that he would look after him during his first few days underground. In a last-ditch attempt to keep Albert out of the pit, his father refused to give this consent, or to be his guardian when he got hired on. Albert told his dad that if he wouldn't sponsor him to go underground, he would get someone else. His frustrated father had to give in: if Albert went into the coal mine, *he* was going to be the one to look after his son.

Albert got hired on at Number 20 Colliery in August of 1950, at the age of 20. Although it was unusual to start off with heavy work, Albert went loading coal on his very first day: Albert's father was loading coal, and Albert went as apprentice with him. In 20 Colliery at that time, the method of mining was still room-and-pillar. This meant that those loading coal would start at the side of the level and dig the coal away until they had created a large, empty room. When the room would get so large that there was danger of a roof collapse or some other major problem, the miners would go in the level and start digging another room, leaving 40 or 50 feet of coal between the mined-out room and the new one. The 50 feet was known as the "pillar," and served as roof support between the rooms.

Albert was not long finding out that mining coal was very hard work. In those days, the loaders had to "cut, shoot and load" the coal themselves. Under the solid coal face that they were going to bring down, they had to cut a horizontal opening that was six inches high by five feet wide. This was called "undermining," and it was done with a "radial" machine driven by compressed air. Roughly the size and shape of a large timber, this machine was jammed tightly between the roof and the pavement, just beside the coal face. The radial machine would pound a straight, slowly rotating steel bar into the solid coal face, its three picks cutting a six-inch horizontal arc under the coal as it moved the cutting bar in a semi-circle. When that steel bar cut as far as it could into the coal, they would replace it with a longer one and continue cutting, changing the steel several times until the cut was as far in under the coal as they wanted. The longer steels would cut away the "corners" of the arc left by the shorter steels.

With this space cut out under the wall of coal, Albert and his father would bore holes into the coal face using a compressed-air jackhammer. Then they'd get a shotfirer to load the holes with powder and "shoot"—bringing down the coal. Then came the hardest part—shoveling the coal into coal boxes that they pushed on rails in to the wall face.

This whole operation left Albert exhausted after his first day underground. Adding to the labour and adventure, when they were finished and on their way out the level for home, there was a horse lying in the middle of the road. It had a broken leg and couldn't move, so Albert and his father had to crawl over the injured horse to get out. Albert says that the guy who was using the horse to haul coal had to stay with it until a vet came into the pit to kill the animal. He was told that the vet would reach into the horse's rectum and cut a main artery so that it would quickly bleed to death. It is no wonder that Albert remembers his first day in the pit! When he got home, he collapsed on the couch, and when his mother called him for supper he was so sore he could hardly move.

Albert worked at this "cut, shoot and load" routine for his first three years. His father never let up his pressure on Albert to use his education and go to night school, at least to get a better job in the mine. This time Albert followed his dad's advice and took up night studies toward becoming a mine official. That course of studies led to his transfer to 1B Colliery as a shotfirer. Albert didn't like the shotfirer's job because they wanted to put him on salary, which would end his opportunities to make overtime money. So it was a mixed blessing when 1B Colliery closed in 1953, not long after Albert went there as shotfirer. This got him out of the shotfirer's job, but it also left him "on the grass" for about a year.

During that year Albert and Eunice Wilkinson

from Glace Bay got married, even though Albert was now unemployed. They managed financially because Eunice was working, making $17 a week, while Albert was getting the same amount from unemployment insurance. On top of that, Albert was making $10 a day working in a bootleg pit. Their combined income was over $80 a week—very respectable money back in 1953—but the bootleg pit only operated four or five months until winter set in.

About six months later, Albert got hired on again at 20 Colliery, and from 1954 to 1967 he did "just about everything" in the pit. His best and biggest paying job was brushing. One week, when the average coal miner's wage was about $60, he and his buddy made $252, prompting the company's head office in Montreal to call management and ask, sarcastically, if it was a coal mine or gold mine they were running there. However, that money-making party ended. The level Albert was brushing stopped when its wall was finished. Now, Albert's short history as a mine official was about to catch up with him.

He was called into the office one day in 1967, and manager Art MacKenzie "coaxed" him to take the official's job as supervisor. Whether he had a choice or not is in question, but when Albert left the office that day he was a supervisor, and it didn't take him long to find out that he hated the job. He had to give orders now to the men who had been his "buddies" for so long. He went back to management planning to quit the supervisor job, but he was told that there was nothing else for him. He toyed with the idea of quitting the mine altogether but his oldest son Rick was in college and Rick's younger brother Kevin was in high school, so Albert decided to stick with the job and try to make the most of it. Albert says that "after a year or two, it turned out pretty good."

In 1969, 20 Colliery was starting to close down, so Albert went to 26 Colliery as an official.

Albert said that a lot of exciting and dangerous things happened while he was in 26 Colliery. He was in the office the day of an underground fire, June 19, 1975. He was marking time just before going home when his boss burst in—"They tell me that we have a fire in 11 South!" He asked Albert to go back down to help put it out. Eunice was in the hospital at the time and Albert had a heavy family agenda, but he agreed to go down to the fire. Once he got there and saw the flames, he asked himself, "Why in hell am I here in this fire, when my shift is over, and I should be going home?" Other officials and miners at the scene were also questioning the wisdom of staying to fight the fire. Albert's boss, the production manager, sensed their apprehension and said, "Anyone here who does not want to stay can leave now, and nothing will be said about it, but I am asking you to stay." Most of them stayed.

The fire was only on the level at the top of the wall, and only in the roof overhead, but it was stubborn. They put water and stone dust on it, "chasing" it out the level, but when they got it extinguished for about 250 feet, they could see that the fire was going again in behind them back in the level. So they had to go back in and put it out again. After doing this several times, they realized they were fighting a losing battle, so they decided to build a barricade, or "stopping," about 500 feet out from the wall face to try to suffocate the fire. They used stone, stone dust and bags full of stone dust—hot, grueling, heavy work. By the time they had the stopping built almost to the roof, the flames were right there on the other side of it. They never did get the fire out. They built other stoppings and shut the mine down for three months until they were sure the fire had smothered itself. Albert says that the guys deserve a lot more credit than they were given, for staying there and fighting that fire.

Albert lost his brother Fabian in the explosion in Number 26—February 24, 1979. Twelve men were killed there. A story about Fabian Young follows this one, but for now we note that it was two years after his brother died that Albert lost most of his left hand.

It happened after a three-month strike—August to October in 1981. The company had to "reconstruct" a wall—not the wall itself but all the mining equipment on the wall, which was worn out and had to be replaced. It was a "Shearer" wall, and Albert and his crew were given the job of removing the Shearer, while other crews removed the rest of the equipment.

If Albert's crew had taken the Shearer all apart, they would have had four or five pieces to move: a cutting drum on each end, a gear box, a motor, and other smaller parts. Instead, Albert and his men decided that, rather than separate the gear box and motor into two parts—about a three-hour operation—they would leave them connected and take them out as a unit.

They "bulled" the five- or six-ton gearbox-and-motor combination off the wall and a little way out the level, where they lifted it with an air hoist and prepared to push a tram under it. A tram is simply a coal box with its sides cut off, looking like a platform on wheels. With this weighty unit lifted and ready, Albert sent some men for the tram. He noticed a long slab of sawn timber lying on the road under the unit where they would have to push the tram. That slab had to be removed. Albert reached with his left hand to pull it out of the way. Just as he grasped the slab, the chain holding the tons of Shearer parts let go and the gearbox-motor unit dropped right on Albert's hand.

Albert says, "Here I was, caught there!"

One of his men, Ernie O'Brien, ran to the air hoist but had trouble getting it to lift the unit. After what seemed a very long time to Albert, Ernie got the unit raised enough so that Albert could get his hand out. Albert said that there was no pain or any blood, but he did not look closely at his hand. He knew that it was horribly mutilated. His fingers were still on but they had to be in one hell of a mess.

The accident happened about 2 a.m. on the back shift. Albert was on the surface about 3:30 a.m., and at St. Joseph's Hospital around 4 a.m.

Dr. Wadden looked at Albert's hand and said, "I can't do anything with that here," gave Albert a needle, and sent him to the City Hospital in Sydney where a plastic surgeon attended him. Albert still had not taken a close look at his hand, but Dr. Dunn had and he told Albert, "If I operate here, you know what is going to happen"—suggesting that he would have to take the hand off. He said that he could do something if he had the right equipment, and he left it up to Albert whether to go to Halifax or not.

Albert decided to try Halifax. The ambulance left about 6 a.m. for the Victoria General Hospital. When they got to the top of Kelly's Mountain—about 30 miles—he almost told the ambulance driver to turn around and go back to Sydney. It struck him that this whole deal was hopeless. He didn't voice his feelings, so they kept going; but as it turned out the Halifax trip really was not that beneficial.

Around noon, Albert was met in Halifax by his brother-in-law "Junior." This was a blessing for Albert's wife, Eunice, because the last she had heard was a 4 a.m. phone call from the pit to say that Albert had been hurt and was on his way to the Glace Bay Hospital. She did not know what had happened, and Albert was now moving between hospitals so fast that she could not find out. Junior called and told her that Albert was all right but his hand was badly busted. Eunice thought that this would be the end of Albert's working days. She was not far wrong. Albert never worked in the pit again. He put in seven more years with the company, but it was on the surface.

In Halifax, Albert was in the care of a Dr. Parkhill, who spent a full nine and a half hours on the first operation on Albert's hand. Next morning, Albert was in a hospital room, still black with coal dust, but his hand was clean, bandaged, and suspended by a cord and pulley. He still had not really studied the damage. When the doctor took the bandages off two days later, he told Albert, "You did quite a job on it." Albert saw that his index finger was gone, but his other three fingers and most of his hand were still there. There was a huge blood blister the size of a hard ball on the palm side, but the back of his hand looked normal except for the fact that all the skin was missing. The whole palm of his hand was horribly busted. The doctor had taken veins from Albert's right foot, and put them in his hand to carry blood to what was left of the fingers; and he had used wires to take the place of bones, planning to replace the wires with some bone from Albert at a later date.

It was a good plan, but it didn't work. Ten days later, when gangrene set in, the hand had to be amputated from the small stump of his index finger to the wrist joint behind and opposite his thumb. His reconstructed thumb is still there. He stayed in Halifax for seven weeks, and was off work for three months.

When he went back, Albert worked in the computer room on the surface of Number 26, until the fire in 1984 closed the mine. He tried for a pension at that time, but was denied. The manager told Albert that they would find something for him, and sent him to Donkin while they were driving the shaft there. This job was done by a contractor, so Albert felt that he was doing next to nothing and didn't like it in the least. After working for the company for 38 years, Albert retired in 1988. He has mixed feelings about his whole experience, and is in a better position now to understand why his father was "sore as hell" when Albert decided to go into the coal mine in the first place. He says that if he had it all to do over again, and knew what he knows now, he would have to be nuts to go into a coal mine.

Michael Fabian (Fabe) Young

THE YOUNGS BOTH WORKED HARD—Theresa looked after their eight children, and Fabian worked in the coal mine. Fabe thought he had a good idea of what Theresa's work was like, but Theresa could never know much about a miner's life underground. That is the only thing they couldn't share, but that didn't seem to matter. They were happily married for 24 years. Just a few days after their wedding anniversary the words in their wedding vows, "until death do us part," became a reality. At the age of 47, Fabe was one of 12 miners killed in an explosion in Number 26 Colliery—February 24, 1979.

Growing up, Fabe lived at 137 11th Street and

That *Bloody* Cape Breton Coal

Theresa lived at 139, just two houses apart in the New Aberdeen area of Glace Bay. They must have known each other for quite a while but never got really thick until 1952. After a three-year courtship they married on February 19, 1955. Sometime during these early years together, they journeyed to Valleyfield in Quebec to stay with a relative while Fabe checked for employment. But Fabe could not speak French and his Quebec chances were slim. After four months they came back to Glace Bay, and Fabe "put his name in" for the pit. Theresa says that it wasn't very long before he was called to Sydney for his pre-pit medical exam. He passed with flying colours and was hired on at Number 20 Colliery in 1954.

Longwall mining had replaced the room-and-pillar method in 20 Colliery. We don't know what his first break-in job was, but likely it was carrying timber or some kind of maintenance work on a level. After that, he would have been "promoted" to helper in the gob where he would take down and replace roof supports on the wall. Perhaps he was sent as one of three men shifting the shaker pan line, moving 200-pound pans one at a time, shifting them from where the coal was mined out to where the coal face was now. Whatever they had him doing, Fabe would know what it was like to work on his knees in very close quarters, and curse every time he forgot where he was and tried to stand up, ripping his back against a bent cap piece over a timber, or on a low and jagged piece of roof coal. Theresa probably wondered why his bare back had so many scratches and cuts.

After about six years in the pit, it wasn't his back

that took the beating. A fall of stone broke his nose and he was taken to the hospital. That was one day after Theresa had given birth to their son Glen. She was resting in the hospital when Fabe came in to see her and the baby, a patient visiting a patient. Theresa says that Fabe had a permanent black scar on his nose from then on—the mark of coal mining accidents—coal dust trapped under the ripped skin.

In 1971, Number 20 closed, but it began to shut down three or four years before that. Most likely that is why Fabe was transferred to 26 Colliery in 1969. His brother Albert says that eventually Fabe got a steady job in the "stall." Working in the "stall" was roughly the same as loading a section of coal during the hand loading days of longwall mining, the days when 25 to 30 loaders would each shovel their 18- to-21-foot sections of coal. The difference was that now the whole wall was cut and loaded by a machine. That machine had to have the wall of coal in front of it in order to cut. This is where Fabe's job came in.

When the machine—in this case the Anderton Shearer—was through cutting roughly 500 feet of wall, it ended up alongside the coal it had cut, with no coal left in front of it. In order to get the coal in front of the machine again, some coal had to be taken from the wall beside the machine and the machine pushed over, into that empty spot. That empty spot was called the "stall." The stall was created with a combination of a radial machine, blasting powder, and a man with a pan shovel. Once in the stall, the 500-foot wall of coal was once again in front of the Anderton Shearer, and it could again cut the length of the wall. With the double-drum Anderton Shearer cutting both down and up the wall, the guys working at the stalls at both ends of the wall were kept busy. Fabe was one of them.

Meanwhile, events were taking place that were to make Fabian Young famous in the coal mining industry. Unfortunately, he had to die first!

In 1978, radio and TV personality Ann Terry MacLellan was appointed to look after public relations for Devco [the Cape Breton Development Corporation]. One of her first projects was to get a series of pictures for a book on coal mining in Cape Breton. She contacted Sydney photographer Warren Gordon and asked him to visit different sites on Devco properties. Warren decided to go to Number 26 and photograph some miners as they came up to the surface after their shift underground.

To Warren, that was a simple plan. He went to the shaft opening near the end of the shift, set up his tripod, and waited for the miners to surface. He was in for a rude awakening! He was easygoing and no doubt enjoying his job, but Warren didn't know miners at the end of a day's work. The men who come out of the pit are hell-bent to get to the showers, clean up, and go home. Anybody knowledgeable would be well out of the way when the miners bolted out of the cage and stampeded for the showers. Warren was caught off guard. Not only did he see no hope of a picture of a miner, he saw immediately that he would have to get the hell out of the way if his equipment was to survive. He grabbed his tripod and ran. He was ready to give up on his project, but decided to wait until the last cage came up.

His patience paid off. There were always a few

miners who did not want to be in the roaring fore-front of those headed for the showers.

Fabian Young was one of the few to step leisurely off the cage and make his way to the wash house. Warren Gordon saw what he wanted: a dusty coal miner finished with his shift, someone he could talk to. He took him by the arm and asked if he would pose for a picture. Warren got his photograph.

Warren figures he took that photo in 1978. The job for Devco was done, and that was all there was to it. He liked the picture and put it on display. Shortly after, a neighbour of Fabe's brother Albert came to Albert and told him that Fabe's picture was in the window at Warren Gordon's studio in Sydney. Albert himself did not go to check it out, but he told Theresa and suggested that she might go and see if, indeed, it was Fabe's picture. She went three or four weeks later but Warren had taken it out of the window after a week or so and had put it in storage. So the matter was forgotten—until a year later, after the explosion in Number 26 Colliery in which Fabe was killed.

On Friday, February 23, 1979, Fabe went to work on the back shift. That was the last time Theresa saw him. About 3:30 a.m. an explosion ripped through the place where Fabe was working, killing him and eleven other coal miners. His brother Albert was called out and changed clothes, ready to go down and give what help he could, but manager Art MacKenzie told Albert that they had enough men down there now, that he should stay on the surface. Art knew that Fabe was dead, but he never said as much. Albert went over to the office where they were already consoling a father who had lost his son in the explosion, and when Albert walked in they all fell silent. Albert knew then that Fabe was dead. Someone asked him, "Did you hear?" and told Albert the grim news. Albert thanked him for telling him straight out.

Albert was not left guessing.

It was 6:50 a.m. when Theresa got the news from her mother and sister. It was not an early morning phone call. Both of them had heard about the explosion, and came to tell Theresa in person. Theresa says that it was hard to believe, and "very hurtful." The hardest part was that she had seen Fabe for the last time when he went out on back shift Friday evening. And it was a closed coffin. She never saw him again to say goodbye, even after he was dead.

It was now February 28, 1979, and because of so many funerals overcrowding the funeral parlours, Fabe was waked at the glebe house. When Albert and his brother Herb saw the snapshot of their brother Fabe on his closed coffin, they were disappointed at its poor quality, but that was all Theresa had. Then Albert remembered Fabe's picture in Warren Gordon's window. Albert vowed to track it down.

Fabe's was the last of the twelve funerals. But there was to be a memorial service at the Glace Bay Forum for all the miners killed in that explosion. Albert, his brother Herb, and brother-in-law Donnie Popwell did not go to the memorial service. Instead, they went to Warren Gordon's studio to see if they could track Fabe's photo. They wanted a better picture than the one they saw at the wake.

Albert told Warren Gordon about the photo that had been in his studio window. Warren said he often took pictures home because of space limitations, but he was willing to check the studio. He went in back and came out a few minutes later with a file folder marked "Young." "Is this it?" Was it ever! Albert was speechless. Warren asked, "Do you know this guy?" Albert said: " I sure do—he is my brother, and he was killed in the explosion on Saturday!" Warren Gordon was deeply respectful, and told Albert about the stampede experience that led up to this quiet, solid photograph.

It was still the day of Fabe's funeral, and Albert wanted Theresa to see the picture. But it was a powerful photograph, and no one wanted to take it to her for fear of upsetting her even more. For sure, Albert wasn't going to show it to her. So he asked Herb and Donnie if they would take it to her. They wouldn't do it either. So they took it to Theresa's sister's place and asked Ann Marie to show it to Theresa, but she wouldn't do it. As luck would have it, Theresa's mother and dad were at Ann Marie's. Their mother, Mayme Wrice, said that she would take it to Theresa. When Theresa saw the picture, she had a "bad reaction" but, as Albert says, "nothing serious."

Theresa still lives in the same house she and Fabe lived in since shortly after they got married— 84 Centre Avenue. She has been there 45 years. She lived with Fabe for 24 years, and she's been without him another 24 years. Their son Todd was 4 when Fabe was killed. She says that she does not mind talking about Fabe, and the picture brings

Fabe back to her a little bit.

Today, Warren Gordon's photograph of Fabian Young is justifiably famous. It has been selected by the Cape Breton Miners' Museum in Glace Bay as their logo. It will be used for all their promotions worldwide, and to help tell their story.

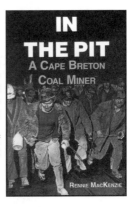

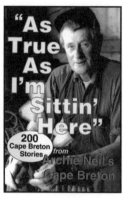

ETHICS
AND LAW
FOR TEACHERS

Kenneth Crook
Derek Truscott

NELSON EDUCATION

NELSON / **E D U C A T I O N**

Ethics and Law for Teachers
by Kenneth Crook and Derek Truscott

Associate Vice President, Editorial Director:
Evelyn Veitch

Publisher:
Joanna Cotton

Acquisitions Editor:
Mike Thompson

Marketing Manager:
Rosalind Wright

Developmental Editor:
Sandra de Ruiter

Permissions Coordinator:
Robyn Craig

Copy Editor/Proofreader:
Gail Marsden

Indexer:
Edwin Durbin

Senior Production Coordinator:
Hedy Sellers

Design Director:
Ken Phipps

Interior Design:
Peter Papayanakis

Cover Design:
Brenda Barratt

Cover Image:
© Frederic Eibner

Compositor:
ICC

Library and Archives Canada Cataloguing in Publication Data

Crook, Kenneth H., 1960-
Ethics and law for teachers/Kenneth H. Cook, Derek Truscott.

Includes bibliographical references and index.
ISBN 0-17-625136-7

1. Teachers—Professional ethics—Canada. 2. Teachers—Legal status, laws, etc.—Canada. I. Truscott, Derek, 1959- II. Title.

LB1779.C76 2006
174'.93711'00971
C2005-906493-5

This book is dedicated to:

Raymond and Una Truscott—for instilling appreciation of the value of ethics, and the power of the written word

and

Gerald A. Neely—lawyer, writer, educator, and good friend

About the Authors

Kenneth Crook is a retired lawyer whose past practice consisted largely of trial work for insurance clients. He has been a member of the British Columbia Bar since 1987. Formerly a partner in the Vancouver law firm of Alexander Holburn Beaudin & Lang LLP, he is now an Associate Counsel within that firm. He has lectured and written extensively in the areas of insurance law, civil procedure, and professional malpractice.

Derek Truscott received his Ph.D. from the University of Windsor in 1989. He is currently an Associate Professor in the Department of Educational Psychology at the University of Alberta. He has published and presented extensively on ethics, standards of professional practice, and life-threatening behaviour.

Table of Contents

Preface

This text evolved out of the realization that there was no single Canadian text that covered both ethical and legal principles for teachers, despite the fact that the understanding of such is a core element in a teacher's education. While there are a number of American texts that canvas this area, the American education system is significantly different from the Canadian one in its historical development, its current organization, and in the values that underpin it. Also, while there are Canadian texts devoted solely to education law, or educational ethics, the former are largely directed towards lawyers, while the latter are directed at educational theorists. Both types of texts have their place and purpose, but it is our view that teachers in training ought to be presented with an opportunity to appreciate the interconnectedness of ethics and law.

The practice of teaching is regulated both by law and by professional codes of ethics and conduct. Laws and codes cannot cover every possible ethically challenging situation that teachers will face, however, and teachers will always have to rely on their own ethical judgement of what the right course of action should be. Such ethical judgement is not simply a matter of personal preference; it must be based on sound ethical principles and reasoning. And because ethical judgements deal with matters of right and wrong, they usually involve our core values and can therefore evoke strong feelings in us. It is not uncommon that these feelings are so strong that our judgement can become clouded. For this reason, an exploration of our own values is an integral part of ethical training. Throughout this book we include questions and prompts for self-reflection that will help you explore your own values relevant to professional behaviour. By doing so, you will have the opportunity to refine your values and gain a clearer understanding of how they are consistent—and perhaps discrepant—with the professional and societal values that underlie the profession of teaching.

In reading this book you will find that many of the examples are taken from legal decisions, often those of the Supreme Court of Canada. The advantage of this, as opposed to hypothetical situations, is that they illustrate in real, live terms the most pressing ethical questions involving teachers in Canada. The cases were largely selected because they involve true ethical dilemmas and the cases should be read critically. You may not agree with the Court's reasoning (and often there is dissension within the Court itself on what is the proper answer) and at the end of the day, within limits, you may not accept their decision. What is important is that you come away with an awareness of the issues facing educators in Canada, and an appreciation of how your conduct will be governed by the codes of ethics and conduct of the profession and the law in the area. What is wholly unimportant at this stage is that you are aware of individual case names and legal citations; we include them only to facilitate more research by the student who may wish to delve further into any particular case. To the greatest extent possible we have simplified the cases, and in many instances focused on only one argument of many presented in the court, while still maintaining an accurate account of the facts of the case and the judge's reasoning.

The first three chapters of the book are introductory in nature; we discuss the nature of ethical systems, the history of education in Canada, and provide a summary sketch of the Canadian legal system. These provide the tools with which to understand the eight chapters that follow, which focus on the primary ethical and legal concerns of teachers. The closing chapter presents a model for how to think in a reasoned, justifiable manner when an ethical issue arises. Throughout the book there are short boxes containing other case law that may be of interest to the reader and specific references to the codes of ethics and conduct; while not central to the text these may provide a starting point for further reflection by the reader.

No book is created in a vacuum and the starting point for this text was the reading lists and syllabus already being used to teach education students in the Canadian universities. A review of all of the codes of ethics and conduct in Canada was made as well as many of the subsidiary publications by the various teaching federations that related to the topic. Finally, we looked at the reasoning of the many judges who have struggled with these ethical problems.

It is our experience that most students when beginning a course on ethics and law in their profession, be it law, psychology, or education, are most interested in how to avoid being sued or running afoul of their code of conduct. As their knowledge increases they become increasingly interested in what are the ethical challenges of the field, and ultimately in developing their own views on how they should be answered. Our hope is that this text may aid them along this path.

ACKNOWLEDGEMENTS

The authors wish to thank the following reviewers for their insight and suggestions that have had a great deal of influence on both the presentation and content of this volume: Elizabeth Campbell, University of Toronto (OISE); Ann Chinnery, University of Saskatchewan; Michael Manley-Casmir, Brock University; Wanda Cassidy, Simon Fraser University; Yvette Daniel, University of Windsor; Kevin McDonough, McGill University; Frank Peters, University of Alberta; Sue Sydor, Brock University; Richard Turcotte, University of Alberta; and Daniel Vokey, University of British Columbia. We would also like to acknowledge our debt to the staff at Thomson Nelson: in particular Cara Yarzab, the senior acquisitions editor; Mike Thompson, the acquisitions editor; Sandra de Ruiter, the developmental editor; and Gail Marsden, the copy editor. We are also indebted to our colleagues at the University of Alberta and Alexander Holburn Beaudin & Lang as well as a number of teachers who provided valuable comments on the text. Above all, of course, we are indebted to our families for their continued support. Finally, we would like to thank Susan Daly of Alexander Holburn for her assistance in the legal research.

CHAPTER 1
AN INTRODUCTION TO PROFESSIONAL ETHICS

You have a student in your class who has been struggling in all of his subjects with a C- average, and he is talking about dropping out as soon as he is old enough. You know that he has a very difficult home life and often looks tired and ill-prepared for his day. The only interest he has expressed about school is taking Computer Studies as an elective, and he shows some aptitude. You know that if he could experience success in one area it could really make a difference for his future. School policy requires a B average in core subjects in order to take electives, however. You speak with him about the situation and he seems to respond to your encouragement to improve his grades. Sure enough, by the end of term his average has improved sufficiently and he enrols in Computer Studies.

As you are packing up after class a few days later, some of the student's friends approach you and tell you that his girlfriend has been doing his homework and assignments for him.

1. *Do you experience any conflict about what to do in this situation? What possible courses of action might you consider?*

2. *What are your thoughts about why you are conflicted about what to do? Why is there not one course of action that is obviously correct?*

3. *What do you think the average person would expect a teacher to do in this situation? How important are these expectations to you when deciding what to do? Why?*

All of us rely on assumptions of right and wrong to guide our behaviour. That is, we all possess a personal ethical sensibility. Most of us have not had the opportunity to think deeply about these assumptions, however. Such unexamined assumptions still shape our view of the world. If you were to discuss the preceding situation with others, even other teachers, you may be surprised by how differently they see the situation. Some may not even see it as an ethical situation. And our understanding of a situation, combined with our (perhaps unarticulated) standards of right and wrong, is a major determinant of how we will behave.

As important as personal ethics are, to be a member of a profession is to undertake an additional level of ethical responsibilities. Professional ethics are not the same as personal ethics, even though the content of professional ethics often derives from ethical principles that we apply in our day-to-day lives. In stating that teaching is a profession in Canada[1] one is not only claiming for its members a certain knowledge or expertise in the area of education, but also a recognition of an obligation to society, parents, and students to act in a certain manner, both individually and collectively. Thus to say one is a professional is to be held to a higher ethical standard than that of an individual.

There is no equivalent of the Hippocratic oath for teachers to serve as a summary description of this obligation. While most, but not all, of the codes of ethics for teachers attempt to capture the essence of teachers' professional ethics by stating that the primary professional responsibility is owed to the students,[2] all of the codes also set out obligations to fellow teachers and staff, to society as a whole (as for example, in the promotion of religious tolerance), and in many cases to the professional body itself. On reviewing the codes of ethics across Canada[3] and the thousands of judgements by the courts on education, it is clear that while there is no unanimity on the specifics of teachers' professional ethics, there are core values that are common and from which one can begin to derive a description of an ethical identity for the profession.

The subject of professional ethics is often perceived by the layperson as a series of rules of conduct and that knowledge of them, in conjunction with

---

1. This book is predicated on the assumption that teaching is a profession. While there is considerable discussion within the field (e.g., Carr, D., 2000. *Professionalism and ethics in teaching*. New York: Routledge), there is also sufficient consensus to accept that teaching is a profession and therefore an enterprise with its own unique ethical requirements. More will be said on this issue in Chapter 4.

2. Federation of Nunavut Teachers' *Code of Ethics*; Manitoba's Teachers' Society *Code of Professional Practice*; New Brunswick Teachers' Association *Code of Professional Conduct*; Newfoundland and Labrador Teachers' Association *Code of Ethics*; Saskatchewan Teachers' Federation *Code of Ethics*.

3. It should be noted that the Quebec system is quite different as, at this point, they do not have a code of ethics. Some of the material one would expect to be contained within such a code is in their *Education Act*. At the time of writing, the possibility of a code, or its equivalent, is under discussion in that jurisdiction.

knowledge of the general laws in the area, should be enough to prevent teachers from going astray. Under this view, a book consisting of the codes of ethics of the profession, and the law that has developed on the practice of teaching, would be exhaustive of the area. Such a book would only be of use, however, if ethics were a static subject, reducible to decisions of what is right versus what is wrong. In fact, the existence of an ethical quandary in professional life may not even be recognized; the right thing to do may not be clear even with knowledge of the codes and the law; or there may be no right answer. And what might constitute a right answer at one time in history may, at a later time, be perceived as an error of ethical judgement.

The reality is that everyday situations faced by teachers are embedded with ethical implications and call for ethical judgement. This book aims to help teachers address such questions as: What do I owe my students, their parents, and society? What are the societal, professional, and legal expectations of teachers? What kinds of punishment are justifiable when a student misbehaves? What do I do when my personal and professional ethics conflict? How do I arrive at a defensible ethical course of action? The answers to these questions are not necessarily reducible to observable facts or agreed-upon rules of behaviour. Nor should they be left to personal whim or preference. Rather, they should be based on sound ethical standards and reasoning. The purpose of this book, therefore, is to promote: first, an *awareness* of situations and circumstances in which ethical judgement is required; second, ethical and legal *knowledge;* and, finally, the *skills* to reason ethically and arrive at a justifiable decision.

The major sources of knowledge used in this book are the codes of ethics and conduct of the provincial and territorial teachers' bodies, and Canadian law and legal decisions. New ethical questions and issues arise more quickly and in greater variety than ethics codes, legal decisions, or textbooks can address them, however. Furthermore, specific answers to questions of ethics usually depend a great deal on the individual circumstances and require extensive thought as to how to behave ethically. For these reasons, professional teachers must become familiar with the foundational principles in each of the areas of ethics, professional standards, and the law. These constitute the core knowledge that teachers need to guide them when a professional consensus has already been reached, and the guiding principles to reason ethically when faced with unique situations. In addition to this core knowledge, comprehensive attention is devoted to the major critical ethical and legal issues that confront teachers: teacher–student boundaries, rights of students, discipline in the classroom, teachers as societal agents, and diversity and fairness. In each of the chapters, teachers' ordinary ethical responsibilities and some of the more troublesome ethical dilemmas are discussed.

Finally, a model for ethical decision making is presented in order to provide teachers with the skills for ethical reasoning. An important aspect of these skills is the ability to explain *how* a decision was reached. With this skill the teacher moves from merely knowing the difference between what is right and what is wrong, to being able to articulate the path of reason used to arrive at the decision.

PROFESSIONAL ETHICS

Ethics is the analysis and determination of how people ought to act toward each other; the rightness or wrongness of behaviour. As such, ethics are primarily *aspirational* in nature and focus on the highest ideals of human behaviour and motivations. Professional ethics is the application of ethical analysis to defining acceptable and unacceptable behaviour of a group of professionals, such as teachers. The terms *ethical* and *moral* are often used interchangeably, particularly in educational scholarship. Philosophers use the term *moral* to describe an assessment of a person's actions when judged against a system of ethics. The common use of the term, however, is often rather ambiguous. *Morality* tends to be associated with rules of behaviour that we have been taught to believe, such as "Don't tell lies." This, of course, is why the term is so often used in educational scholarship; students learn lessons about how to behave from teachers. This is also why teaching is understood to be a moral enterprise.[4]

The adoption of a code of ethics defines a group as professional. If a group of practitioners desires to be acknowledged as a profession and thereby have society grant them the right to practise independently and exclusively, their ethics must be based upon a commitment to ensuring that the members of society who are recipients of their services are protected from harm. A code of ethics creates an implied social contract with the public that balances professional privilege with a commitment to consumer welfare.

WHAT THE CODES SAY

"The impact which the teaching profession has on our society is immeasurable and the quality and character of the individual members of the profession are prominent factors in the economic and moral levels of that society. Therefore, the profession must establish rules of conduct for all who are engaged therein to ensure the highest possible performance standards."

—From the P.E.I. Code of Ethics

In theory, professional ethics can be *descriptive*—what members of the profession actually do; and they can be *prescriptive*—what members ought to do; or *proscriptive*—what members should not do. In practice, most codes of ethics attempt to strike a balance between description and prescription/proscription. Such a balance is not an easy one to strike, however. If a professional body attempts to align its codes of ethics too closely with how its practitioners' behave, it would have to be updated continuously. Such amending would not necessarily be because of an evolution toward more ethical behaviour, but more likely because professional attitudes change.

---

4. See, for example, Nyberg, D. (1990). Teaching values in schools: The mirror and the lamp. *Teachers College Record, 91*, 595–611.

If, on the other hand, the professional body adopts a more prescriptive code, it will likely reflect how the most strident or influential members of a profession feel about the issues that the profession faces. Such a code risks ceasing to reflect the shared values of the profession and thereby being ignored or rejected.

Ultimately, a professional code of ethics should not contain anything that is ethically peculiar or unique. The existence of a professional code of ethics does not indicate that different ethical principles apply to that profession. Rather, it indicates that the members of that profession have a distinct expertise and face ethical challenges that non-members do not. A professional code of ethics should, therefore, represent the application of foundational ethical principles via an ethical system to activities characteristic of or unique to the profession.

While many codes of ethics for teachers contain statements prescribing and proscribing particular conduct, these really do not properly belong in an ethical code.[5] Such statements properly belong in professional standards and law. Professional standards bridge the gap between ethics and legal standards. All professional standards should be consistent with the ethics of the profession. The most important of these is a *code of conduct*. A code of conduct contains definitions of minimally acceptable behaviour for professionals and is intended to function as enforceable rules of practice. The rules are definitive, prescriptive, and proscriptive, and are the standard against which to judge a teacher's conduct in such matters as disciplinary hearings. From time to time professional groups within teaching will also develop guidelines for practice. These guidelines tend to address new developments or areas that present particular challenges to ethical behaviour. They usually bridge the gap between ethics and conduct and integrate specialized knowledge into practice.

The law deals with minimum acceptable standards of behaviour for members of a society—the "do's and don'ts" of behaviour. Laws relating to professionals deal with regulatory matters, principally around standards for admission into the profession, as well as case law that reflects societal expectations of professional behaviour. Because ethical standards are developed by the profession, and given that legal standards represent the values of society at large, sometimes professional ethics and standards are not consistent with the law.[6] Such situations are rare but can be particularly troubling. Fortunately, the courts usually assume that professional codes of ethics or conduct are ethically appropriate, and are therefore extremely reluctant to make rulings that contradict a profession's codes.

---

5. It should be noted that different bodies (professional associations, school boards, etc.) are responsible for the creation and enforcement of professional standards and codes in different jurisdictions. For example, both Ontario and British Columbia have independent professional regulatory colleges, while in other provinces teacher federations or unions are mandated to guide the profession.

6. As, for example, when the courts find that a professional body's standard is not high enough.

1. Is a code of ethics for all professionals desirable? Conversely, should each individual establish her or his own personal standards? Explain your position.
2. Do you think that the codes of ethics should have prescriptive and proscriptive statements? Alternatively, should it be comprised of only descriptive principles? Why?
3. When professional ethics conflict with the law, should teachers obey the law, or decide whether to follow the law or not based on their own personal ethics? Explain your position.

ETHICAL SYSTEMS

Professionals are expected to behave in an ethical manner such that it is not sufficient to say that one chose a particular course of action because it "felt right" or "just seemed to be the right thing to do at the time." Rather, a professional's decisions must be justifiable. This requires a system of ethics to guide decisions.

An ethical system ought to provide a general framework based on principles that are relevant for all members of the group under similar circumstances, whereby appropriate actions can be deduced from the principles by reasoning. Such a system must be specific enough that one knows what to do, and general enough that one knows how to be ethical when encountering new situations. Fortunately, it is not necessary to go into detail regarding all of the competing ethical systems and sub-systems; Canadian society follows almost exclusively the teleological and deontological systems in its professional, social, and legal practices.[7]

Teleological

Teleological[8] systems of ethics operate from the perspective of outcomes or goals. They can also be thought of as *consequentialistic* in that they are concerned with consequences. By far the most common and accepted teleological ethical system is *utilitarianism*.[9] Its basic premise is that an act is right if, all other things being equal, it produces or is likely to produce the greatest amount of good for the greatest number of people. Thus the ethical

---

7. An example of an alternate ethical system can be found in Noddings, N. (1984). *Caring: A feminine approach to ethics and moral education.* Berkeley: University of California Press.

8. The word stems from the Greek words *telos*, meaning "end" and *logia*, "reason." Therefore, "reasoning from ends."

9. Mill, J.S. (1833/1985). *John Stuart Mill on politics and society.* Glasgow: William Collins.

correctness of one's actions is judged on the consequences of the act. A utilitarian approach for teachers would require that they not follow a code of ethics, but rather that they consider the consequences of each possible outcome for each situation that they face. This, of course, can quickly become unwieldy as one tries to consider all of the possible outcomes of all of the possible actions one could undertake. Also, one is faced with the additional difficulty of being unable to predict all of the possible outcomes of one's actions.

A variant of utilitarianism that addresses most of these problems is known as *rule utilitarianism*, which can be stated as, "We should behave in accordance with rules that, all other things being equal, produce or are likely to produce the greatest amount of good for the greatest number of people." Such an approach has the advantage of allowing a profession to codify rules of ethics, and each professional only then has to know which rule to apply to a given situation.

If we consider the example from the beginning of this chapter from a pure utilitarian system perspective you would consider the consequences of the possible responses to the knowledge that the student may have cheated. If the student is found to have cheated, he will likely lose what little enthusiasm he has for school. On the other hand, you do not want the student to learn the lesson that he can cheat in order to get ahead in life. Similarly, the other students think that he has cheated and would learn the same lesson.

From a rule utilitarian system perspective you consider that even though being deceitful can produce desirable outcomes, when it is exposed the resulting outcomes are typically so undesirable that any potential benefits are not worth the risk. You would, therefore, be inclined to act in accordance with the rule, "I will promote honesty rather than deceit."

The greatest philosophical limitation of both forms of utilitarianism beyond their practical difficulties is that they leave unanswered the question of what counts as "good." Some argue that what is good is *hedonistic* or pleasurable; others argue that what is good is what is *ideal* such as honesty, justice, or beneficence; while others argue that it is some mixture of these. And if we could find agreement on what is good, how would we then compare different forms of good and bad outcomes? Is one student experiencing profound humiliation worse than an entire class missing the fun of a dance? Does the outstanding success of one student outweigh the moderate failure of five?

Deontological

The deontological[10] system of ethics maintains that the rightness of an action depends upon whether it is in accordance with, and is performed out of respect for, certain absolute and universal principles. Autonomy, equality, and justice are examples of such principles. Thus, neither the intention to bring about good results nor the actual results of an act are relevant to assessing ethical

---

10. From the Greek word *deont*, meaning "being right." Therefore, "reasoning from what is right."

worth.[11] The deontological system requires that one accept that all people should be treated as equally worthy. That is, that no person be treated as a means to an end, and any person's happiness must count as much as anyone else's. Its basic premise is, "Act as if the principle governing your action were to become a universal law." The test of this is, are you treating others as you would be treated? If you consider behaving toward someone in a way that you would not want yourself, then the principle should not be universally applied and you would not be behaving ethically.

To return to our example of the student who may have cheated, from a deontological system perspective you would ask yourself what ethical principles would be promoted and compromised by the various choices of action. If you chose to not act on the information that the student may have cheated, you would not be acting honestly and with integrity. Given that we generally want others to be honest with us, you would conclude that the ethical course of action is to investigate the possibility that the student cheated. Note that, from a deontological system perspective, you would do so even if you had reason to expect that it would result in undesirable consequences for the student.

The difficulties with a deontological approach to ethics come from two sources. First, there is no consensus as to which principles are universal and absolute. Some people may state that they are quite willing to be lied to if it spares them discomfort, while others might be adamant that they always be told the truth. Second, situations arise whereby principles are at odds with one another. So it could be argued that the principle of equality requires that all students should receive an equivalent portion of an education system's resources, while the principle of autonomy requires that we devote additional resources to maximize the achievements of each student to the extent of their capacity.

Teleological and Deontological Systems Compared

Clearly each system has its strengths and weaknesses. The teleological system provides us with a calculative framework of weighted parameters that allows implementation in an objective fashion. Furthermore, it allows for consideration of the consequences of one's actions on the social and family context in which the student is embedded.

The calculative framework of teleology, however, is also the greatest weakness of the system. By focussing on the social good—greatest amount of good for the greatest number of people—utilitarianism allows for the sacrifice of the individual in the name of the common good. Such an "ends justifying the means" approach stands against the basic value that our society places on the fundamental worth, rights, and duties of the individual. As a society we tend to emphasize the individual person as a being of ultimate worth, and to believe that questions of right or wrong should be decided with reference to universal and absolute principles that preserve, within limits, the autonomy of the person.

---

11. Kant, I. (1959). *Foundations of the metaphysics of morals.* New York: Bobbs-Merrill.

QUESTIONS for REFLECTION

1. Can you think of any important ethical decisions you have had to make in your life and what your decision says about your personal ethical system?
2. How would you respond to the argument that art has no utility and should therefore not be taught in our schools? Can you make an argument from a teleological and a deontological system perspective?
3. By spending extra class time covering a topic you are able to help a struggling student master the material, but most of the rest of the class become bored and lose much of their enthusiasm for the subject. What are the ethical implications of this action from a teleological perspective? From a deontological perspective?

FOUNDATIONAL ETHICAL PRINCIPLES

Systems of ethics will only take one so far in an effort to be an ethical teacher. Whether a teleological or deontological system is employed, teachers need a set of basic ethical principles that can serve as further guidance for professional behaviour. Five ethical principles have become generally accepted as being centrally important for any profession: respect for autonomy, nonmaleficence, beneficence, fidelity, and justice.

Respect for Autonomy

The ethical principle of respecting autonomy deals with honouring the dignity of all persons, the right of individuals to make choices about self-determination, and freedom from the control of others. It can be seen in respecting the right of students to form their own judgements based upon knowledge, and to keep parents and the school community informed of and appropriately involved in decisions about educational programs. It is also reflected in respecting the confidentiality of students in that it acknowledges that each person has the right to decide who has access to their private information.

Note that there is an important distinction between freedom of action and freedom of choice: while people should have the freedom to make choices, their freedom of action is limited by the autonomy of others. So one may accept an individual's right to hold bigoted views, but one does not accept that person's right to promulgate hate literature because that would interfere with the autonomy of the intended victim.

Nonmaleficence

Nonmaleficence means not causing others harm. In more general terms for professionals, nonmaleficence means not inflicting intentional harm nor engaging in actions that risk harming others, as well as being obligated to protect students against harm. Most ethicists agree that, all other things being equal, our obligation to protect and not harm our students is stronger than our obligation to contribute to their welfare. In the medical arena the concept of harm tends to be less controversially understood as physical bodily damage, pain, or death. Teachers rarely deal in such matters and are more likely to be involved in instances of mental harms or thwarting significant personal interests such as self-confidence or privacy.

Beneficence

The principle of beneficence involves actively contributing to the well-being of others. At a basic level that applies to all members of a society, it involves the responsibility to provide aid to those who are in need of assistance. For members of a profession, it includes establishing and maintaining a minimum level of competence in order that professional services might be delivered in a manner that furthers the welfare of our students (see Chapter 4), or seeking to meet the needs of students by designing the most appropriate learning experiences for them. In some respects nonmaleficence and beneficence can be thought of as being on a continuum from not harming others to benefiting them, with beneficence placing a correspondingly greater demand to take positive action, rather than merely refraining from harmful acts. In addition to providing benefit, beneficence also obligates teachers to balance the potentially beneficial consequences of an action against the potentially harmful ones, particularly the autonomy of their students.

Fidelity

Faithfulness, loyalty, honesty, and trustworthiness fall under the principle of fidelity and are at the core of the fiduciary relationship between teachers and their students, parents and society. This principle is particularly important to teachers because it is the foundation for trust, which is at the core of the bond between people, and because of the power differential inherent in the teacher–student relationship (see Chapter 7). Upholding the ethical principle of fidelity involves placing the interests of the student ahead of one's own, even when doing so is inconvenient or uncomfortable.

Fidelity also extends to relationships with colleagues and the community. Teachers have a responsibility to honour contracts with employers, for example, and to act in accordance with the rules of their professional associations. Teachers should also be willing to review with colleagues, students, and their parents/guardians the quality of service rendered by the teacher and the practices employed in discharging professional duties.

Justice

Justice is the ethical obligation to act fairly. In the context of professional ethics it refers to ensuring that all people are treated fairly regardless of their status within society and avoiding bias or unfair discrimination in one's professional actions. The ethical teacher behaves in a manner that respects the dignity and rights of all persons without prejudice as to religious beliefs, sexual orientation, gender, physical characteristics, age, or ancestry. An ethical teacher should also recognize a responsibility to promote a respect for human rights. Justice also deals with fairness and equity in the allocation of access to an education. Because teaching functions as a profession within the context of society, teachers have responsibilities to the societies in which they live and work and by extension to the welfare of all members of those societies. A just society would be one where human rights and liberties are safeguarded, material resources are equally distributed, and there is greater public involvement in societal decision making. Thus, the ethical teacher develops teaching practices that recognize and accommodate diversity within the classroom, the school, and the community. Justice issues are dealt with in detail in Chapter 11.

QUESTIONS for REFLECTION

1. Do you agree that there are universal ethical principles or rules? If so, which ones and why? If not, why not?
2. Do you agree with the view that respect for autonomy should be the most important principle governing the ethical practice of teaching? Why or why not?
3. Do you think that the principle of nonmaleficence would prohibit you from ever inflicting harm on someone in order that good may come out of it? Why or why not?

THE ETHICAL TEACHER

Ethics thus are an essential part of professional practice and the development of what we refer to as an ethical identity is essential for the continued recognition of teaching as a profession. Knowledge of the codes of ethics and the relevant law is part of this ethical identity. Of equal import, however, is an awareness of when ethical issues exist, and an ability to deal with them in a reasoned manner. Teachers, perhaps more than those in any other profession, must work to develop and maintain a professional ethical identity. On a practical level this is because the acknowledgement of teaching as a profession, as opposed to mere employment, has been slow to be recognized and prone to be taken away. On a much broader societal level, teachers have an even greater ethical responsibility than other professionals because a teacher's practice has a strong influence on the moral lessons students learn directly and indirectly.[12] Being an ethical teacher means approaching activities with sensitivity to the ethical issues involved and being prepared to reason ethically in order to act in ethically justifiable ways. The remainder of this book is devoted to providing guidance for achieving this.

WHAT THE CODES SAY

"Education is continually about human beings interacting responsibly with each other. When formulated as questions, the ethical standards can facilitate a process of inquiry into the personal and professional ethics of one's educational practice."

—*From the Ontario* Ethical Standards for the Teaching Profession

---

Summary

Ethics represent the core values of a profession. If teachers claim to be professionals and thereby seek to be granted the right to practise independently, they must abide by a code of ethics that strives to ensure that students, parents, and the community are protected from harm. A professional code of ethics represents the application of foundational ethical principles via an ethical system to activities characteristic of or unique to the profession. The major ethical systems are teleological (consequence-based) and deontological (principle-based). The foundational ethical principles are autonomy, nonmaleficence, beneficence, fidelity, and justice. Being an ethical teacher requires an *awareness* of situations and circumstances in which ethical judgement is required; ethical, professional, and legal *knowledge;* and the *skills* to reason ethically and arrive at a justifiable decision.

Questions for Discussion

1. Consider two people who perform the same worthwhile action and achieve the same beneficial result, but for one the action was much more difficult to perform. Which individual would you consider to be more ethical? Why?

---

12. Campbell, E. (1997). Connecting the ethics of teaching and moral education. *Journal of Teacher Education, 48,* 255–263.

2. If ethical standards can be objective, how can one avoid becoming dogmatic? If ethics are subjective, how can anyone be held accountable for their behaviour?
3. What should a teacher do if she or he does not accept the ethical standards of the profession? Can one still be a teacher? Why or why not?

Further Reading

Campbell, E. (2003). *The ethical teacher*. Maidenhead, England: Open University Press.

Carr, D. (2000). *Professionalism and ethics in teaching*. New York: Routledge.

Sockett, H. (1993). *The moral base for teacher professionalism*. New York: Teachers College Press.

Strike, K. A., & Ternasky, P.L. (1993). *Ethics for professionals in education: Perspectives for preparation and practice*. New York: Teachers College Press.

CHAPTER 2
THE DEVELOPMENT AND ORGANIZATION OF EDUCATION IN CANADA

During the course of a social event a parent asks you, "Why is it that we have two elementary schools, one for Catholics and the one where my child attends less than two blocks from each other? Isn't this just a waste of taxpayers' money?"

1. *Do you think this is a question you should be expected to know the answer to? Why or why not?*

2. *How would you answer this parent's question? If you don't know, how would you go about finding an answer?*

3. *Does knowledge of the organization of Canada's educational system play a role in your personal ethics of teaching? Explain.*

The development of the Canadian education system reflects the social, political, and religious history of our nation. This history is characterized by a series of political compromises and accommodations originally designed to protect the interests of the French and English colonists and their existing Protestant and Catholic school systems that had been established in the years prior to Confederation. The formation of Canada created a framework for the provision of education that has had long-lasting effects and continues to shape education in Canada today. An appreciation of the history of the Canadian education system is central to understanding much of what society expects of schools and teachers and has profound legal and ethical consequences, particularly as reflected in important and sometimes bewildering court decisions.

PRE-CONFEDERATION EDUCATION

French parish priests developed the first European system of education in Canada during the early 1600s in the regions of North America now recognized as Nova Scotia and Quebec. Education was under the control and sponsorship of the Roman Catholic Church in the same manner as it was in France at that time. By 1756 there were some 88 established parishes in New France (as it was known, now Quebec), each with its own school. These schools offered basic instruction in religious doctrine, reading, writing, and arithmetic. While there was no public support for education in the form of taxes, the Church provided indirect support by supplying priests and nuns, and the King of France made direct cash and land grants to the Church for educational purposes in the colonies. Local priests provided education to the children of the colonists in each settlement that established a parish.

Lower Canada

In 1763 the British conquered New France and introduced their system of education that was supported by a mix of public monies and private tuition, as opposed to the Church as it was under French rule. Such a drastic change dealt a very hard blow to the existing education system and two generations of French Canadians grew up practically without the benefit of schooling. For the next hundred years of Canadian history a variety of acts were passed under British rule in an effort to establish a centralized government—and educational system—while at the same time appeasing French Canadians by allowing them some freedom to live as they saw fit. This compromise dealt primarily with religious freedom, which was inseparable from education under the former French system. With the passing of the *Quebec Act, 1774* the rights of Quebec Catholics to practise their faith "subject to the King's Supremacy" were protected. In 1829 the Legislature of Lower Canada (previously New France, now Quebec) was given authority over schooling and schools were placed under the control of a locally elected school board rather than a church body, with government grants to build schools and pay teachers. This, in turn, lead to the establishment of non-Catholic (known as "dissentient") schools in Quebec and two distinct denominational education systems: French Catholic and English Protestant.

Upper Canada

In Upper Canada (now Ontario), schooling developed in a more haphazard manner than the French tradition of church-supported parish schools. English-speaking immigrants from the United States, Scotland, Ireland, and England found life hard and devoted little time to cooperative undertakings such as schools. The first schools were established in the late 1700s without government assistance essentially by anyone who felt so inclined. In the period between 1800 and Confederation (1867) a system of education developed that was partially supported by government grants with the majority of funds provided by tuition fees. Although the schools were not church run, English-speaking parents did expect that their children's schools would stress the importance of the Bible and God.

By the time of Confederation there existed three broad classes of schools: common schools, grammar schools, and separate schools. The *School Act, 1841* allowed for the establishment of local school boards and schools, and the empowerment of trustees to hire and fire teachers and make rules for the good government of schools. Boards of education were set up to apportion monies received from the legislature and to control the texts used. These common schools were intended to provide schooling for the "common" or average person. Sadly, the teachers in these schools were typically barely literate themselves and often characterized as alcoholic. This is perhaps not so surprising given that they were poorly paid and could rarely afford their own lodgings; many communities took turns among the parents boarding the teacher in lieu of pay.

Grammar schools were designed to give students the opportunity to learn the language and literature of Greece and Rome in order to prepare for further university studies. Interestingly, grammar schools were not intended to be post-common school education—the subjects taught rather than the age of students distinguished them—and they were almost completely populated by children of well-to-do families. Today's system of elementary schooling for younger children who, when they become teenagers, progress to secondary schooling to receive an education broader than the "Three R's" is a construct of the latter decades of the last century.

The *School Act, 1841* also enshrined the rights of those professing a religious faith different from the majority in a township or parish to establish their own school. Trustees of these "separate" schools were granted the same power as those in common schools to regulate what was taught, the textbooks used, and the appointment of teachers but were required to report to the District Superintendent of Common Schools. By 1863 separate schools could share in municipal as well as provincial monies.

Thus, at the time of Confederation the need for protection of a separate school system, based primarily on religious affiliation but with roots in national origin (French vs. English), was already established in English-speaking Upper Canada (now Ontario) and French-speaking Lower Canada (now Quebec).

THE *CONSTITUTION ACT, 1867*

With the formation of Canada through the passing of the *British North America Act, 1867* (re-enacted and re-titled the *Constitution Act, 1867* by the *Constitution Act, 1982*) a framework for the provision of education was established. The form that schooling would take in the new country was not a prominent issue in the negotiations around Confederation; essentially only Section 93 of the *Constitution Act, 1867* deals with education. Instead, by granting exclusive legislative authority to the provinces (as we now know them) to make laws in relation to education, schools "as they existed at the time of Union" would be allowed to continue. Thus, Section 93 of the *Constitution Act, 1867* was designed to protect the two dominant religious groups:

93 (1) Nothing in any such Law shall prejudicially affect any Right or Privilege with respect to Denominational Schools which any Class of Persons have by Law in the Province at the Union:

(2) All the Powers, Privileges, and Duties at the Union by Law conferred and imposed in Upper Canada on the Separate Schools and School Trustees of the Queen's Roman Catholic Subjects shall be and the same are hereby extended to the Dissentient Schools of the Queen's Protestant and Roman Catholic Subjects in Quebec;

(3) Where in any Province a System of Separate or Dissentient Schools exists by Law at the Union or is thereafter established by the Legislature of the Province, an Appeal shall lie to the Governor General in Council from any Act or Decision of any Provincial Authority affecting any Right or Privilege of the Protestant or Roman Catholic Minority of the Queen's Subjects in relation to Education:

(4) In case any such Provincial Law as from Time to Time seems to the Governor General in Council requisite for the due Execution of the Provisions of this Section is not made, or in case any Decision of the Governor General in Council on any Appeal under this Section is not duly executed by the proper Provincial Authority in that Behalf, then and in every such Case, and as far only as the Circumstances of each Case require, the Parliament of Canada may make remedial Laws for the due

Execution of the Provisions of this Section and of any Decision of the Governor General in Council under this Section.

This protection of both the Roman Catholic minorities in Upper Canada, Nova Scotia, and New Brunswick, and the Protestant minority in Quebec was pivotal to Confederation being achieved, as a commentator from the time observed:

> That but for the consent to the proposal of the Hon. Sir Alexander Galt, who represented especially the Protestants of the great province of Quebec . . . that in the Confederation Act should be embodied a clause which would protect the rights of minorities, whether Catholic or Protestant, in this country, there would have been no Confederation. . . . I say, therefore, it is important, it is significant that without this clause, without this guarantee for the rights of minorities being embodied in that new constitution, we should have been unable to obtain any confederation whatever.[1]

The importance of this "Great Compromise" cannot be overstated; not only did it allow for Confederation it also shaped education in Canada in ways very different from either England, France, or the United States. In particular, by placing the control of education under provincial auspices, there is no explicit constitutional guarantee of an education in Canada, apart from the religious minority provisions, nor are there Canadian standards for the services that must be provided.

Catholic and Protestant separate schools and school boards now exist in a variety of forms across Canada. This reflects the status of denominational schools in the provinces prior to entry into Confederation, and the outcome of legal and political challenges since. The most significant challenge to Section 93 occurred in Manitoba in 1890 when the legislature abolished the Catholic and Protestant systems in favour of a non-denominational system in which religious exercises are subject to the regulations of an advisory board. Despite a series of court cases and attempts by the federal government in 1896–1897 to introduce remedial legislation, Manitoba remains a strictly non-denominational public system.

PROVINCIAL CONTROL

While Section 93 protected the rights of separate schools it did not "freeze" those rights; provinces were free to make new laws concerning education, subject to a right of review to ensure that such legislation did not degrade the

---

1. Tupper, C. (1896). Debates of the House of Commons, 6th Sess., 7th Parliament, 59 Vict. 1896, col. 2719, at 2724, March 3, 1896.

privileges enjoyed up to that point by the denominational schools. Some have argued—unsuccessfully—that because secondary education did not exist at the time of Confederation the rights conferred onto the separate school system did not extend past elementary education and by extension there was no obligation to provide funding for such an education system (Bill 30, an act to amend the *Education Act* (Ontario), *1987*). The Supreme Court noted that the intent of Section 93 was to secure the denominational minorities' interest in separate but suitable education for their children into the future and as such had to be read in a manner that would allow for changes to achieve its goals.

As subsequent provinces entered Confederation their statutes varied to some extent the wording contained in Section 93. By way of example, the *Alberta Act, 1905* provides that:

> 17 Section 93 of The British North America Act, 1867, shall apply to the said province [Alberta], with the substitution for paragraph (1) of the said section 93, of the following paragraph:
>
> 1. Nothing in any such law shall prejudicially affect any right or privilege with respect to separate schools which any class of persons have at the date of the passing of this Act [September 1, 1905], under the terms of chapters 29 and 30 of the ordinances of the North-west Territories, passed in the year 1901, or with respect to religious instruction in any public or separate school as provided for in the said ordinances.

Thus the protection offered varies depending upon the wording of the statute and the conditions existing at the time of entering into Confederation. In the case of Ontario, Nova Scotia, New Brunswick, Prince Edward Island, and British Columbia Section 93 applies directly; although it should be pointed out that as only Ontario had denominational schools established "by law" the guarantees contained in Section 93(1) apply only to that province. Manitoba entered Confederation with a variant on Section 93 that omits subsection 2. The provincial statutes became part of the constitutional fabric by virtue of incorporation into the 52(2) of the *Constitution Act, 1982*. Finally, in the case of Quebec (Constitution Amendment, 1997) and Newfoundland (Constitution Amendment, 1998) recent amendments have removed denominational educational rights altogether; or, in the case of Newfoundland, guarantees religious observances in school when requested by the parents and allows for non-denominational religious courses.

OTHER CASES OF NOTE

What right do other religious groups have for publicly funded schools? See *Adler v. Ontario,* [1996] 3 S.C.R. 609 and then compare to the United Nations Human Rights Committee case of *Waldman v. Canada,* CCPR/C/67/D/694/1996.

FIRST NATIONS EDUCATION

An extremely important exception to Section 93 of the *Constitution Act, 1867* was the education of First Nations people that remained a federal responsibility by virtue of Section 91(24). Registered (or status) Indians are persons whose names are included on a register kept by the Department of Indian and Northern Affairs Canada, and their schooling is a constitutional responsibility under the *Indian Act*. The education of status Indians living away from reserves and non-status Indians was and is a provincial responsibility.

The early history of the federal government's implementation of their responsibility for First Nations education was to enlist the services of the churches to operate schools. A number of different forms of schooling were tried, from local day schools to the now-infamous residential schools. The general goals of these schools were to Christianize Aboriginal children and to assimilate them into Euro-Canadian culture. By the 1960s the federal government began to take a more direct role and implemented programs to integrate status Indian children into provincial school systems through payment transfers, as well as operating federal schools. In the 1970s and '80s moves began to be made toward developing a First Nations educational system with the authority and administration being controlled by individual First Nations. More will be said about the issue of First Nations in Chapter 11.

THE *CANADIAN CHARTER OF RIGHTS AND FREEDOMS* AND EDUCATION TODAY

With the enactment of the *Charter of Rights*, the guarantees contained within Section 93 were further enshrined in the law, the extent of which will be dealt with at length in the next chapter. In addition, however, the *Charter* was intended in part to promote and protect the two official languages by providing that Canadian citizens whose mother tongue is English or French and who reside in a linguistic minority community are entitled to have their children educated in the language of the minority (*Charter of Rights*, 1982, section 23). The section was again a political compromise and was intended to be remedial of a number of defects found in the existing provincial legislation by not only allowing a choice of language instruction but by requiring that facilities be provided for it.

OTHER CASES OF NOTE

What is the interplay between the equality sections of the *Charter* and the right of Quebec francophone parents to have their children educated in English? See *Gosselin (Tutor of) v. Quebec (Attorney General)*, [2005] S.C.J. No.15.

PUBLIC AND PRIVATE SCHOOLS

Schooling in Canada today continues to be shaped by a cultural and legislated belief that education be at least a partial reflection of the community within which it operates. Thus, we distinguish between public schools and private (or "independent") schools. The public school system continues the belief that education should be available to all who fall within a certain age group, and that this education should be administered by the state. It is funded to a large extent through public funds (although schools are now increasingly being required to raise additional monies on their own) and in many cases is viewed as non-denominational or purely secular. Private school systems, which may be recipients of some public funds, are largely self-supporting and managed by boards or individuals, sometimes as corporations (either for profit or not). They exist because their members believe that certain aspects of educational growth, such as religious tenets or academic rigour, are not being provided in the public school system. Their curriculum is governed, to some extent, by provincial legislation (for example, see British Columbia's *Independent School Act*) but is not as set as would be found in a public school environment.

OTHER CASES OF NOTE

To what extent can a parent teach their own child as they see fit? Consider *R. v. Kind*, [1984] N.J. No. 243, 50 Nfld. & P.E.I.R. 332 and then compare to *R. v. Jones*, [1986] 2 S.C.R. 284 and *R. v. Powell*, [1985] A.J. No. 456.

The public school system is further divided between non-secular schools and denominational separate schools (usually Catholic); the latter receive full public funding and are subject to state control. Most of the constitutional cases involving education turn on the question of funding public denominational schools; at this time only three provinces (Alberta, Saskatchewan, and Ontario) have such schools. Like public non-denominational schools their curriculum is state controlled; however, in order to qualify as a denominational separate school board they must offer religious instruction. The terminology is confusing as "public schools" are often used in case law to refer to public non-denominational schools as opposed to denominational public schools. The determination of which usage is intended can usually be determined by the context.

MINISTERS OF EDUCATION AND DEPARTMENTS OF EDUCATION

Within each of the provinces and territories the administration of the school system falls under the authority of the Minister of Education who has the right to control what is taught in the schools, subject to the right of religious instruction,[2] and to make policies in respect to education within the province. Within the provinces of Ontario, Alberta, Saskatchewan, and the territories of the Yukon, Northwest Territories, and Nunavut, legislation provides for denominational minorities to operate separate school systems (typically Roman Catholic); most also provide for First Nations schools operated by bands.[3] The Ministry is also responsible for the licensing of teachers (except in British Columbia and Ontario where that role resides with the College of Teachers), and therefore has considerable control over teachers as a professional group.

Typically in the case of public schools, the Minister will have the right to create or eliminate school divisions or districts, and delegates the routine operation to school boards. The power of a school board is therefore subject to ministerial control, including its dissolution. The school board itself is composed of elected members from the local community; it is the intent that it represents the diverse views of all sub-communities within that larger group rather than the views of the individual elected members.[4] In particular, a school board cannot be ruled by a particular religious or moral point of view, even if that view is one accepted by the majority of the school board. While the primary teaching materials are determined by the Minister, supplementary learning resources are usually selected by the school board; an important role that has resulted in a number of pivotal decisions on the power of school boards. (This aspect will be discussed in greater depth in Chapter 10.)

SCHOOL BOARDS AND PARENT COUNCILS

School boards are also responsible for the hiring of teachers, subject to the provincially established qualifications. Teachers may be employed under a continuing, temporary, interim, probationary, part-time, or substitute teacher contract—the terms of which are subject to the provincial acts, and the collective agreements reached between the teaching associations and the boards. (The role of teaching associations is discussed in Chapter 4.) In order to provide some measure of employment security, internal review boards were instituted to govern the dismissal and suspension of teachers; these were a relatively late innovation with Alberta, Saskatchewan, and Ontario creating them in the 1930s while they did not come into existence in British Columbia until the 1970s.[5]

Many of the school acts recognize the right of parents to be involved in the management of their children's education (for example, the Preamble to the *Alberta School Act* provides "WHEREAS parents have a right and a responsibility to make decisions respecting the education of their children"), and allow for the

---

2. For example, the *Alberta Education Act*, Chapter E–1.12, s. 6.

3. For example, the *Yukon School Act*, Vol. 4, Ch.155, s.230.

4. *Chamberlain v. Surrey School District No. 36*, [2002] S.C.J. No. 87.

5. Piddocke, A., Magsino, R., & Manley-Casmir, M. (1997). *Teachers in trouble: An exploration of the normative character of teaching*. Toronto: University of Toronto Press.

establishment of a parent advisory council for individual schools (for example, the *B.C. School Act*) or districts. Such councils, as the name suggests, are to advise schools as to how greater scholastic achievement can be achieved, on suspensions of students (*Yukon School Act*), and the conditions of the premises and extracurricular activities. Although Parent Advisory Councils can only make recommendations, they have an important role in giving a voice to the local community in the schools. There is a wide range of structure of such committees; some councils, for example, have extensive bylaws and place restrictions on their members in order to avoid bias. For example, the bylaws for the Vancouver School Board state that "The DPAC shall be non-partisan politically, as shall its members when speaking/acting on its behalf." In general members of the councils are voted in for one-year terms and must be parents of children attending that school. Some school acts (e.g., British Columbia) specifically exclude members of any school board from serving on a council, although such provisions may be contrary to the *Charter*.[6]

Summary

French parish priests developed the first European system of education in Canada during the early 1600s under the control and sponsorship of the Roman Catholic Church. When the British conquered the French settlers they brought their own system of education that was a mix of public monies and private tuition. A variety of acts were passed under British rule in an effort to appease French Canadians by allowing them religious freedom, which was inseparable from education under the former French system. By the time of Confederation local school boards oversaw schools, board trustees hired and fired teachers, and boards of education apportioned monies received from the legislature. Those professing a religious faith different from the majority in a township or parish were also allowed to establish their own school and school boards. With the passing of the *Constitution Act, 1867*, this system of public and separate schools was adopted, and it continues to shape education in Canada today.

Questions for Discussion

1. How has the professional status of teachers in the eyes of Canadians been shaped by the history of our educational system?
2. Do you think the "Great Compromise" was good for education? How might you have resolved the problem of disparate educational systems? Why?

---

6. *Ontario Public School Boards Assn. v. Ontario (A.G.)* (1999), 175 D.L.R. (4th) 609.

3. Should there be national standards of education? What are the advantages and disadvantages of your position?
4. What is the impact on the profession of teaching that most of the law dealing with education is directed toward minority religious protection?
5. Some commentators have criticized private schooling as taking away resources from public schooling, or for creating a multi-tiered approach to education. Do you agree with this?

Further Reading

Axelrod, P. (1997). *The promise of schooling: Education in Canada 1800–1914.* Toronto: University of Toronto Press.

Guppy, N., & Davies, S. (1998). *Education in Canada: Recent trends and future challenges.* Ottawa: Minister of Industry.

Manzer, R.A. (1994). *Public schools and political ideas: Canadian educational policy in historical perspective.* Toronto: University of Toronto Press.

Martel, A. (2001). *Rights, schools and communities in minority contexts: 1986–2002 toward the development of French through education, an analysis.* Ottawa: Office of the Commissioner of Official Languages.

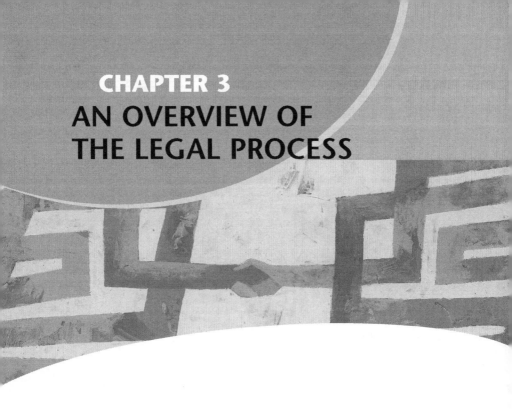

CHAPTER 3
AN OVERVIEW OF
THE LEGAL PROCESS

One of your fellow teachers is well-known for his physically affectionate teaching style that includes rubbing, patting and slapping students' buttocks. Most of your colleagues feel that his behaviour is perfectly acceptable and he is, in fact, quite popular with most of the students and their parents. A female grade 6 student made a complaint about his having touched her in a manner that made her uncomfortable, however. Despite numerous character references from upstanding members of the community and no evidence of sexual intent, he was found guilty of child sex assault and given a conditional discharge.

1. *How do you feel about the verdict? Do you think it was fair? Why or why not?*

2. *This teacher was required to give a DNA sample and was placed on the sexual offenders registry. Do you think it's appropriate that he was treated as a criminal? Explain.*

3. *What role do you think community opinion should play in legal decisions? What about the opinions of other teachers? Can you justify your position?*

The profession of teaching has been significantly shaped by the legal system in Canada. It has also been closely regulated by each of the provinces and territories; in British Columbia alone there are in excess of forty statutes and regulations that have some bearing on education in the province. It is unrealistic to think that you, as a teacher, would be familiar with all the statutes relating to education; likewise it would be impossible to keep abreast of the literally thousands of cases on the topic. This chapter will therefore serve as a general introduction to the law as it pertains to teachers. One caveat, however, is that the law is constantly evolving and the information in this book therefore should not be viewed as a definitive legal opinion on any issue.

At its most fundamental level, the purpose of a set of laws is to codify behavioural expectations and by so doing avoid conflicts. In its most visible form there is the legislation passed either by the federal or provincial governments in the form of statutes, and the subsidiary regulations that relate to them. The *New Brunswick Education Act*,[1] for example, is a statute, while the details of teacher certification are set by regulation.[2] Most legislation can be readily changed by the government passing it; some however, notably the *Charter*, are more difficult to change as they are meant to be an enunciation of the basic shape of the nation.

A less visible source of law arises from the decisions of judges in individual cases. The decisions in individual cases form part of the larger case law in Canada; an earlier decision will have precedent value, meaning that judges will be guided by that court's reasoning, particularly if the decision comes from the same jurisdiction (i.e., province or territory) and from an equal or higher level of court (provincial, Supreme or Queen's Bench, provincial Court of Appeal, then Supreme Court of Canada). Judges are said to be bound by a higher court's decision in that unless they can distinguish their set of facts from those of the case in the higher court they must follow the same reasoning. This, however, is only a general rule; each case is different on the facts and all judges wish to achieve a just result.

The second purpose of a legal system is the resolution of conflicts when they arise. Although not all legal scholars would agree, the three essential features of our legal system as it pertains to the resolution of such disputes is that it is *adversarial*, *visible*, and *remedial*.

Our system of law is based on the premise that "legal truth" and justice will emerge when both sides in a dispute have an equal opportunity to present their cases and to challenge the other party's evidence and credibility. In fact, it is a rare case where both sides are represented equally; often some parties have more money than the others, and the calibre of lawyer will vary as will the strength of the witnesses.

Many people find the adversarial nature of the legal system disquieting. In fact, lawyers do have a duty to try and resolve their client's disputes by agreement before resorting to court action. Increasingly, cases are being dealt with

---

1. S.N.B. 1997, c E-1.12

2. Teacher certification, N.B. Reg. 2004-8

through alternative dispute resolution such as either mediation, where the parties negotiate towards a settlement with the assistance of a neutral mediator, or by arbitration where a third party is chosen by the disputants to decide the issue. The advantage of either route is that they are usually quicker and therefore cheaper for the parties. If a case cannot be resolved without the involvement of the court system then lawyers must do their utmost to act as partisan advocates on behalf of their client within the law and their legal ethics. It is only when a case reaches the courtroom that the full impact of the adversarial system becomes evident.

The courts are highly bound by tradition and rules of procedure. The idea is to preserve the dignity and decorum of the institution so that the public can depend upon its order and authority. In order for this to impact the public at large, not just those directly involved in the proceedings, the courts are open to the public. It is said, "justice must be seen to be done." While a court may in certain circumstances ban the publication of information about a case or exclude the public entirely from the courtroom in order to protect the people involved, as in the case of children who are victims of sexual abuse, generally an open court is considered to be essential to its function.

The legal system is a dynamic combination of parts functioning together for a purpose: to maintain social order by providing remedies to correct a wrong or settle a conflict. When a criminal case (see below) goes to trial the judge or jury will decide if the accused is guilty or not and, if the accused is found guilty, the judge or jury will decide on a sentence. Sentencing can have a variety of objectives, including denouncing unlawful behaviour, deterring the offender, separating the offender from society, rehabilitating the offender, providing reparations for harm done to the victims, and promoting a sense of responsibility in the offender. When a civil dispute (see below) goes to trial a judge or jury will reach a decision regarding injuries and who is at fault and will normally render a judgement that is combined with an appropriate remedy to rectify the injury or damage. Such remedies include payment of money to compensate for damages, performance or discontinuance of specific activities, or payment of money to punish the wrongdoer.

AREAS OF LAW

The law can be classified in a number of ways. One distinction is between *substantive* and *procedural* law. Substantive law includes laws that define the rights, duties, and obligations of the citizens of the state, while procedural law deals with the procedures by which substantive law is applied. Another important broad distinction is between the areas of *criminal* and *civil* law. Both criminal law and civil law can play a significant role in a teacher's life.

Criminal

Criminal law deals with offences as set out in the *Criminal Code of Canada* (1985) and related federal statutes. A finding of criminal guilt can result in a fine or loss of liberty in jail or prison; given the seriousness of the consequences a case against the accused must be proven beyond a reasonable doubt. The more serious offences are indictable; less serious offences are summary. Since criminal acts are considered to be offences against the state, the prosecution of these violations is conducted by the state, referred to as the Crown. The role of the court is to adjudicate between the Crown and the accused. To protect the rights of the accused given such a powerful discrepancy in status, elaborate and detailed procedural regulations exist to ensure that the accused is treated fairly. These include the duty of a prosecutor not to obtain a guilty verdict, but to further justice.

The welfare of children has always been one of the areas of concern of the criminal law and it is therefore not unexpected that there are a number of provisions that impact directly on teachers. The criminal law excludes some individuals from being teachers: section 161(b) of the *Criminal Code* allows that when a person has been found guilty of certain sexual offences against children under the age of fourteen the sentencing judge can, as part of the sentence, prohibit the accused from obtaining or continuing in a position of trust or authority, such as being a teacher, which involves children under the age of fourteen. There has been some criticism that this section has been underutilized despite its mandatory wording that the sentencing judge must consider it.[3]

In addition there are sections of the *Criminal Code* that deal with persons in authority (which would include teachers) making sexual advances to children (section 153) between the ages of fourteen and eighteen (see Chapter 7), as well as the sections of wider application pertaining to sex with minors, and sexual assaults.

WHAT THE CODES SAY

"If a member is convicted of an indictable offence under the Criminal Code of Canada, the STF General Secretary places the Notice of Conviction before the Professional Ethics Committee. No referral to the Executive is required, nor is preliminary investigation required."

—From the *Teaching Profession of Saskatchewan* Code of Ethics

The treatment of youth in the criminal justice system is always a matter of controversy, and one that has significantly changed over the past three decades. Canadian law recognizes three different levels of culpability: childhood, up to age 12, is without criminal liability; from 12 to 18 there is limited accountability under the *Youth Criminal Justice Act*[4]; after that there is full accountability under the criminal law.

---

3. Protecting Our Students: Executive Summary and Recommendations, page 16

4. *Youth Criminal Justice Act*, S.C. 2002, c. 1 (royal assent February 19, 2002; in force April 1, 2003).

The *Young Offenders Act*,[5] passed in 1985 was a significant change from its predecessor, the *Juvenile Delinquents Act*,[6] in that it adopted less of a child welfare approach and stressed increased culpability for specific acts, greater protection of society, and an increased attention to the rights of youths while still recognizing a lesser degree of culpability for youth crimes. During the 1990s there was an increased public outcry for "tougher" laws for youth crimes, despite the fact that the actual youth crime rate was falling, which resulted in a series of amendments to the *Young Offenders Act*.[7] Ultimately, the *YOA* was replaced with the *Youth Criminal Justice Act* in 2002 that, while not as significant a change as its predecessor was from the *Juvenile Delinquents Act*, nevertheless constituted serious reform. Although it has been criticized for not going far enough the *Youth Criminal Justice Act* is more specific that accountability should be a factor in sentencing, and that in the most serious cases there is greater likelihood of the youth being raised to adult court.[8]

Civil

Where criminal law is concerned with the enforcement of state-sanctioned behavioural codes, civil law deals with the resolution of disputes between individuals (which can include government bodies). The litigants are referred to as the plaintiffs, who bring the action to court, and the defendants. The burden of proof, which is who has to prove the case, lies with the plaintiff who must prove the case on the balance of probabilities. Civil law covers a wide range of actions, including contract, wills and trust law, and the law of tort.

It is the latter that is the primary concern for teachers. The word "tort" stems from the Latin *tortus*, meaning, "twisted" or "crooked." Tort law serves a number of purposes: it can compensate a wronged party at the expense of the party at fault, it can set standards of behaviour and enforce them through the threat of civil proceedings, but most importantly it allows a mechanism for parties to settle their differences in a controlled setting.

Torts can either be intentional or unintentional. An intentional tort would include such acts as deliberate interference with another person through assault, battery, false imprisonment, or the infliction of mental suffering. The primary form of unintentional tort is that of negligence where the defendant's conduct is argued to be below the standard set by society.

To successfully bring an action in negligence a plaintiff must establish five elements. First the plaintiff must show that the defendant owed him or her a

---

5. *Young Offenders Act*, R.S.C. 1985

6. *The Juvenile Delinquents Act*, S.C. 1908, c. 40, s. 31; later R.S.C. 1970, c. J-3, s. 38(1).

7. To put Canada's youth laws in perspective Canada incarcerates youth at a rate twice as high as the United States and ten to fifteen times higher than many European countries (Anand, S. (2003). "Crafting Youth Sentences: The Roles of Rehabilitation, Proportionality, Restraint, Restorative Justice, and Race under the *Youth Criminal Justice Act*," *Alberta Law Review*, 40 (4), 943–963.)

8. The *YCJA* is discussed in greater detail in Chapter 8.

duty of care. In the case of teachers it is traditionally thought that this duty arises in two ways: first, the teacher has a delegated authority over the student coming from the parents or guardian of the child, and secondly as teachers they act as an arm of the state in fulfilling the latter's interest in the child's education. These descriptions of the basis of a duty of care are not exhaustive; a teacher's duty of care might arise from undertaking responsibility for an extracurricular activity, or by undertaking a task, such as offering medical aid to an injured student.

The second requirement is that the plaintiff must establish that the defendant failed to use reasonable care; this is not a standard of perfection, and not all injuries will be found to be the result of negligence.[9]

The most difficult requirement to understand is that of causation. Causation encompasses two different concepts; factual and proximate causation. Factual causation is usually summarized as the "but-for" test; but for the defendant's conduct the plaintiff would not have been injured. In the real world, however, there can be multiple causes for events or the actual train of events may be suspected but not ultimately knowable. Because of that the Supreme Court of Canada in *Snell v. Farrel*[10] emphasized that cause need not be proven with scientific precision and reiterated that the civil standard of the balance of probabilities continues to apply. In the case of multiple causes the defendant will be found liable only to the degree to which he is found at fault; thus a plaintiff may be found to be contributorily negligent and recover only a portion of her damages. In the case of multiple defendants at fault the court can decide whether there is joint (that is each defendant can be responsible for paying the entire damages) or several liability where the plaintiff is limited to recovering only that particular tortfeasor's portion of the damages from the person. This is a significant issue when, as in many cases, only some of the defendants are insured and thus financially able to compensate the plaintiff.

Proximate causation requires that there be a reasonable connection between the conduct complained of and the injury resulting. The test here is whether the damage is foreseeable by a reasonable person in the defendant's position. However, there is a concurrent legal principle that the defendant must take the plaintiff as they find him, often expressed as the "thin skull" rule.

The fourth requirement is that there must be, in fact, damage to the plaintiff; in cases where the damage is very slight the court can invoke the *de minimus* principle and order that no damages are awarded.

Finally, there must be no conduct on the part of the plaintiff that would preclude him from recovery, with the most common example being him engaged in a criminal act at the time of the injury; the Supreme Court of Canada, however, in recent years has limited the invocation of this principle, instead relying upon findings of contributory negligence.

---

9. This is discussed further in Chapter 6.

10. [1990] 2 S.C.R. 311

Occupiers' Liability

Of greater import to school boards than individual teachers is the liability that arises through one being an occupier of a premise. Being an occupier does not necessarily require that you own the property; a tenant, for example, can be responsible for the condition of the premises. Using a common example, if a school fails to keep the walkways free of snow and ice and a student slips and is injured then an action under occupier's liability could be pursued against the school board.

THE *CHARTER OF RIGHTS AND FREEDOMS*

In April 1982, as part of the patriation of the Canadian constitution, the *Canadian Charter of Rights and Freedoms*[11] was enacted. The effect of this cannot be overstated; for the first time there was a written social contract between the State and the citizens of Canada in which the latter were guaranteed certain fundamental rights and freedoms. Unlike other legislation enacted by the federal or provincial governments, the *Charter* is the "Supreme Law of Canada"[12] by virtue of which it has two attributes. First, all other laws are subordinate to it and secondly the mechanism for its amendment is considerably more difficult than for regular statutory instruments in that it requires a resolution of both the House of Commons and the Senate, and by resolutions of the legislative assemblies of two-thirds of the provinces, representing at least fifty percent of the population.[13]

The application of the *Charter* is set out in section 32 that provides:

32(1) This Charter applies

(a) to the Parliament and government of Canada in respect of all matters within the authority of Parliament...

(b) to the legislature and government of each province in respect of all matters within the authority of each province.

On its face then, the *Charter* would apply only to governmental actions and would not apply to private actions. However, a number of cases have applied *Charter* reasoning in private settings as being a codification of Canadian values. In the case of teachers and education, being a function of the provincial government there is no issue but that the *Charter* applies.

---

11. *Canadian Charter of Rights and Freedoms*, Part 1 of the *Constitution Act, 1982*, being Schedule B to the *Canada Act 1982* (U.K.), 1982, c. 11, s. 32

12. S. 52

13. S. 38

The *Charter* begins with the preface that "Whereas Canada is founded upon principles that recognize the supremacy of God and the rule of law," which seems inconsistent with our generally held belief that Canada is a non-sectarian nation.[14] The preface was a late addition to the *Charter*, and not the subject of debate in the house;[15] the Supreme Court of Canada has rejected the suggestion that the preface forms a "mini Bill of Rights"[16] and has essentially ignored the section.

While the *Charter* is the supreme law of Canada the fundamental rights and freedoms it enumerates are not "trump"; rather they are subject to "such reasonable limits prescribed by law as can be demonstrably justified in a free and democratic society."[17] The purpose of this section can easily be demonstrated using the timeworn example of someone mischievously shouting "fire" in a crowded theatre; the individual's freedom of speech is limited for the greater good of the public. The mechanism for determining whether a limit is "reasonable" is set out in the *Oakes*[18] test, which requires that the end result sought is sufficiently important and the means to this end are reasonable and demonstrably justified. In establishing that the means to the end are reasonable and demonstrably justified the government must provide cogent and persuasive evidence that the method chosen is designed to reach the objective, that it impairs as little as possible the rights and freedoms of the individual, and there be a proportionality between the deleterious effect of the measures and their salutary effect.

A second significant limitation on the *Charter* is section 33; the "not withstanding" clause that was enacted as part of a compromise with the provincial legislatures whereby the provinces can enact legislation and expressly declare its effect notwithstanding that it may infringe upon the *Charter* guarantees set out in sections 2, and 7 through 15 of the *Charter*. Such legislation automatically expires in five years (though it may be renewed) and it was generally thought at the time that few provincial governments would risk the censure of their electorate by imposing on *Charter* rights.

The *Charter* sets out four categories of fundamental freedoms: freedom of conscience and religion; freedom of thought, belief, opinion, and expression, including freedom of the press and other media of communication; freedom of peaceful assembly; and freedom of association.[19] It then sets out a series of legal rights which, among others, include the right to life, liberty

---

14. For example, section 27 of the *Charter* also provides that it be interpreted in a manner consistent with our multicultural heritage.

15. Hogg, P.W. (1982).*Canada Act 1982 Annotated*.Toronto: The Carswell Company Limited.

16. See, for example, Justice Wilson's comments in *R. v. Morgentaler*, [1988] 1 S.C.R. 30

17. S. 1

18. *R. v. Oakes*, [1986] 1 S.C.R. 103

19. S. 2

and security of the person,[20] to be secure from unreasonable search or seizure,[21] not to be arbitrarily detained or imprisoned,[22] and the right to be told upon such detention the reasons for such and the right to retain counsel.[23] Finally, section 15 provides for equality rights guaranteeing equal protection before and under the law without discrimination, in particular that based on race, national or ethnic origin, colour, religion, sex or age, mental or physical disability.

The remedies available under the *Charter* are diverse; section 24(1) allows a person whose rights or freedoms have been infringed to apply to the courts for whatever remedy is appropriate and just in the circumstances. This could include the exclusion of evidence,[24] a declaration that a law is invalid either in whole or part,[25] or "reading in" to an existing law a remedial interpretation.

In addition to guaranteeing certain rights and freedoms the *Charter*, in section 23, provided parents who speak the minority official (that is, French or English) language in the province with instruction of their children in that language "where the number of children of citizens who have such a right is sufficient to warrant the provision of them out of public funds."[26] In many respects, the provision of language rights has supplanted the issue of religious instruction in the school system as one of the most troubling areas for provinces. Some provinces have attempted to avoid making controversial, and thus potentially politically damaging, decisions in this area by seeking rulings from the courts. However, s. 23 is intentionally vague in its reference to "where numbers warrant"; in some provinces, notably Quebec, the number may be as few as one; in others it may be as high as 100.[27] In the Supreme Court of Canada decision of *Mahe v. Alberta*[28] the Court stated that while section 23 was intended to promote the concept of an "equal partnership" between the two languages there was no requirement that the services be identical; thus, where the numbers did not warrant it it was not necessary to establish a separate school board, but it may be necessary to provide linguistic minority representation within the existing school board

---

20. S. 7

21. S. 8

22. S. 9

23. S. 10

24. S. 24(2)

25. S. 52(1)

26. S. 23(3) *Canadian Charter of Rights and Freedoms*

27. Young, J. & Levin, B. (2002). *Understanding Canadian Schools: An Introduction to Educational Administration, 3rd ed.*, p. 37. Scarborough, ON: Thomson Nelson.

28. [1990] 1 S.C.R. 342

in proportion to the numbers of minority language students within that board. These representatives should have the responsibility of determining how the funds are used for the promotion of the minority language and the procurement of appropriate teachers.

There are a number of factors, however, that threaten the assimilation of the French language culture, particularly outside Quebec, within the education system. These factors include a lower birth rate and immigration rate for fran-cophones, and a gradual decrease in the French mother tongue.[29] Compliance with s. 23 of the *Charter* may not, in itself, be enough to protect the French culture outside of Quebec, particularly where the numbers are such that French is the language only of the school room, but not of the playground.

Summary

A basic understanding of the legal system and of the expectations of the profession of teaching by the Canadian courts can serve as a guide to how the courts would likely judge teachers if their actions were to be brought before them. The Canadian legal system is adversarial, visible, and remedial in nature and deals with disputes either through the criminal or civil courts. If teachers are involved with the legal system, they tend to be defendants in civil suits, which deal with professional negligence. Negligence involves five elements: a duty of care, a failure to provide reasonable care, an injury, causation between the failure and the injury, and an absence of factors on the part of the injured party that would preclude recovery.

Questions for Discussion

1. What is the difference between ethical and legal standards for professionals?
2. Is a teacher ever justified in breaking the law? If so, under what circumstances? What system of ethics does your answer represent?
3. Why are legal decisions not always a good guide for professional behaviour?
4. Should a teacher who has broken a serious law unrelated to teaching practice, such as embezzling a charitable organization, be prohibited from teaching? Why or why not?

---

29. For further examination of this problem see Martel, A. *Rights, Schools and Communities in Minority Contexts:1986–2002*, a report prepared by the Office of the Commissioner of Official Languages, Minister of Public Works and Government Services Canada 2001, Cat. No. SF31-49/2002 ISBN: 0-662-65326-2.

Further Reading

Bala, N. (2002). *Youth criminal justice law.* Toronto: Irwin.

Gall, G.L. (1995). *The Canadian legal system.* Toronto: Carswell.

Yates, R. A., Yates, R. W., & Baines, P. (2000). *Introduction to law in Canada.* Scarborough: Prentice-Hall Canada.

CHAPTER 4
TEACHING AS A PROFESSION

In talking to your brother-in-law, who has been a teacher and school administrator for a quarter century, you find that he observes the problem with being a teacher is everyone thinks that they can do it if not better, at least as well as he can, unlike any other profession.

1. *Do you think teaching is a profession?*

2. *What does it mean to be in a profession as opposed to a job?*

3. *Is your university education enough to qualify you as a professional?*

4. *Are all, or only some, teachers professionals?*

The degree to which the public can trust a profession ultimately rests upon its ability to regulate its members. Every profession is accountable to the public for setting standards for admitting members to the profession, and for identifying and sanctioning members who may be at risk to harm or may have harmed a recipient of their services. But the question is often raised, "Is teaching a true profession?"

CHARACTERISTICS OF A PROFESSION

To be considered a profession, an occupation must be (1) an intellectual activity based on a particular knowledge base rather than a routine, (2) practical rather than theoretical, and (3) oriented toward service to society. Many occupations might be said to meet the first two criteria, but few meet the third. The three most established professions, sometimes referred to as the *learned professions*, are the clergy, law, and medicine. Each requires years of education and practice to acquire necessary expertise and performs a vital service to society. The clergy tend to the spiritual needs of the faithful. Lawyers enact our legal system to maintain civil order. And physicians treat the sick and injured. Members of each of these professions are expected to serve the needs of society's citizens regardless of income, status, or heritage. Thus a profession is expected to adhere to specific specialized responsibilities and moral duties in serving the public.

When the learned professions first emerged there were no clear categories of who belonged and who did not, nor were there any clear criteria of what constituted admission to the profession. Members were typically self-taught or apprenticed under someone considered to already be a member. Nevertheless, most societies regarded them as having a privileged status. Modern day usage of the term *professional* can also refer to being engaged in an occupation as a paid job rather than unpaid, leading to some confusion. This is a secondary meaning, however, and serves only as a distinction from amateur. A professional is someone who belongs to a profession and upholds his or her professional responsibilities. That is, if one does not *act* professionally—by failing one's moral responsibility to society—one is not truly a professional.

Is teaching a profession? Certainly the learned professions have a much longer history of organization and development. And some commentators[1] have argued that teachers are "semi-professionals" for various reasons—such as lack of a theoretical base, relatively low status within society, and limits on self-regulation. But these are superficial characteristics of a profession. Teachers unquestionably have a time-honoured role in the service of society. Preparing children to be contributing members of a community is arguably the most

---

1. E.g., Carr, D. (2000). *Professionalism and ethics in teaching.* New York: Routledge; Etzioni, A. (1969). *Semi-professions & their organization.* New York: Free Press; Winch, C. (2004). What do teachers need to know about teaching? A critical examination of the occupational knowledge of teachers. *British Journal of Educational Studies, 52,* 180–196.

essential of occupations. It is in the classroom and in the school where students exercise their understanding of the concepts of democratic participation in society. And it is the professional teacher who performs this service.

THE NATURE OF PROFESSIONAL STANDARDS

Entrance Standards

One of the more obvious tasks of a profession is to set entrance standards deemed necessary to offer services to the public as a "teacher." As we discussed in Chapter 2, as a result of the great compromise that was confederation, each province and territory has established unique standards. Currently, most jurisdictions only allow persons who have obtained the Bachelor degree to call themselves teachers. Beyond degree status, there are varying requirements for specific coursework and supervised practice prior and subsequent to earning the degree.

Codes of Conduct

Regulators of teachers must also ensure that properly qualified teachers practise competently. While some jurisdictions employ a code of ethics for these regulatory functions, as discussed in Chapter 1 the aspirational nature of ethics codes makes them poorly suited for the task. A code of conduct does a much better job of setting a minimum standard of professional behaviour for safe practice. Effective codes of conduct have the following characteristics:

1. They are non-optional, non-aspirational and non-trivial, so that any violation would justify formal disciplinary action.
2. They primarily protect society.
3. They are as clear as possible concerning what behaviour is acceptable and what is not.
4. They deal with the teacher's behaviours, not the content or outcome of professional judgement.
5. They are self-explanatory and do not require undue interpretation or additional materials.

As with entrance standards, each provincial and territorial regulator has the authority to establish or adopt a code of conduct. All jurisdictions in Canada, with the exception of New Brunswick, the Northwest Territories, and Saskatchewan, have done so. An important practical concern that arises out of this situation is that teachers who move from one province or territory to teach in another are responsible to practise in accordance with the code of conduct of the new jurisdiction.

Professional Guidelines

Given that codes of ethics set aspirational standards, and codes of conduct set minimal standards, guidelines are used to bridge the gap between the two. Obviously, they should be consistent with both codes of ethics and conduct,

Teaching as a Profession

while going further to integrate specialized knowledge into standards of quality practice. Professional guidelines are developed to provide guidance in general areas that are of concern to all teachers, and in specialized areas that present specific difficulties. Although these guidelines are neither usually definitive nor enforceable in and of themselves, regulators and the courts will often refer to them to establish desirable practice. Teachers should be familiar with guidelines published by their regulatory college, professional associations, and any speciality organizations relevant to their area of teaching.

PROFESSIONAL ACCOUNTABILITY

Various formal mechanisms have been established within the profession and by law to protect the public from harm by teachers. Ideally, professional mechanisms for accountability should be sufficient to deal with the vast majority of situations. In those rare instances when professional standards and mechanisms are not sufficient, external (i.e., legal) mechanisms can be invoked.

Discipline Processes

In most jurisdictions the regulator (whether college or association), a member of the public, or a member of the profession can initiate a complaint. Initially, the complaint may be made orally or in writing, although a written complaint must be made if it proceeds beyond preliminary considerations. In many jurisdictions the code of ethics or conduct requires that, if the complainant is a teacher, the named colleague also be informed of the intent to make a complaint.

WHAT THE CODES SAY

"A member shall avoid derogatory criticism of an associate except when it is directed to a person or an authority who is in a position to rectify the cause. Such criticism shall not be directed unless the associate has been informed in writing detailing the complaint."

—*From the Federation of Nunavut Teachers'* Code of Ethics

Typically, an appointed representative of the regulator will discuss the standards the teacher will be held to and the nature of the discipline process with the person making the complaint (the *complainant*). At this point the complainant may do nothing further, make a formal written complaint, or elect for an informal complaint resolution process (if the jurisdictional legislation allows for it). If the complaint is of a serious nature, the regulator may proceed with an investigation regardless of the wishes of the complainant.

If the complainant elects to proceed, and provided the complaint is not obviously frivolous or in bad faith, the regulator's representative will typically send a letter to the named teacher requesting a response and, if needed, a letter to the complainant requesting further documentation. The regulator may then appoint an investigator who reviews all materials, contacts any relevant parties, collects any necessary further documentation, and prepares a report summarizing the evidence. The method of investigation typically varies based on the nature of information necessary to clarify the complaint, and may include interviews, review of school files, and other correspondence. The regulator may also seek legal advice or an expert opinion as to whether any relevant codes or standards have been violated. •

Once all necessary information has been gathered, the regulator typically has the option to dismiss the complaint, initiate a mediated or negotiated settlement, or proceed to a discipline hearing. If the complaint is dismissed, the complainant usually has the right to appeal. If a negotiated settlement is pursued, the teacher undertakes whatever actions are agreed to be necessary to remedy the wrongdoing. In some cases this may involve the teacher undertaking sensitivity training or upgrading, for example. If the teacher breaches the terms of the settlement, the regulator typically will forward the matter to a discipline committee. If the terms are completed successfully, the case can be closed.

If the case proceeds to a discipline hearing, the committee will hear evidence from the regulator and the teacher. At this point in some jurisdictions the complainant becomes a witness and the regulator becomes the complainant. In other jurisdictions the complainant maintains "status" and has the right to legal representation, to question witnesses, and so forth. Typically, legal counsel represents both the regulator and teacher. If an expert witness was involved, the witness testifies on behalf of the college and can be cross-examined by the teacher's legal counsel. In most jurisdictions the teacher is permitted to call his/her own expert to testify.

Disciplinary committees are better equipped to deal with a teacher who has a multitude of relatively minor offences over a period of time with different students, and can impose a greater range of penalties, including placing restrictions on a teacher's certificate such as the age of students that can be taught[2] or requiring that teachers take courses in boundary issues or anger management.[3] In some instances disciplinary hearings will be undertaken in addition to criminal proceedings; thus, a teacher who was originally charged on a number of counts of assault and as a result agreed to a peace bond was subsequently the subject of a discipline inquiry that exonerated her.[4] The penalties available to discipline committees are diverse, from a written reprimand to revocation of the teacher's registration. Other possibilities include imposing terms, limits, or conditions on the teacher's practice such as supervision, fines, personal therapy, or successful completion of courses or exams.

As the discipline committee acts in a quasi-judicial manner, and may impose rather severe penalties, there is a right of further appeal by the teacher

---

2. *Ontario College of Teachers v. D.J.*, [2000] O.C.T.D.D. No. 45.

3. *Ontario College of Teachers v. MacDonald*, [2001] O.C.T.D.D. No. 13.

4. *Ontario College of Teachers v. Newton*, [1999] O.C.T.D.D. No. 10.

to the lower courts in each of the provinces and territories. The legislation governing this right of appeal varies between jurisdictions, but most allow the courts to uphold, quash, or alter the committee's decision. In hearing an appeal the courts will usually defer to the expertise of the regulator, and by extension the discipline committee, to govern its own affairs.

Complaints Against Teachers

It is almost impossible to form a precise idea of how many complaints are handled by provincial or territorial regulatory bodies due to the absence of a uniform system of classifying cases and inconsistent reporting practices. Some smaller jurisdictions, such as Prince Edward Island, receive only one or two complaints per year. The largest jurisdiction, Ontario, which has 180,000 teachers, receives some 200 complaints per year. As many as 20 cases per year are handled through negotiated or alternate dispute resolution procedures in some jurisdictions, with many more than that handled informally. But the numbers of complaints that go to a formal discipline hearing are very low, from none to 50 per year in any given jurisdiction.

COMPETENCE

Competence is the cornerstone of professional practice; society expects professionals to be able to perform the central tasks that define their profession. Incompetent actions on the part of teachers are unethical, unprofessional, and, under certain circumstances, grounds for malpractice because such actions are unlikely to be of benefit and likely to be harmful. A teacher who is not competent to practise, therefore, should not teach. To be competent is to be able to do something. Competence is generally considered by most ethics scholars to be comprised of four major dimensions: *knowledge, skill, judgement,* and *diligence.*

WHAT THE CODES SAY

"Members regard as their first duty the effective education of their students and maintain professional competence in their teaching."

—*From the Yukon* Code of Ethics

Knowledge

Knowledge involves having absorbed and understood a body of information sufficiently to understand and conceptualize the range of professional issues that teachers can reasonably be expected to encounter. Knowledge is a necessary but not sufficient foundation for competence. In Canada basic knowledge is initially demonstrated by completing a degree program in education, usually with a certain set of required courses. Knowledge can be understood as covering a continuum from basic information that all teachers should know, such as ethics, to specific knowledge necessary for specialized areas of practice, such as special education. Obviously, however, the knowledge base for teaching is not static and continued study is considered necessary to maintain an adequate knowledge base. To be considered knowledgeable, teachers must stay current to those matters relevant to their practice.

Skill

Skill is the ability to apply knowledge effectively in practice. As with knowledge, skills cover a continuum from basic teaching skills of lesson planning and classroom management, to technical proficiency for specific teaching procedures. Much more difficult to assess and even more difficult to instil, but also considered to be necessary, are personal skills such as self-awareness, tolerance, and interpersonal sensitivity. It is generally accepted that supervised field experiences are necessary to acquire the fundamental skills for the practice of teaching.

Judgement

Judgement involves knowing when to apply what knowledge and which skills under what circumstances. It also involves self-reflection on how one's own values, attitudes, experiences, and the social context influence one's actions, choices, and recommendations. Good judgement incorporates the intent of increasing the probability that activities will benefit and not harm the students, parents, and communities to whom teachers are responsible. Judgement is much harder to assess and is usually indirectly addressed during supervised experience.

Diligence

Diligence involves consistently attending to one's knowledge, skills, and judgement as they are applied in one's professional activities, and being careful to give priority to students' needs over any other concerns. Diligence involves a willingness to work hard to provide the best service possible for each and every student, honestly evaluating one's own professional performance, and seeking additional training when appropriate. A diligent teacher seeks out professional guidance to identify the knowledge, skills, and judgement essential for improved practice. Being diligent also incorporates self-awareness of any personal or situational circumstances that might diminish one's competence.

MAINTAINING COMPETENCE

The knowledge, skills, and judgement considered basic to being even minimally competent are not static. In constantly striving to be a better teacher, the average competence of the profession continues to rise over time. Teachers must, therefore, continually keep abreast of new developments in the field in order to maintain competence. These new developments are typically knowledge in the form of new practice findings, and skills in the form of new teaching and assessment procedures. But there are from time to time developments in professional judgement when what was once considered marginal but acceptable behaviour is no longer, such as corporal punishment (see Chapter 7), and new practice guidelines that are periodically produced by professional organizations.

WHAT THE CODES SAY

"The teacher should maintain his/her efficiency by study, by travel or by other means which will keep him/her abreast of the trends in education and the world in which we live."

—*From the Nova Scotia Teachers Union* Code of Ethics

Equally important is that teachers as persons are not static. The profession is generally understood to be stressful. Teachers also age, experience joy and suffering, form new relationships and end others, and generally change as people. Thus one's judgement also changes—often for the better, but sometimes for the worse. Teachers must also, therefore, stay abreast of their own personal changes and continually evaluate how these changes impact their competence.

What should become obvious from the above discussion is that there is no single way to maintain competence. It is incumbent upon teachers to continually monitor their teaching relative to the state of the profession. When developments occur that "raise the bar" teachers must assess the extent of the gap between these new concepts and their own knowledge, skills, and judgement and take appropriate steps to upgrade. It is also necessary to monitor oneself continually as a person and professional, assess how any changes affect one's skill and judgement, and take appropriate steps to maintain competence. Among the activities to consider are the following:

- Continuing education
- Peer consultation/supervision
- Personal counselling
- Formal consultation
- Formal supervision
- Additional training
- Retraining

ENHANCING COMPETENCE

For various reasons teachers may wish to enhance or change their areas of expertise. In that case, teachers should obtain whatever additional knowledge and skills are necessary to practise competently in the new area. Teachers must become familiar with the standards of knowledge, skills, and judgement considered necessary for competent practice in the area they are considering expanding into, compare them with their own, and develop a plan to acquire what is lacking. The means for achieving this goal are identical for those used to maintain competence, although of course teachers will typically have to undergo more extensive training.

Another consideration in enhancing competence is whether doing so involves the acquisition of established and proven knowledge and skills, or more recent ones. With regard to the former, training or retraining is more straightforward and mainly has to do with acquiring expertise in the area of practice. With more recently developed knowledge and skills, however, the issues are somewhat more complex. It is incumbent on teachers to ensure that any new approaches and procedures that are adopted will benefit and not harm students. This requires critical evaluation of the new procedures and their incorporation into existing areas of expertise. Evaluation of the relevance and soundness of new procedures can be accomplished through several routes, such as examining the professional literature on the topic, consulting other professionals with expertise and experience in the area, and the exercise of critical judgement.

AVOIDING IMPAIRMENT

Beyond becoming out-of-date relative to the state of the profession, teachers must be vigilant with respect to becoming impaired. Because competence is based on performance, not ability, circumstances may arise whereby one's ability to apply knowledge, skills, and good judgement becomes impaired. Reasons can range from burnout or distress, to substance abuse or dementia. Whatever the reason, one must do what one can to avoid becoming impaired, be vigilant with respect to impairment, and take appropriate steps to limit harm to others if one should become impaired.

OTHER CASES OF NOTE

Can a professional body order a teacher to receive psychological counselling? *British Columbia Teachers' Federation v. Vancouver School District No. 39*, [2003] B.C.J. No. 366.

The following suggestions should be considered to help avoid becoming impaired:

* Develop and nurture a strong interpersonal support system.
* Develop a close, cooperative relationship with a group of peers to share the frustrations and excitement that surround your work.
* Take time to nurture your personal well-being.
* Stay involved in professional development activities.

SELF-REGULATION

The essence of being a self-regulating profession is that each member is both regulated and a regulator. Remember that this is because teachers have special expertise that the average member of society cannot understand. All teachers, therefore, will find themselves at some time faced with having to respond to unprofessional or incompetent behaviour on the part of a fellow teacher. Most codes of ethics prohibit teachers from publicly criticizing other teachers; some codes go further and set out when critical comments are to be made, to whom they can be made, and require that the teacher being criticized be given the opportunity to respond.[5] In some provinces the enabling act for the Teachers' Federation also prohibits malicious, careless, or irresponsible criticism of a fellow teacher that undermines the public's confidence.[6]

WHAT THE CODES SAY

"The teacher should not make defamatory, disparaging, condescending, embarrassing, or offensive comments concerning another teacher."

—*From the Nova Scotia Teachers Union* Code of Ethics

These restrictions, however, have been the subject of some adverse judicial commentary, most notably in the Alberta Court of Appeal decision of *Eggertson v. ATA*. Ms. Eggertson was, in addition to being a teacher herself, a mother of two elementary school-age children. During the course of a parent–teacher interview she made critical comments to her children's current teacher as to the quality of her predecessor. During a subsequent meeting set up by the principal of the school for the purpose of reviewing Ms. Eggertson's complaints she reiterated her view that her children did not learn a thing the previous year. A complaint was made by the children's current teacher and Ms. Eggertson was found to have violated s. 13 of the Alberta Teachers' *Code of Conduct*, which required that teachers' criticisms of each other be done in confidence to the proper official and only after the other teacher has been advised. Internal appeals were unsuccessful; in particular the Professional Conduct Appeal Committee held that neither Ms. Eggertson's status as a parent, nor the freedom of speech guaranteed by the *Charter* allowed her to criticize in this manner a fellow teacher.

The Alberta Court of Appeal[7] disagreed: the decision of the administrative bodies did not place sufficient weight to the right of a parent to be involved in their child's education. The comments, although contrary to s. 13 of the *Code*,

---

5. Saskatchewan Teachers' Federation *Code of Ethics*.

6. S. 38, *Teachers Federation Act*, Saskatchewan.

7. *Eggertson v. Alberta Teachers' Association*, [2003] A.J. No. 384.

were in the context of meetings devoted to the academic achievements of the children and the attendees were also concerned about the children's progress and were not mere disinterested members of the public. The strict and literal reading of s. 13 adopted by the PCAC, the Court noted, would have the effect of stifling discourse between parents and teachers when the parents also happened to be teachers.

The restriction on criticizing other teachers is also extended by many of the *Codes of Ethics* to critiquing the Teachers' Federation itself. For example the Yukon Teachers' *Code of Ethics* provides that "Members do not act in a manner harmful or prejudicial to the Association"; it is a moot point whether public criticism of the policies of the Association would contravene the *Code*.

The following steps may be of some help when attempting to deal with these situations in an ethical and responsible manner.

Confirm the Issue

First, as best as you are able, try to assess the situation dispassionately. Are you certain that you are able to determine the appropriateness of your colleague's actions? Are your motives personal, as opposed to protection of the public? Do you have direct knowledge of your colleague's actions? You should be very reluctant to act based upon rumours you have heard from others. Similarly, if you are approached by someone who claims to have first-hand knowledge of the unprofessional behaviour of a colleague, you should be helpful and encourage them to take appropriate action but should be careful about how active a role you take.

Consult

Discuss your concerns with trusted peers, making sure to protect the identity of your colleague and anyone else involved. Do they agree that action should be taken? Are there any professional guidelines or standards relevant to the issue? Does the situation truly fall below acceptable professional standards?

Respect Student Confidentiality

Except in situations that involve a threat of serious physical harm or suspected child abuse, the student's right to confidentiality takes precedence over any professional obligation to correct or offset harm. If a teacher becomes aware of a colleague's behaviour in the context of a professional relationship, therefore, the student's or their parent's consent (depending on whether the student is old enough to give consent) to reveal information must first be obtained. If consent is not granted, no further action on your part should be undertaken unless the situation involves a mandatory reporting duty.

Speak with Colleagues

If the issue appears to be primarily the result of a lack of sensitivity, knowledge, or experience, attempt to reach an agreement with your colleague on the issue and whatever appropriate action is to be taken. Your goal at this point should be to correct the problem, not to punish. Try to be calm, respectful, and constructive; imagine how you would like to be treated if you had made a professional mistake and were being confronted. Try to be open-minded and to understand your colleague's side of the story. A face-to-face meeting in professional surroundings is usually best.

Involve Others in an Action Plan

If your colleague is unwilling to address the issue, or if the action is of a seriously harmful nature, such as the sexual exploitation of a student, you should take your concerns to the provincial or territorial regulatory body best suited to investigating the situation and to stopping or offsetting the harm. You should be willing to make a written, signed complaint and/or testify in a disciplinary hearing if you proceed this far. You should record details of your actions and include time, date, and the basic content of any conversations if you reach this step.

Summary

The degree to which the public can trust the profession of teaching rests upon teachers' ability to protect the public from harm caused by their members. Teachers are therefore accountable to regulate themselves by setting entrance standards to the profession, developing codes of conduct to set minimum standards of competent practice, publishing professional guidelines to facilitate highly competent practice, and sanctioning members who are at risk to harm or have harmed the public. Competence is comprised of four major components: *knowledge, skills, judgement*, and *diligence*. Several avenues are open to teachers for professional development to keep up with these changes. Teachers should take steps to avoid becoming impaired and to limit harm to others should they become so. One of the more difficult situations they have to deal with is the possible incompetent behaviour of another teacher. If a teacher suspects a colleague has harmed or is at risk to harm, the teacher should first be sure to have adequate knowledge of the issue, consult with others if unsure, attempt to resolve the issue informally with the colleague, and involve others if necessary or if the issue is a serious one.

Questions for Discussion

1. Why might some people not consider teaching to be a profession? Do you think teaching is a true profession? Why or why not?
2. Do you think the entrance standards for teachers are high enough? Or are they too high? Explain your answer.

3. How do you think the profession should deal with teachers who violate codes and laws because they have a different personal morality? Why?
4. To what extent do you think that burnout is inevitable in the profession of teaching? Why or why not? What self-care practices do you have in place to facilitate your continued personal and professional well-being?
5. To what extent should private schools be allowed to set their own standards for teachers? Should a person without a teaching degree be allowed to teach in such a setting?

Further Reading

Campbell, E. (1996). Ethical implications of collegial loyalty as one view of teacher professionalism. *Teachers and Teaching: Theory and Practice, 2,* 191–208.

Carr, D. (2003). Moral educational implications of rival conceptions of education and the role of the teacher. *Journal of Moral Education, 32,* 219–232.

Piddocke, A., Magsino, R., & Manley-Casmir, M. (1997). *Teachers in trouble: An exploration of the normative character of teaching.* Toronto: University of Toronto Press.

Winch, C. (2004). What do teachers need to know about teaching? A critical examination of the occupational knowledge of teachers. *British Journal of Educational Studies, 52*(2), 180–196.

CHAPTER 5
PRIVATE LIFE, PUBLIC ROLE

The newspapers are covering the story of a teacher who is a spokesperson for the local Gay Pride Parade. During the course of being interviewed he identifies himself as being a teacher at a Catholic school; he also criticizes the Catholic Church for its position on gays and lesbians.

1. *As a teacher should he be censured for playing a public role in such an event?*

2. *Would it make a difference if he had not identified himself as a teacher?*

3. *What if he had stated that he was heterosexual and was only acting in support of those who are homosexual?*

4. *What if he was being interviewed as a spokesperson at a rally for a political party critical of the current government?*

Probably one of those most powerful concepts of teaching is that of being a role model and mentor. The role model a particular teacher played in our own schooling experience has inspired most of us; likewise, we remember other teachers in a less favourable light and strive to avoid being like them. While many of our teachers have faded from memory, at least one will remain with us. And who of us does not want to be remembered as one of those good teachers in the lives of our students? Without going too deeply into the philosophy of teaching, most will agree that what made those teachers "good" was not how much of the subject material they helped us master. Rather, it was how their unique character inspired us in just the right way at a certain point in our lives: their personality, interests, passions, opinions. No matter how carefully curriculum may be circumscribed, it is a teacher who interprets and applies curricula, and it is the person of the teacher who inspires—or discourages.

While most will agree that this is how it should be, a dilemma arises when who the teacher is as a person, as opposed to simply choices he or she makes, is seen to be at odds with the role model a teacher should serve. As discussed in the last chapter, teachers share in common many attributes with people in other professions: they have mandatory requirements of belonging to professional bodies, such as the provincial teacher federations; they have a code of ethics or conduct under which they must govern their affairs; they are given a certain degree of autonomy as professionals in how they fulfil their professional duties; and to varying degrees the profession is self-governing. And like other professionals, teachers are expected to be competent in their practice.

Unlike other professionals, however, a teacher might be competent—that is teaches knowledgeably, skilfully, with good judgement, and with respect for the autonomy of students—and might still cause harm by failing to be an *example* of virtuous behaviour. And remember that the ethical principle of non-maleficence—do no harm—is central to any profession, including teaching. Thus the question can be asked, is this teacher the kind of *person* who should be teaching our children? If one is seeking the best surgeon to cure a child of a disease, the fact that the surgeon's private life might be characterized by being a cruel spouse, neglectful parent, and opposed to charitable organizations would probably not change our minds provided he or she has the required surgical expertise. If one is seeking the best education for one's child, however, these same personal attributes become relevant to our decision. Parents are understandably concerned, therefore, with the values and personal characteristics exhibited by teachers in the classroom and the community. We see then that the contract that teachers have with society as a whole, and in particular the community in which they teach and with parents whose children they are responsible for, is very important.

This places teachers in a number of conflicts. Teachers are expected to serve a role as agents of desired change, while also being preservers of existing values. And while parents rightly expect teachers to be role models for their children, there is no unanimity as to what constitutes a suitable model. Even for a teacher working in a private or separate school setting, where there is a more defined description of the values of the community and by extension the school, conflicts arise as to what are the exact attributes of a qualified teacher.

For the most part, teacher associations recognize the importance of role modelling[1] by requiring that teachers act "in a manner which maintains the honour and dignity of the profession"[2] and not engage in "conduct unbecoming of a member of the profession"[3] in order to avoid bringing "dishonour to the teacher or the profession."[4] The Saskatchewan Teachers' Federation's *Code of Ethics* explicitly addresses the issue of role modelling in the commentary on Article 1, "The Honour of the Teaching Profession":

> Teachers are also subject to the standards of teacher conduct that prevail within society at large. Numerous court decisions have made it clear that society expects teachers to behave in a manner that encourages their students to live ethically and will in no way exert a degrading influence on the conduct of others. Teachers have a duty to understand their social function as role models and to work within the prevailing social standards.

The Ontario College of Teachers' *Ethical Standards for the Teaching Profession* also addresses role modelling by stating that teachers ought to

> model respect for human dignity, spiritual values, cultural values, freedom, social justice, democracy and the environment.

And then there is the question of the degree to which a community can impose its expectations on the teacher as an individual, particularly outside of the classroom, without violating the teacher's personal rights. Again, the Saskatchewan Teachers' Federation's *Code of Ethics* addresses this issue in the commentary on Article 1:

> It is recognized that accepted patterns of behaviour vary across the province and are subject to change over time. At times the teacher's personal and professional principles may conflict with the behavioural expectations of a school or community. So far as it is possible without compromising

---

1. The British Columbia Teachers' Federation *Code of Ethics* and the Manitoba Teachers' Society *Code of Professional Practice*, which are essentially identical documents, are silent on this issue.

2. Alberta Teachers' Association *Code of Conduct*; Newfoundland and Labrador Teachers' Association *Code of Ethics*; Prince Edward Island Teachers' Federation *Code of Ethics*; Saskatchewan Teachers' Federation *Code of Ethics*.

3. For example, New Brunswick Teachers' Association *Code of Professional Conduct*.

4. Federation of Nunavut Teachers' *Code of Ethics*; Nova Scotia Teachers' Union *Code of Ethics*; Yukon Teachers' Association *Code of Ethics*.

these principles, the teacher may adapt to the expected lifestyle while working towards change in the community's behavioural standards.

As we have discussed, the development of education in Canada (see Chapter 2) was intricately tied to religious affiliation and so, when the question of community expectations versus personal rights of teachers has reached our courts of law, religious freedoms are often involved. While related issues arise when discussing the teaching of controversial subjects (see Chapter 10), this chapter is devoted to the difficult question in ethics and law of balancing the individual rights of teachers relating to their private life, with the rights of the public that they are responsible to as role models for their children.

QUESTIONS for REFLECTION

1. Do you think teachers should be expected to be role models? Why or why not?
2. What sorts of roles are expected of teachers? What kinds of personal qualities are relevant to these roles teachers are expected to model?
3. What kinds of in-school behaviours are relevant to the roles teachers are expected to model? What kinds of out-of-school behaviours are relevant to the roles?
4. Do you think teachers can be morally neutral and not impart their own values onto students? Is it at least possible for some important values to be kept out of the process of role modelling?

SEXUAL ORIENTATION

Most people would identify freedom from discrimination as being central to a just society; barring an individual from a position solely on the basis of their gender or ethnic heritage, for example, would be widely accepted as unfair. Applying such a universal statement to the individual circumstances of a teacher, however, may not be so easy, as the Supreme Court of Canada case of *Vriend v. Alberta*[5] illustrates.

Delwin Vriend was employed as a laboratory coordinator in 1987 at King's College, an institution in Alberta set up to promote learning in a Christian environment. During the three years of his employment he had received regular pay increases and positive work evaluations. On being asked by the president of the college whether he was homosexual Mr. Vriend indicated that he was. Shortly thereafter the college's Board of Governors

---

5. [1998] 1 S.C.R. 493

passed a position statement condemning homosexuality and requested his resignation solely on that basis. Mr. Vriend refused and filed a complaint with the Alberta Human Rights Commission.

The ethical and legal dilemmas posed by the *Vriend* case are profound. The school, for its part, was set up to a substantial degree to foster an environment where Christian values could be promoted. As the Bible condemns homosexual relationships it was inappropriate, according to the college, that Mr. Vriend continue on as a member of the staff. To require that the college continue to hire gays and lesbians was contrary to the freedom of conscience and religion guaranteed not only in the *Charter*, but also by a long series of legal decisions in Canada.

However, discrimination against gays and lesbians has been increasingly recognized as a social evil, particularly in a school setting where tolerance should be promoted. The Supreme Court of Canada[6] has already clearly stated that gays and lesbians "whether as individuals or couples, form an identifiable minority who have suffered and continue to suffer serious social, political and economic disadvantage" and that sexual orientation should be protected from discrimination under the *Charter*.

The *Vriend* case went to the Supreme Court of Canada on the narrow issue as to whether the Province of Alberta's *Individual's Rights Protection Act* was unconstitutional by virtue of denying rights based on sexual orientation.[7] The Supreme Court held that the failure to include sexual orientation was simply an indirect way of permitting discrimination against gays and lesbians. Furthermore, by refusing to protect sexual orientation, in the same manner that other attributes such as age or gender were protected, the Act discriminated between homosexuals and heterosexuals as the former class of people was unfairly impacted by the omission in the legislation. Finally, the Court was very dismissive of the province's submission that the Act did not create the discrimination against homosexuals (because the Act was silent on it) but rather that it existed in society. The Court described the argument as superficial because the Act was intended to protect against such discrimination as unfortunately existed in society. As the Act's stated purpose was the protection of rights and dignity of *all* persons in Alberta the omission of sexual orientation could not be demonstrably justifiable and the legislation was declared unconstitutional.

---

6. In the 1995 decision of *Egan* v. *Canada*, [1995] 2 S.C.R. 513.

7. The degree of acceptance of gays and lesbians varies from province to province. In Alberta the *Individual's Rights Protection Act (IRPA)*, first enacted in 1973, protected against discrimination on a number of bases including race, religion, sex, and age but not sexual orientation. Despite repeated efforts to convince the legislature to amend the Act, the Alberta government refused on the bases that sexual orientation was a "marginal ground," that the legislation was powerless to change human attitudes, and that there had been very few complaints brought on that basis. Based on the wording of the IRPA the Alberta Human Rights Commission held that under the existing legislation Mr. Vriend had not been discriminated against and dismissed his case.

Reaction to the *Vriend* decision was mixed; some commentators read it as a declaration of the Court that religious schools could not practise faith-based hiring practices, while others stated that the case allowed religious schools to refuse employment to teachers based on their sexual orientation. In fact the decision did neither. It did reiterate the protection that gays and lesbians are afforded in Canadian society, and it found that legislatures, either through omission or commission, must recognize this protection in drafting their human rights codes. The right of separate schools to specify the personal characteristics of the teachers they employ, as role models of virtuous character, however, remains intact.

The Supreme Court of Canada had the opportunity of readdressing the issue of the conflict between religious expectations of teachers as role models and personal rights in the decision of *Trinity Western University* v. *British Columbia College of Teachers*.[8] Trinity Western University, a private institution, was associated with the Evangelical Free Church of Canada. It had been established with the purpose of offering an "academically responsible education within a distinctive Christian context." In 1985 Trinity Western University, in conjunction with the secular Simon Fraser University, started a teacher-training program offering baccalaureate degrees in education upon completion of a five-year course, four years of which were spent at Trinity Western University, the fifth year at Simon Fraser University. In 1995 Trinity Western University applied to the British Columbia College of Teachers to obtain permission to have full responsibility for the program.

Trinity Western University, consistent with its religious mandate, required students and staff to sign a Community Standards document that provided that they were, among other things, to:

> Refrain from practices that are biblically condemned. These include but are not limited to drunkenness (Eph. 5:18), swearing or use of profane language (Eph. 4:29, 5:4; Jas. 3:1–12), harassment (Jn. 13:34–35; Rom. 12:9–21; Eph. 4:31), all forms of dishonesty including cheating and stealing (Prov. 12:22; Col. 3:9; Eph. 4:28), abortion (Ex. 20:13; Ps. 139:13–16), involvement in the occult (Acts 19:19; Gal. 5:19), and sexual sins including premarital sex, adultery, *homosexual behaviour*, and viewing of pornography (I Cor. 6:12–20; Eph. 4:17–24; I Thess. 4:3–8; Rom. 2:26–27; I Tim. 1:9–10). Furthermore married members of the community agree to maintain the sanctity of marriage and to take every positive step possible to avoid divorce. [Emphasis added.]

The B.C. College of Teachers rejected Trinity's application on the basis that:

> Labelling homosexual behaviour as sinful has the effect of excluding persons whose sexual orientation is gay or lesbian.

---

8. *Trinity Western University v. British Columbia College of Teachers*, [2001] 1 S.C.R. 772.

The Council believes and is supported by law in the belief that sexual orientation is no more separable from a person than colour. Persons of homosexual orientation, like persons of colour, are entitled to protection and freedom from discrimination under the law.

The Supreme Court of Canada, in reviewing the decision of the College of Teachers, observed that the college was correct in considering the protection of gays and lesbians in determining whether to accredit a private institution. However, they failed in not also taking into account the right of religious freedom of Trinity Western University. The effect of the College of Teachers' decision was to limit the freedom of association of a particular religious group. Not only was Trinity Western University affected but also so were those students who, because of their religious affiliation, would be forced to attend a secular university for at least one year.

There was no evidence before the Court that teachers graduating from the Trinity Western University program fostered discriminatory practices in the public school system, either through their teaching habits or by conduct in their personal lives. The freedom to hold beliefs, the Court observed, was wider than the freedom to act on those beliefs. Thus while a teacher might be censured for acting in a discriminatory manner, holding such beliefs was within their rights. In the absence of such evidence, which could have been obtained by asking for reports on student teachers, opinions of school principals and superintendents, or through discipline files involving Trinity Western University graduates and other teachers affiliated with a Christian school of that nature, there was no basis for denying Trinity Western University's application.[9]

There was, however, a strongly worded dissent by Justice L'Heureux-Dubé who disagreed with the distinction drawn by her colleagues between the freedom to hold beliefs and the freedom to act upon them. She observed that not only would a homosexual student be discouraged from applying to the college, but also a homosexual staff or faculty member would be forced to resign. The majority decision of her colleagues, in her view, miscast the nature of the decision that the BCCT was required to make. As part of its mandate as being a self-governing profession the college was required to accredit only those teachers who would be adequately prepared to teach in a public school environment.

Justice L'Heureux-Dubé was of the view that a student teacher who signed the *Code of Community Standards* of Trinity Western University, even if they did not personally agree with those standards, gave a public expression to discrimination against gays and lesbians. It was reasonable, in her view, that the college would not want to accredit those teachers whose publicly held views were contrary to the inclusive environment of the public school community.

---

9. If, for example, there were a disproportionate number of Trinity graduates who were disciplined for making homophobic comments in their local newsletters (which might be "conduct unbecoming a member"—see *Kempling v. British Columbia College of Teachers*, [2004] B.C.J. No. 173) then an evidentiary basis might have been established.

Unlike the majority of the Court, the Justice approached the case on the basis that as a self-governing profession the BCCT was in the best position to judge how to ameliorate the effects of a student teacher coming from a particular religious schooling, which as part of its mandate discriminated against gays and lesbians. The BCCT's requirement that the final year of a teacher's education, including the supervision of their student teaching assignment, be done under the auspices of Simon Fraser University was a decision of the college, acting within their own area of expertise, that this final year would potentially broaden the minds of teachers who had signed this discriminatory document. The majority decision, in her view, ignored the critical need in public education systems that teachers be sensitive to the concerns of homosexual and bisexual students. The public, including gays and lesbians, was entitled to rely upon the pedagogical expertise of the college in ensuring that teachers would maintain this inclusive outlook.

QUESTIONS for REFLECTION

1. Do you think that sexual orientation is a choice or an immutable quality? How does your belief relate to your opinion about whether someone who is homosexual can be a good role model?
2. Should sexual orientation be considered a relevant characteristic of teachers in secular schools? Do you agree with the Court that it can be in religious schools?
3. Could a homosexual teacher be an effective role model in a secular school with no policy on sexual orientation, but where the community values are strongly opposed to homosexuality?
4. Could a teacher who is homosexual and celibate be an effective role model in a Christian school?

PRIVATE BEHAVIOUR

Sexual orientation is only one aspect of teachers' private lives that is relevant to their employment. The case of *Caldwell v. Stuart*[10] provides us with an insight as to how personal conduct might, in some circumstances, lead to professional concerns. Ms. Caldwell, a practising Catholic, was hired by a private Catholic high school as a teacher of mathematics and commercial subjects. Although the school would have preferred to have an all-Catholic staff, shortages of applicants meant that 30 percent of the teachers were non-adherents. In the case of Catholic applicants a certificate was required from their parish priest that the teacher was a practising Catholic; non-Catholics were expected to adhere to the tenets of their own faith.

---

10. *Caldwell v. Stuart*, [1984] 2 S.C.R. 603

After five years of teaching at the school Ms. Caldwell married a divorced man in a civil ceremony. Upon learning of this the school advised her that they would not be renewing her contract in the subsequent year on the basis that her conduct violated their teaching contract, which required that their (Catholic) teachers exhibit the highest model of Christian behaviour. Her complaint to the Board of Inquiry under the *British Columbia Human Rights Code* was dismissed on the basis that the *Human Rights Code* allowed for discrimination based on "bona fide qualifications in respect of his occupation or employment." This adverse decision was upheld by the Supreme Court of Canada who observed that while Ms. Caldwell would be entitled to reinstatement were she hired in a secular or public school, in the case of the Catholic school there was a religious element that forms part of the nature of a Catholic education. Part of the qualifications of teachers in such a setting is that they act as exemplars to the students through their adherence to the Catholic faith. The Court observed that the special role teachers played allowed such discrimination, even though a Catholic school would not, for example, be allowed to impose similar requirements on a secretary. In reaching this decision the Court concluded by noting, "freedom of religion remains and the right to separate schools continues" as guaranteed by section 92 of the *Constitution Act.*

In a case[11] that received considerable commentary at the time a husband and wife, both of whom were teachers, sent in a nude, but relatively modest, photograph of the wife to a men's magazine contest. The local school board, on learning of the photograph, suspended both teachers for a period of six weeks. The teachers won an internal appeal on the basis that the board should not have applied a local community standard but rather applied the more lenient nation-wide standard. The matter went to the British Columbia Court of Appeal on the issue of what constituted "misconduct," and was the standard to be applied one of a local or nation-wide nature.

The Court of Appeal noted that the B.C. Teachers' Federation condemns the public display of all pornographic material, and defines pornography as exploitation for a sexual purpose. Both teachers admitted that, after the fact, they had regretted their actions and were concerned about losing their jobs, and that the magazine was not the sort of publication they would recommend to their students. On that basis, the Court found that according to the standards of the province-wide Federation the photograph constituted misconduct on the part of the teachers and a period of suspension was imposed. In a passage subsequently adopted by the Supreme Court of Canada[12] the Court of Appeal noted:

> The reason why off-the-job conduct may amount to misconduct is that a teacher holds a position of trust, confidence and responsibility. If he or she acts in an improper way, on or off the job, there may be a loss of public confidence in the teacher and in the public school system, a loss of respect by students for the teacher

---

11. *Shewan v. Abbotsford School District No. 34* (1987), 21 B.C.L.R. (2d) 93, 47 D.L.R. (4th) 106

12. In *R. v. Audet*, [1996] S.C.J. No. 61

Private Life, Public Role

involved, and other teachers generally, and there may be controversy within the school and within the community which disrupts the proper carrying on of the educational system.

QUESTIONS
for REFLECTION

1. What do you think are the ethical implications of a married teacher having an affair? Would it make a difference if no one in the school (staff or students) ever knew of the affair? Why or why not?
2. Could a person who has an inclination toward dressing in cross-gender clothing in private still be an effective role model as a teacher? What difference would it make, if any, if the community would strongly disapprove?
3. What should be done if a teacher is unjustly described as being sexually immoral and this causes the community, including students, to lose respect for the teacher as a role model?
4. Can an unmarried person well known for sexual promiscuity still function as an effective teacher? Would it make a difference what age group the person taught?

CRIMINAL BEHAVIOUR

The requirement that a teacher's private life not bring the profession into disrepute can extend beyond sexual and religious choices. Criminal activity may, for example, result in a teacher being reprimanded for professional misconduct. In the discipline decision of the *Ontario College of Teachers v. GWD*[13] a teacher was found to be guilty of professional misconduct when he became involved in an altercation with a police officer and was convicted of assaulting a police officer in an attempt to resist arrest even though the act took place outside school hours and no students were involved. Similarly, a conviction of trafficking cocaine, and incidentally being known in the drug subculture as "Teacher," was grounds for dismissal.[14] Other conduct that has been found to be misconduct includes refusing to provide a breathalyser sample, engaging the services of a prostitute,[15] and attempting to bribe a school official in order to protect employment during a period of downsizing.[16]

As community standards change conduct that once was cause for dismissal, such as simple possession of marijuana, would likely no longer be accepted as cause for dismissal in the public school system. However, in a

---

13. [1999] O.C.T.D.D. No. 15

14. *OCT v. Hungerford*, [1999] O.C.T.D.D. No. 17

15. *OCT v. Knott*, [2000] O.C.T.D.D. No. 11

16. *OCT v. Kuhn*, [1998] O.C.T.D.D. No. 10

school established in part for religious reasons an argument could be made that a higher standard of behaviour is required of teachers and that the conviction could be grounds for firing.

Wrongdoing that predates a person entering the teaching profession may also result in censure: where an applicant lies about his or her qualifications in order to obtain a teaching certificate, this constitutes professional misconduct even though at the time the individual was not a teacher.[17] The case of *OCT v. Raciot*[18] takes this principle a step further. Ms. Raciot applied to the University of Ottawa for entrance into their Bachelor of Education program for French studies that required that a candidate had to have a Bachelor of Arts degree. In fact Ms. Raciot had completed only a third of the requirements for a B.A. but through an administrative error this was overlooked. She successfully completed her Bachelor of Education program and on that basis was issued a teaching certificate and employed by the City of London school board.

When the administrative error was discovered Ms. Raciot admitted the deception and offered to make up the missing courses. The University of Ottawa elected not to revoke her degree in Education. The Discipline Committee of the College of Teachers, however, characterized her behaviour as "disgraceful, dishonourable and unprofessional. In addition, the Committee believes that this reprehensible behaviour must be dealt with severely as it undermines the integrity of the profession, which depends upon its members providing accurate information concerning their qualifications." In addition to her teaching certificate being revoked, a substantial fine was imposed.

QUESTIONS for REFLECTION

1. Should the *Raciot* case be different if the lie was about high school marks in order to obtain entry into a university program? What if a teacher stole a car as a minor and has never committed another crime? How far back in time does blameworthiness extend?
2. While obviously heinous crimes such as murder are reprehensible, is all criminal behaviour an example of poor role modelling? Even jaywalking? Smoking a marijuana cigarette? Where should the line be drawn?
3. A teacher took part in an animal rights protest that turned violent and a police officer was severely, though accidentally, injured. The teacher pleaded guilty to assault and the judge gave an absolute discharge so that no criminal record resulted. Should the teacher disclose the fact to the school board? Why or why not?
4. Have you ever broken the law? To what extent do you think this fact is relevant to your ability to be an effective role model? Are you an exception or an example of the importance of criminal behaviour for role modelling?

---

17. *OCT v. Haines*, [1999] O.C.T.D.D. No. 12

18. [2001] O.C.T.D.D. No. 5

CONDUCT AS CITIZENS

Finally, a teacher's general behaviour as a citizen of the community outside of the classroom is also relevant to her or his fitness as a role model. At the start of this chapter we observed that in assessing a doctor one would not be concerned whether the doctor was kind to her or his spouse. Having thought about the interrelationship between the personal life of a teacher and the teacher's position as a role model it is interesting to note that, in fact, the Courts have found that it is was within the jurisdiction of a teacher's professional body to investigate the circumstances surrounding allegations of spousal assault.[19] Obviously the circumstances surrounding the allegations would be germane to the reasonableness of any finding that body made: it is, however, a strong reminder of the unique nature of a teacher's role within society.

WHAT THE CODES SAY

The teacher does not engage in activities which adversely affect the quality of the teacher's professional service.

—*From the Alberta Teachers' Association* Code of Professional Conduct

Although the *Charter* contains a guarantee of freedom of speech, by virtue of their positions teachers do not have unfettered freedom of speech, even when the subject is independent of the classroom. Mr. Ross, a resource teacher at the Magnetic Hill School, was active during his off-duty hours making racist and discriminatory comments through his books, articles, and television appearances. In particular, he claimed that Christian civilization was being undermined by a Jewish conspiracy. Although the school board knew of his comments, Mr. Ross claimed that because they were made in off-duty hours they did not directly affect his teaching, and so no disciplinary action was taken until a parent, who was a member of the Jewish faith, complained that the school board's inactivity condoned Mr. Ross's behaviour and promoted discrimination in the school system. Mr. Ross was then reprimanded for his behaviour and warned that continued public discussion of his views could result in dismissal. Mr. Ross continued to make racist statements outside the classroom and so the board placed him in a non-teaching position, and ordered him not to publicly express any anti-Semitic views.

Mr. Ross appealed the board's decision to the New Brunswick Court of Queen's Bench who ruled that it infringed on Mr. Ross' freedom of speech outside of the classroom. The Court of Appeal upheld the lower Court's decision, saying that while "the author of the discrimination is a teacher, who might be considered a role model to students," and thereby in some circumstances could be removed from the classroom for saying things that would otherwise be

---

19. *Stolen v. British Columbia College of Teachers*, [1995] B.C.J. No. 1980

protected by his right to freedom of expression, there were no "pressing and substantial reasons" for doing so in Mr. Ross's case given that the conduct complained of took place entirely outside of the classroom. In arriving at that decision, the Court noted that to do otherwise would be to condone the suppression of views that were not politically popular at any particular time; it was only in the clearest circumstances that an individual's rights of free expression could be restricted and, in its view, that had not been established in the case of Mr. Ross.

At the Supreme Court of Canada[20] Mr. Ross argued that both his freedom of expression and his own freedom of religion had been infringed by the disciplinary order. The Court accepted that both of Mr. Ross's freedoms had been violated, but held that this could be justified if it could be demonstrated that doing so addressed a pressing and substantial concern in a free and democratic society, and that it was done in a manner that was proportional to meet that goal (the *Oakes* test). The Court held that the first part of the test was met, given the need to promote an inclusive educational environment. However, once Mr. Ross was removed from the classroom there was no evidence that his continued employment would foster a poisoned environment and thus the *Charter* protected the expression of his views, distasteful as they were. So Mr. Ross could be removed from a teaching position for his discriminatory comments, but once he was not in the role of a teacher, could not be prevented from stating his views. The unique role of teachers as mentors was stressed in the Supreme Court of Canada's decision:

> It is on the basis of the position of trust and influence that we hold the teacher to high standards both on and off duty, and it is an erosion of these standards that may lead to a loss in the community of confidence in the public school system. I do not wish to be understood as advocating an approach that subjects the entire lives of teachers to inordinate scrutiny on the basis of more onerous moral standards of behaviour. This could lead to a substantial invasion of the privacy rights and fundamental freedoms of teachers. However, where a "poisoned" environment within the school system is traceable to the off-duty conduct of a teacher that is likely to produce a corresponding loss of confidence in the teacher and the system as a whole, then the off-duty conduct of the teacher is relevant.

Mr. Ross would likely not have been allowed to make his inflammatory comments in the classroom, given the Supreme Court of Canada's observation that:

> There can be no doubt that the attempt to foster equality, respect and tolerance in the Canadian educational system is a laudable goal. But the additional driving factor in this case is the nature

---

20. [1996] 1 S.C.R. 825

of the educational services in question: we are dealing here with the education of young children. While the importance of education of all ages is acknowledged, of principal importance is the education of the young. . . [E]ducation awakens children to the values a society hopes to foster and to nurture. . . The importance of ensuring an equal and discrimination free educational environment, and the perception of fairness and tolerance in the classroom are paramount in the education of young children.

While the nature of Mr. Ross' comments may be so reprehensible that his removal from the classroom setting would be seen as justified by most observers, in other instances it may be more difficult to separate legitimate political discourse from unacceptable conduct. Consider the example of Metropolitan Separate School Board and Ontario English Catholic Teachers' Association[21] where an eminently qualified religious studies teacher was barred from teaching that program on the basis of her public criticism of the Catholic Church's attitudes towards the role of women in the church. Many Catholics, particularly in North America, are troubled by the non-ordination of women in the Catholic faith. Ms. Manning had been quoted in a number of newspaper articles as a spokesperson for Coalition of Concerned Canadian Catholics (CCCC), which is critical of the Church's position. In some of the articles she was identified as being employed by the Board; the School Board felt that in so doing Ms. Manning was using the Board as a "soap-box" to express her own views. From their perspective, while Ms. Manning was entitled to express those views, her identifying herself as a teacher in a particular separate school board could not be condoned. In addition, there were a number of letters written to the Board complaining of Ms. Manning's deviation from traditional church orthodoxy.

The School Board argued before a Labour Board of Arbitration that s. 93 of the *Constitution Act, 1867* allowed them to refuse to appoint Ms. Manning on the basis of her public criticism. They relied upon a number of earlier decisions that supported the right to dismiss for denominational cause in Catholic schools as being protected by that constitutional right.[22]

The Board of Arbitration, while conceding that the School Board had the right to decide who could teach a particular subject, held that in this case the Board's decision was not made for denominational reasons but rather political ones. It was found that because Ms. Manning's identification as a board teacher of religion in articles critical of the Church was uncomfortable for the School Board they chose to deal with it by removing her from that post. This, the Board of Arbitration held, was not a denominational

---

21. Re: *Metropolitan Separate School Board and Ontario Catholic Teachers' Association* (1994), 41 L.A.C. (4th) 353

22. In particular, the cases of *Essex County Roman Catholic Separate School Board v. Porter* (1978), 89 D.L.R. (2d) 445, 21 O.R. (2d) 255 (C.A.), and *Essex County Roman Catholic Separate School Board v. Tremblay-Webster* (1984), 5 D.L.R. (4th) 665, 84 C.L.L.C. Para.14,030, 45 O.R. (2d) 83 (C.A.)

decision but merely taking the easy way out, and ordered that Ms. Manning be reinstated as a teacher of religion at the school.

While not determinative of the case, one interesting aspect of this decision is that the School Board felt that it would have been preferable if Ms. Manning had raised her concerns within the classroom, rather than in a more public forum. The question of whether, as an agent of social change, a teacher should have the ability to speak out within the classroom on controversial subjects is a fascinating and difficult issue to be dealt with in Chapter 10.

With the widespread adoption of the Internet interesting ethical issues arise as to how a teacher's private "surfing" habits may impact on their suitability as role model. In the *Ontario College of Teachers v. King* disciplinary[23] case, Mr. King, while a member of the College, was teaching at a private kindergarten school in Hong Kong. As part of his equipment both a laptop and desktop computer had been made available to him. All staff members were provided with a policy on Internet usage, which included a prohibition of visiting porno-graphic sites. A firewall program identified that Mr. King had visited, but not downloaded content, from a number of sites containing child pornography. All of this activity occurred outside school hours, and was unknown to any of his students. Nor did such viewing constitute a crime in Hong Kong. Mr. King was dismissed from his position at the school, then faced a hearing in front of the College as to whether his conduct was unbecoming a member.

The College found that the viewing of the material was reprehensible and appalling, that it was immaterial where or when it occurred, and on that basis suspended Mr. King's certificate and ordered that he undergo psychiatric testing as well as sensitivity training.

QUESTIONS for REFLECTION

1. How does the decision in *King* accord with the Supreme Court of Canada's view in *Trinity* between the right to hold beliefs so long as you don't act on them—if the Internet viewing was completely private how is this different than an unexpressed view on homosexuality? Is there an ethical difference if it had been a personal computer at home?
2. Do you hold values for which you would sacrifice being a teacher? Are there any important personal values that you suppress in order to be a teacher?
3. A teacher is well known to go on weekend alcoholic "benders." To the sur-prise of the students and fellow teachers, the teacher consistently displays excellent ability in the classroom and is generally well liked as a person and professional. Do you think the teacher ought to be professionally sanc-tioned? Why or why not?
4. Are there circumstances where modelling social disobedience may benefit students and the community? If so, which circumstances? If not, why not?

---

23. [2003] O.C.T.D.D. No. 59

Summary

Teachers are expected to teach by example as well as classroom instruction. This requires that teachers are role models and, as such, must display consistency between in-school and out-of-school behaviour. Difficulties certainly arise because just what behaviours are allowed and disallowed will vary within and across communities. In general, teachers must be seen to be reliable, trustworthy and, in the case of denominational schools, upholders of religious tenets including those relating to sexual orientation and behaviour.

Questions for Discussion

1. Should society allow schools to be set up that may discriminate through their sincerely held beliefs as to what constitutes proper behaviour according to the tenets of their religion? Given the importance of freedom of religion shouldn't individuals be allowed to set up schools where their children are taught according to their faith? Should it make a difference whether the teacher's role excludes direct instruction in religion?
2. What sort of role model do you think you represent? Which of your personal characteristics and qualities are central to this representation? Which of these characteristics and qualities could you change? Which would you like to change to make you a better role model? Why?
3. What harms are done to students by setting a bad example? What are the benefits of being a good role model? Consider for example teachers who smoke during breaks—is this contrary to setting a good example?
4. Should school boards warn prospective teachers about certain acts that, while not illegal, are considered by the local community to be unacceptable and therefore may be grounds for sanctions? What about circumstances where a community is in transition and standards are in flux?

Further Reading

Grace, E. (1993). Professional misconduct of moral pronouncement: A study of "contentious" teacher behaviour in Quebec. *Education and Law Journal, 5,* 99–142.

La Forest, G. V. (1997). Off duty conduct and the fiduciary obligations of teachers. *Education & Law Journal, 8,* 119–137.

Piddocke, A., Magsino, R., & Manley-Casmir, M. (1997). *Teachers in trouble: An exploration of the normative character of teaching.* Toronto: University of Toronto Press.

CHAPTER 6
NEGLIGENCE AND TEACHERS

You are a substitute teacher who is filling in for a junior high school gym teacher. The class is learning to play rugby, a sport you have never played in your life. The students are anxious to play the game but you have some concerns about your lack of knowledge and the risks that you perceive may be presented if you allow the students to play.

1. What is your responsibility?

2. What should you do in the circumstances?

3. Would it matter if you had taught the students previously?

In Chapter 3 we discussed in general terms a number of legal concepts including that of negligence. In this chapter we will consider in greater depth how the law of negligence affects the teaching profession, paying particular attention to the duty of care owed by teachers to supervise. At the close of the chapter we will consider in brief a number of concepts that you should also be aware of including occupiers' liability, vicarious liability, educational malpractice, and prevention of suicide and self-harm.

THE STANDARD OF CARE AND DUTY TO SUPERVISE

While a teacher, or a school district, is not a guarantor of the safety of children they are responsible for they still must meet a reasonable standard of care. The classic description of the standard to be met is that of a careful or prudent parent;[1] while this standard may have been appropriate in the 1800s changes both to the size of classes and the activities carried on within them have demanded a revision. The Supreme Court of Canada in *Myers v. Peel,* [2] while accepting the test, noted that:

> It is not, however, a standard which can be applied in the same manner and to the same extent in every case. Its application will vary from case to case and will depend upon the number of students being supervised at any given time, the nature of the exercise or activity in progress, the age and the degree of skill and training which the students may have received in connection with such activity, the nature and condition of the equipment in use at the time, the competency and capacity of the students involved, and a host of other matters which may be widely varied but which, in a given case, may affect the application of the prudent parent-standard to the conduct of the school authority in the circumstances.

A large classroom size, while obviously a factor in the degree of supervision a teacher can offer any one student, is likely not a defence for a claim brought for failing to properly supervise. In the *Myers* case illness of the Grade 12 gym teacher resulted in the Grade 11 teacher having to teach a double class of approximately 40 students. A small group of students asked permission to leave the gymnasium to practise gymnastics in a separate room. As this was not an unusual request, permission was granted. During the course of a dismount from the rings the plaintiff was rendered a quadriplegic due to improper spotting. The Court, in addition to finding that the protective floor mats were inadequate, also held that the level of supervision was not met, in that a prudent parent would not allow his or her child to undertake such a risky activity without supervision.

---

1. *Williams v. Eady* (1893), 10 T.L.R. 41

2. *Myers v. Peel,*[1981] 2 S.C.R. 21.

What is interesting is that at no point did the Supreme Court address the practical difficulty the teacher had in teaching two groups of students with different course requirements; having said that it is clear from the judgement that in such circumstances the teacher should not have allowed part of the class to be wholly unsupervised. A prudent teacher would have changed the lesson plan to allow for all the activities to take place under teacher supervision, or alternatively, indicated to the students that they were restricted to only that apparatus that did not pose substantial risk.

WHAT THE CODES SAY

"The Code of Ethics is based on the following principles . . . Teachers have regard for the safety of their students."

—*From the New Brunswick Teachers' Association* Code of Ethics

Obviously, with today's increasing classroom sizes there will be occasions when it is impossible to monitor all students simultaneously. As a teacher you should be aware not only of the risks posed by the activities but also how reliable the students are. Thus, if you have a group of adolescent students who are "risk takers" extra care must be taken to avoid placing them in a position where they are involved in hazardous activities without your direct supervision. Your ultimate responsibility is for the students' safety; this transcends the need to follow a course curriculum or a lesson plan. If you, as a professional, feel that— either due to class make-up, equipment available, or your own experience— there is an unacceptable degree of risk, you should not undertake the activity and should discuss the matter further with the school's administration and your peers who may have greater experience in the area.

UNUSUAL RISKS AND ACTIVITIES

A large part of the Court's reasoning in *Myers* was based on the inherent and unusual dangers posed by the rings and, for that matter, most gymnastic activities. The question then arises as to whether "the prudent parent" test is appropriate for classroom activities that the average parent would have no experience in, such as supervising a chemistry laboratory or the use of parallel bars as was the case in *McKay v. Govan School Unit*. There a jury had found liability on the part of the school board on the basis of "the prudent parent" test. This finding was appealed on the basis, inter alia, that the jury had been improperly advised as to the standard of care expected of a teacher. The Saskatchewan Court of Appeal, in allowing the appeal, imposed a much higher standard of care than that of the prudent parent by saying that while such a standard might apply to a teacher supervising a baseball or hockey game "A physical training instructor in directing or supervising an evolution or exercise is bound to exercise the skill and competence of an ordinarily competent instructor in the field. The standard of the careful parent does not fit a responsibility which demands special training and expertise."[3] On the basis that the jury instruction was therefore misleading the Court of Appeal overturned the verdict of fault even though in so doing it resulted in the incongruous result that while a higher standard of care was imposed than that adopted by the jury the finding of fault was overturned!

The Supreme Court of Canada while overturning the Court of Appeal's ruling and restoring the jury's finding of liability tacitly accepted that a higher standard would be imposed when the activity posed a greater than normal risk and required additional knowledge on the part of the instructor.

This is not to say that gymnastics, per se, are inherently dangerous and thus have no place in a school setting. It is not negligence or a breach of the duty of care on the part of the school authorities to permit a pupil to undertake to perform a gymnastic manoeuvre (a) if it is suitable to his age and condition (mental and physical); (b) if he is progressively trained and coached to do it properly and avoid the danger; (c) if the equipment is adequate and suitably arranged; and (d) if the performance, having regard to its inherently dangerous nature, is properly supervised.[4] The same reasoning would apply, of course, to other recognizably hazardous activities, such as operating power tools or dealing with dangerous chemicals.[5]

A teacher must also be cognizant of the individual attributes of the student; thus, a younger child might require greater supervision than an older one "who should have known better,"[6] as would a child who is either uncoordinated or obese when asked to perform a task requiring some physical agility.[7] In the case of children with disabilities the standard becomes much higher. In the Supreme Court of Canada decision of *Dziwnka v. The Queen in Right of Alberta*[8] the infant plaintiff, who was deaf and mute, was injured while using a table saw with the guard removed. The teacher had adequately instructed the plaintiff and warned of the dangers of the operation and the student was a competent woodworker. The Court observed that had the plaintiff had the use of all his faculties then no liability would have been found. However, as the condition of the plaintiff could not allow a rapid warning of something going wrong, liability was imposed.

---

3. *McKay v. Govan School Unit* (1967), 60 W.W.R. 513.

4. *Thornton v. Prince George*, [1976] 5 W.W.R. 240; varied on other grounds [1978] 2 S.C.R. 267

5. *James et al. v. River East School Division No. 9 et al.*, (1975), 58 D.L.R. (3d) 311, [1976] 5 W.W.R. 135; affirmed by the Manitoba Court of Appeal at 64 D.L.R. (3d) 338, [1976] 2 W.W.R. 577

6. *Catherwood v. Heinrichs*, [1996] B.C.J. 1373

7. *Boese v. St. Paul's Roman Catholic Separate School District No. 20*, [1980] S.J. No. 211; aff'd. [1979] S.J. No. 87

8. *Dziwnka v. The Queen in Right of Alberta* (1971) 25 D.L.R. (3d) 12.

Even if a teacher is free of fault from allowing a student to be injured the teacher may be found liable if, after the injury, his or her conduct is such that injury is exacerbated. In *Freer v. Okanagon-Skaha School District No. 67*[9] a student who had previously broken his leg while skiing was watching his class participate in a winter soccer game. He was unable to play as his leg was still in a brace. While walking he slipped and re-injured his leg; he indicated to the supervising teacher that he thought he had re-broken the leg. The teacher erroneously believed it might just be a movement of scar tissue and on determining that the student could walk assisted by the brace told him to return to the school, get some ice on the knee, and call his mother to take him to the hospital. Although the Court held that neither the teacher nor the school was negligent in failing to adequately supervise the plaintiff, to have him walk back to the school unassisted, thus putting weight on the injured leg, caused him additional pain and suffering and a nominal amount was awarded.

Nevertheless, as neither the school nor a teacher is a guarantor of safety, there is no duty to supervise commonplace activities that the students can reasonably be expected to perform on their own. A fourteen-year-old student's claim, for example, that the school board was negligent in failing to prevent him from sliding down a banister, particularly after he had been warned on a number of previous occasions, was dismissed.[10] It is interesting to note that the Court in their judgement observed that the plaintiff, while a disciplinary problem, was of normal intelligence. The courts tend to take a robust view of teens bearing some responsibility for their actions as the following quote from Justice Keiller Mackay amply reveals:

> I am of the opinion that boys of 14 years of age are capable of and indeed should be held to exercise reasonable intelligence and care for their own safety. With great respect, I am further of opinion that paternalism in respect to boys of teen age in collegiate institutes should not be extended to a degree which would virtually deprive them of that exercise of intelligence demanded of young people of that age in other walks of life.

And in *Rich*, supra, Morris, L.J. said that it was not the duty of a reasonable, careful, and solicitous parent to endeavour to put a child in a straitjacket.[11]

In many instances an injury occurs that is either unforeseeable or of such a low magnitude of risk that a prudent parent would not hesitate to allow their child's participation. A ball that bounces out of control during a game of catch causing the loss of an eye,[12] a teenager doing a baseball-like slide on fresh

---

9. *Freer v. Okanagon-Skaha School District No. 67*, [2002] B.C.J. No. 2739.

10. *Robinson v. Calgary School District 19* (1977), 5 A.R. 430.

11. As quoted in *Plumb v. Cowichan School District No. 65*, [1993] B.C.J. 1936.

12. *Plumb v. Cowichan School District No. 65*, 1993

fallen snow rendering himself a quadriplegic,[13] the presence of a tree that was climbed unsuccessfully during a baseball game[14]—all were in their particular circumstances tragic, but unforeseeable, accidents.

In the case of younger children, or those with learning disabilities, the need to provide safe premises and adequate supervision are that much higher. Schools have been successfully sued for not having temporary teaching trailers hooked up to the school address system when the latter was used to advise students when it was safe to load onto school buses. In that case, a five-year-old was struck by a school bus when he was discharged from school in the erroneous belief that all the buses had arrived;[15] in contrast, in a similar accident when a sixteen-year-old was run over by a school bus that unexpectedly backed up, the Court noted that the plaintiff was an age that he should have known better and apportioned liability accordingly.

OTHER CASES OF NOTE

Do teachers or school boards have remedies if a parent unjustly accuses them of failing to take proper care of the students? This issue arose in *Campbell v. Cartmell*, [1999] O.J. No. 3553.

EXTRACURRICULAR AND AFTER-CLASS ACTIVITIES

A number of recent cases have brought to the forefront the issue of a teacher's liability for injuries occurring during extracurricular activities. Although outside of regular hours and not on the school premises, these activities are viewed by the courts as being an extension of schooling with the teacher having both the right and responsibility of controlling the student's activities. Arguably, as the risks posed by such activities may be less familiar ones than encountered during normal school hours, there is a higher onus on the teacher to supervise.[16]

Typically, parents are asked to sign a consent form for the activities that will usually specify that the pupils be under the control of the teachers and adult supervisors. While no consent form could cover in minute detail all of the activities that might be carried on, it must be reasonably specific enough to allow parents to make an educated decision as to their child's involvement. An activity that deviates significantly from the consent form, such as a mountain climbing attempt during a forest products tour, not only would fall outside the consent but also, if it could be shown that the teacher was acting outside the scope of his employment, render the teacher personally liable.

---

13. *Fraser v. Campbell River School District No. 72*, [1988] B.C.J. No. 2453.

14. *Catherwood v. Heinrichs*, [1996] B.C.J. 1373.

15. *George v. Port Alberni School District 70*, [1986] B.C.J.1726.

16. *Bain v. Calgary Board of Education*, [1993] A.J.952.

Many parents feel that the school is responsible for the safety of their children throughout the school day, even when the student may have permission to leave the school property, such as to return home to lunch. The courts in Canada at this point seem to draw a distinction between those students who are bussed to the school and those who are not. The duty of supervision continues, in the case of students bussed to school, from the time they are picked up by the bus until they leave the bus at the end of the day; thus, students can be disciplined for their conduct occurring off the school premises during a lunch hour break.[17] In the case of students who do not use bussing, liability would be imposed from the point that the students enter school property[18] and arguably ends when they leave the property.

Occupiers' Liability

Schools, of course, can also be found liable for the condition of the premises. Occupier's liability is a concept all are familiar with; if an injury is sustained as a result of the condition of your premises then a lawsuit may be brought against you even if the person injured was there without your permission. The standard is that of "reasonable care"; if a person slips on a tiny piece of apple in a classroom used as a student lunchroom no liability on the part of the school division will be found if they can show that they had a reasonable maintenance system in place.[19] In the case of students the standard is somewhat higher because students are under a compulsion to attend schools, and there is a duty to supervise students on the part of the school.[20] Thus, if students are directed to enter the school by a certain entrance that proves to be unsafe, the school can be found negligent—not only for their failure to provide safe premises but also through their failure to supervise. As a teacher, while you would likely not be considered the occupier of the school grounds in law, you still have a professional responsibility to your students to be attentive to the conditions of the premises. In some instances this may consist of nothing more than being aware that there is a regular maintenance program in place; in other cases a more proactive response may be required, such as asking that a janitor shovel a path commonly used by students, or picking up broken glass on the playing field.

WHAT THE CODES SAY

"It shall be unethical for a teacher to . . . knowingly disregard the safety of his/her pupils . . ."

—*From the New Brunswick Teachers' Association* Code of Professional Conduct

17. *Lutes (Litigation Guardian of) v. Prairie View School Division No. 74*, [1992] S.J. 198.

18. *Hoyt v. Hay*, [1978] N.B.J. No. 9.

19. *Thiessen v. Winnipeg School Division 1*, [1967] S.C.R. 413.

20. *Cropp v. Potashville School Unit 25*, [1977] S.J. No. 328.

Negligence and Teachers

Vicarious Liability

Although not directly the responsibility of the individual teacher one area of law that has seen a significant degree of change recently is the imposing of vicarious liability on organizations for activities conducted without their knowledge by their employees, or by individuals whom they have some measure of control over. Few, if any, could be uninformed of the tragic sexual abuse of First Nations' children that occurred in the residency school programs or of some of the sexual predatory cases involving adults who are involved with children under the auspices of team sports or boys and girls clubs. Less well known, but of more immediate concern for the teaching profession, is the decision of the Supreme Court of Canada in *E.D.G. v. Hammer*[21] where a night janitor at a public school repeatedly assaulted a Grade 3 student when she was sent down to the boiler room to clean blackboard brushes. Neither her teachers, nor any member of the school's administration, had any reason to suspect these events were taking place over the two-year period and involved at least 20 sexual assaults. Although the child had asked her teacher to be taken off brush duty she did not explain why nor object when her request was denied. Her reticence was in part because of her natural shyness, her status as a member of a visible minority in the school, and because the janitor had told her that if she revealed what was happening he would lose his job and his family. The victim came forward a number of years later after she received a sexual education course in Grade 8.

Although both the teacher and the school board were initially sued, inter alia, in negligence these claims were abandoned during the trial; the trial judge agreed that in the circumstances they would have been unsuccessful. The plaintiff's claim proceeded on the basis of vicarious liability, which is a principle of law that where there is a non-delegable duty on the part of an organization they can be found liable for the activities of an employee even in the absence of negligence on the organization's part in hiring or supervising that employee. It is, in effect, a "no fault" imposition of liability and thus much different from a case proceeding on the basis of normal negligence standards.

The key issue in the case was whether there was a non-delegable duty imposed on the school board to keep children safe while at school. The Court reviewed the statutory responsibilities of the school board under the School Act and found that the duties imposed by that Act were not so broad that they could be held to be liable for sexual abuse by an employee whose activities they had no cause to have knowledge of. Although the Court was considering only the wording of the British Columbia act its reasoning would almost certainly apply across Canada.

EDUCATIONAL MALPRACTICE

Educational malpractice claims are those brought by former students alleging that a teacher or school was negligent in the way that they taught a subject or subjects, and as a result the student did not reach full potential. Allegations

---

21. [2003] S.C.C. 52

against teachers might include that they were unqualified to teach the subject, that they failed to advise the students on how their performance would be evaluated, that the marking system was unfair or flawed, that the curriculum was not adequately covered, or that the materials used were flawed.

At the time of writing it is unclear whether such a claim can be brought at all,[22] with some decisions suggesting that a claim solely based on educational malpractice might not be recognized by the courts as a valid cause of action. Other cases, however, have accepted that educational malpractice claims may be brought[23] although they would be limited to cases where the "conduct is sufficiently egregious and offensive to community standards of acceptable fair play".[24] To date, there have been no cases in Canada where a teacher has been successfully sued for educational malpractice.

Apart from persuading the court that such a claim exists in law at all there are a number of significant hurdles that a potential plaintiff would have to overcome. First, under many of the provinces' School Acts, teachers and employees of the school board are liable only for cases where they are "guilty of dishonesty, gross negligence or malicious or wilful misconduct or libel or slander."[25] Establishing that a teacher was grossly negligent (as opposed to simple negligence) would require very compelling evidence that a teacher was far below the standard of a reasonable teacher in the field. Secondly, on public policy grounds many courts have refused such claims on the basis that the courts should not be interfering with administration of the schools vested in the school boards.[26] Finally, proving causation would in many cases be insurmountable given the other factors that would impact on a student's success in life including the student's own aptitudes and abilities, the job market, and other vagaries of life.

QUESTIONS for REFLECTION

1. Do you think that teachers should be legally liable if they fail to teach a student? If not, what is it about teaching that makes it different from other professions, such as medicine or law?
2. Do you agree with the requirement for "gross negligence" in some jurisdictions? What ethical considerations might underlie such a requirement?

---

22. *Smart v. College of the Rockies*, [2002] B.C.J. No. 3119.

23. *McKay v. CDI Career Development Institutes Ltd.*, [1999] B.C.J. No. 561.

24. *Gould v. Regina (East) School Division No. 77*, (1996) 7 C.P.C. (4th) 372.

25. This reasoning, for example, was used in *Haynes (Guardian ad litem of) v. Lleres*, [1997] B.C.J. No. 1202 under section 112 of the *British Columbia School Act*.

26. Many U.S. cases have been decided on this basis; for example *Donohue v. Copiage Union Free School, Court of Appeal, New York* (1979), 47 N.Y. 2d, 375. In Canada, this reasoning was also adopted in *Haynes* (supra).

There are, to the knowledge of the writers, no cases in Canada where a teacher or school has been held negligent for the suicide or attempted suicide of a student. Nevertheless, some commentators[27] have suggested that there is a potential for lawsuits being brought against a school and/or teachers particularly where there was knowledge of a risk of suicidal behaviour, or the student was under undue outside pressure (such as bullying or drug abuse within the school), or the school and/or teachers failed to respond appropriately to previous attempts at suicide (by counselling or notifying parents).

Given that the courts continue to adopt the in loco parentis test in Canada, a duty of care could be found on the basis that a "prudent or careful parent" would have foreseen the risk and taken steps to ameliorate it. Alternatively, under more normal negligence principles, a duty of care could arise, especially where the teacher had particular knowledge of the risk. The substantial issue, however, in any case would be that of causation; if there was, for example, a known problem of bullying in the school then the finding of a causal connection would likely be made. While bullying is recognized as one of the primary problems facing schools today there have been few cases in Canada that have directly addressed the issue. One exception is *North Vancouver School District No. 44 v. Jubran*[28] where a student successfully launched a human rights complaint on the basis that the school district failed to take adequate steps to prevent him being harassed by other students who were uttering homophobic threats (the student was, in fact, not homosexual). We discuss the *Jubran* decision at greater length in Chapter 11. In other jurisdictions, notably the United Kingdom, the courts have found a duty owed by a teacher to take reasonable steps to prevent bullying,[29] although the court stressed in that case that:

> There is no magic in the term bullying. Any school has to have sensible disciplinary policies and procedures if it is to function properly as a school at all. It will no doubt take reasonable steps to prevent or deal with one-off acts of aggression between pupils and also recognise that persistent targeting of one pupil by others can cause lasting damage to the victim. In seeking to combat this it is always helpful to have working definitions such as those contained in the documentation we have seen. The problem is now well enough recognised for it to be reasonable to expect all schools to have policies and practices in place to meet it; indeed, this school

---

27. Doug Stewart, School of Professional Studies, Queensland University of Technology; Andrew Knott, Partner, Macrossans Lawyers, "Schools and the Duty of Care in Relation to Student Suicide and Self-Harm: An Australian Perspective," *Edu LJ* 1(218).

28. [2002] B.C.H.R.T.D. No. 10; (Human Rights Tribunal) [2003] B.C.J. No. 10 (B.C.S.C.)

29. *Leah Bradford-Smart v. West Sussex County Council*, [2002] E.W.J. No. 127.

developed just such a policy in 'Working Together.' We agree that such policies are of little value unless they are also put into practice. But in order to hold the school liable towards a particular pupil, the question is always whether the school was in breach of its duty of care towards that pupil and whether that breach caused the particular harm which was suffered.[30]

WHEN AN INCIDENT OCCURS

Although the immediate concern is, of course, with the well-being of the injured student, teachers must be vigilant to protect themselves and the school boards from unreasonable findings of liability. Because an action may not be brought for a number of years by an injured party memories may fade and the name of potential witnesses may be forgotten. It is prudent for a teacher to, as reasonably as practicable, interview the student injured and for any bystanders to determine what has happened and why. Not only is this important to prevent further incidents of the same sort but when kept as a written record this may be an important source of evidence in court as well as an aid in recreating at that time what took place. Most schools will have in place an incident reporting form that, at the very least, should be filled out. Depending upon the severity of the injuries additional records should be kept, including signed and dated witness statements from the students if this is appropriate; in all cases the teacher must advise the school administrators of any significant events.

WHAT THE CODES SAY

"Members are advised that they should immediately contact the President in case of an emergency. DO NOT leave the school building as a result of a dispute with the Department of Education or an official. It might be interpreted as a termination of contract if you do."

—*From the Yukon* Code of Ethics

You should be careful not to make any incriminating statements against yourselves, the school board, or the students in the heat of the moment. Rather, deal with the accident first and then attempt to determine fault, if any, later. You must also be cognizant of the need to inform the parents of the student; it may be that a minor injury on the school grounds might make the student more susceptible to further injury later at home. Or, it could be that the child, particularly if young, may complain of symptoms only after a number of hours and may not attribute it to the accident. While bumps and scrapes are

---

30. Supra, para. 38

a normal part of growing up for all of us, hindsight is sometimes critical of the best efforts of those involved at the time.

In the very rare cases where a lawsuit is commenced your school board will either have insurance or will be self-insured to provide coverage in case of liability being found. Assuming your activities fall within the scope of your employment this insurance will protect you financially. However, you will have to cooperate with the insurance company and its lawyers, which will likely be time-consuming and is often unavoidably stressful for the teachers involved. In the ideal world, no accidents would occur; realistically the best we can do as teaching professionals is to take what care we can, and be conscious of minimizing risks.

Summary

Although the standard of care for supervision expected of a teacher is expressed as "that of a reasonable and prudent parent" this may be modified by the degree of risk that an activity poses, the particular attributes of the student in question, the condition of the equipment used, and a host of other considerations. A young child, a more dangerous activity, or a disabled child all may require greater vigilance on the part of the teacher. In some instances, such as gymnastics where the reasonable person would expect specialist training on the part of the teacher, a higher standard is imposed on the teacher to have the knowledge and level of care of the ordinary, competent instructor in that field. This may require a teacher to have special training or to refuse to take part in such activities. Not all injuries, however, are the result of negligence; in some cases the accidents are unforeseeable or the likelihood of their occurrence is too remote to allow recovery. The guiding principle, restated, could be "If this was my child, what would I expect of the teacher?"

Questions for Discussion

1. In the summary we restate the principle as being "If this was my child, what would I expect"—why is this possibly misleading?
2. You have just started teaching a new class of students with whom you are unfamiliar—how should your conduct differ, if at all? If you are a teacher on call or substitute teacher do you have different considerations than a teacher who has normal responsibilities for the class?
3. You are assigned recess supervision; do you have a responsibility of ensuring that the playing field is completely free of all potentially hazardous debris?

Uneven surfaces? To what extent does your professional responsibility extend and is this different from your legal responsibility?

4. Is the standard of care of the reasonable, careful, or prudent parent even appropriate in this day and age? Would a more appropriate test be that of a reasonable or prudent teacher? What changes would occur if the latter standard were imposed?

5. To what extent do you think the courts should be involved in resolving disputes initiated by parents who contend that their child has suffered due to incompetent teaching? Justify your answer.

Further Reading

MacKay, W. and Dickinson, G. (1998). *Beyond the "Careful Parent": Tort Liability in Education.* Toronto: Emond Montgomery.

DeMitchell, T. and DeMitchell, T. (2003). Statutes and standards: has the door to educational malpractice been opened? *Brigham Young Education and Law Journal*, 485–519.

CHAPTER 7
TEACHER–STUDENT BOUNDARIES

You are in your first posting as a teacher and find yourself attracted to one of your students. The student is only 17, though very mature, and shares a common interest in hearing live jazz. During the summer break you meet the student at a local jazz club that serves alcohol. The student offers to buy you a drink and shows all the signs of being interested in you.

1. *What ethical issues arise out of this situation?*

2. *Does it make a difference if you are not, at the time, the student's teacher? Suppose the student will be attending another school next year—does this make a difference to your conduct?*

3. *If the student's parents were present and clearly approved would this make a difference?*

4. *Is the student's age an important consideration? What difference, if any, would it make if you were only a few years older than the student? If you were many years older?*

A teacher is called upon to play many different, and sometimes conflicting, roles: an instructor, an authority figure, a confidant, and a role model. All of these roles must be accommodated within a circumscribed boundary between the teacher and the student(s) being taught. Professional boundaries are the framework that defines the role expectations for the people involved. Establishing and maintaining clear boundaries is a large part of what makes the relationship professional by trying to ensure that students and the community are protected from harm (see Chapter 4). The primary means of harm is the power imbalance in favour of the professional and this is inherent in any professional relationship. The teacher's power relative to that of the student is derived from the socially sanctioned authority and influence of the teacher. For these reasons, teachers are ultimately responsible for managing boundary issues and are therefore accountable should problems related to boundaries occur. Almost all codes of conduct and ethics in Canada admonish teachers to "recognize that a privileged relationship with students exists and refrain from exploiting that relationship for material, ideological or other advantage."[1]

The primary concern in establishing and managing boundaries with students and their parents must be the best interests of the student. As the professional in the relationship, the teacher has the responsibility to ensure that he or she gains only a salary (or fee paid for a service) and, ideally, a sense of professional satisfaction for a "job well done." Beyond this, it must be only the student's best interest that is furthered in a professional relationship. This responsibility is manifested in such behaviours as not meddling in the affairs of their students that are outside of their professional responsibilities. Except for behaviours of a sexual nature or obvious conflict of interest activities such as accepting pay for tutoring one's own students,[2] however, boundary expectations often are not clear-cut

WHAT THE CODES SAY

"A teacher recognizes that a privileged relationship exists between the teacher and his/her pupils and shall never exploit this relationship."

—*From the Newfoundland and Labrador Teachers' Association* Code of Ethics

---

1. British Columbia Teachers' Federation *Code of Ethics*; Federation of Nunavut Teachers' *Code of Ethics*; Manitoba Teachers' Society *Code of Professional Practice*; New Brunswick Teachers' Association *Code of Professional Conduct*; Newfoundland and Labrador Teachers' Association *Code of Ethics*; Nova Scotia Teachers' Union *Code of Ethics*; Saskatchewan Teachers' Federation *Code of Ethics*; Yukon Teachers' Association *Code of Ethics*. The Alberta Teachers' Association *Code of Conduct* and the Prince Edward Island Teachers' Federation *Code of Ethics* are silent on the issue. The Ontario College of Teachers' *Ethical Standards for the Teaching Profession* does encourage teachers to "maintain professional relationships with students."

2. Alberta Teachers' Association *Code of Conduct*; Federation of Nunavut Teachers' *Code of Ethics*; New Brunswick Teachers' Association *Code of Professional Conduct*; Prince Edward Island Teachers' Federation *Code of Ethics*; Newfoundland and Labrador Teachers' Association *Code of Ethics*.

matters of right and wrong. Rather, the best course of action is dependent upon many factors, and decisions require careful consideration of the issues, always keeping in mind the best interests of the student.

MULTIPLE RELATIONSHIPS

Multiple relationships occur when the teacher functions in one professional role and another significant role in relationship to the same person. The other significant role can be professional, authoritative, emotional, or some other. Although these multiple roles can be very beneficial for students, they can also become quite difficult for both parties, and role confusion is common. Multiple relationships should therefore be avoided whenever possible because the expectations of one role may be incompatible or interfere with the other, resulting in harm to the student. Because of the power imbalance, students may find it difficult to negotiate boundary expectations or to defend themselves against violations of boundary expectations that are not in their best interest. As well, students are typically unaware of the need for professional boundaries and may at times even initiate behaviour or make requests that could constitute boundary violations. Of course, because these multiple relationships are inherent in the teaching role, they cannot be completely avoided.

Overlapping relationships, where a teacher has contact but not a significant role in relationship to the student, can be problematic but again are not completely avoidable. Such overlapping relationships can occur in situations where, for example, the teacher is active in a particular religious or cultural community and meets his or her students through those activities, or is active in a local support association for parents of children with a learning disability and interacts with parents of his or her students at meetings. Overlapping relationships require the teacher to be alert to signs that the student or parent is treating the teacher as a teacher (e.g., discussing student academic progress) and not as an individual citizen, and to take steps to clarify that questionable role expectations will not be fulfilled.

Relationships with students outside of the professional relationship where either the teacher or the student is in a position to give special favours, or to hold any type of power over the other, present particular difficulties. Requesting favours from students or any other assistance that involves another relationship in addition to the primary professional relationship, such as babysitting, risks changing the professional relationship. For example, a student who receives a gift from a teacher could feel pressured to reciprocate to avoid receiving a negative evaluation. Conversely, accepting a significant gift from a student risks altering the professional relationship and could leave the teacher feeling pressured to reciprocate by offering "special" treatment. A frank but sensitive discussion of the student's motives can usually provide the necessary information to make an ethical decision. The decision should not be based upon a desire for the gift or to avoid discussing the student's intentions, but on a judgement of whether the teacher–student relationship would be changed in such a way that the student may be harmed.

Socializing with students outside of school-sanctioned activities is a special case. For example, in the discipline case of *Ontario College of Teachers v. Markson*[3] a 14-year-old male student was asked to assist an occasional teacher in the computer lab. The student developed a "crush" on the teacher. The parents, observing this, brought the matter up with the teacher who indicated that a teacher should never be alone with a student. Despite this the student and teacher met during the summer on five occasions where, apart from a hug and a kiss on the cheek by the student, no sexual conduct took place. However, a series of sexually explicit notes and e-mails ensued between the two in which the teacher confided that the thought of other females being involved with the student "drove her crazy" and that "the only experience I want to ever have is with you only from now on." The contents of these notes and e-mails were revealed in part by the boy's mother's discovery of a note while doing his laundry, and in part through a subsequent investigation of the father's laptop, which the student had been using.

The teacher was cited on a number of bases including unprofessional conduct and abusing a student physically, sexually, verbally, psychologically, or emotionally. While the latter charge was dismissed, she was found to have acted in an unprofessional manner.

Other examples of professional misconduct have included taking a student for drives in the teacher's car, purchasing small items for a student, and giving a student a home or cellular phone number.[4] Teachers colleges have noted that infatuation between teenage students and teachers is not uncommon and that there is a positive duty on the part of the teacher to discourage such feelings by distancing himself or herself from the student.[5]

Friendly relationships can also present problems for both teachers and students in that the role expectations in a friendship are for a higher level of personal disclosure and reciprocity than in a teaching relationship. Information revealed in a friendly relationship, as well as the expectation for friendly reciprocity, may then present complications leading to feelings of betrayal when evaluative decisions are made in the teaching role.

Self-disclosure represents another example of role boundary crossing. Teachers, therefore, should be very careful in its use. A number of dangers exist in self-disclosure, including shifting the focus from the needs of the student to the teacher's needs or changing the relationship toward one that is more personal than professional. Such blurring of role expectations can confuse the student with respect to role expectations of the relationship and thereby degrade the quality of their educational experience. As always, the primary question to be asked is, "Is my self-disclosure for the student's benefit?" Self-disclosures such as storytelling or recollections of incidents as instructive or illustrative can be a powerful teaching tool when used judiciously, but should not involve irrelevant details such as current problems, personal fantasies, sexual practices, or gossip.

---

3. [2001] O.C.T.D.D. No. 16

4. *Ontario College of Teachers v J.L.*, [2001] O.C.T.D.D. No. 12

5. *Ontario College of Teachers v. H.J.R.*, [2001] O.C.T.D.D. No. 17

Teachers in large urban centres have a much easier time avoiding multiple relationships because of the large student pool from which to draw; they can more easily separate their professional from their personal life. Urban teachers have the benefit of the relative anonymity of the large city so that overlapping relationships run less risk of harm. Rural teachers, by contrast, have dramatically different experiences as a result of less, if any, anonymity, and different demographics and cultural norms. The pool of potential schools is much smaller so not teaching one's own children, for example, can be next to impossible. And unless one is willing to live as a hermit, overlapping relationships are a fact of life. Thus, the management of role boundaries and multiple relationships is far more complex in rural settings. Rural teachers must be particularly committed to the core ethical values of the profession and adept at upholding them in a flexible manner, while possessing a generous capacity for tolerating ambiguity in their relationships. The fact that the teacher teaches in a small community, however, does not absolve them from having to meet the same standards for professional conduct as their urban peers.[6]

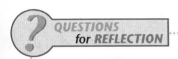

QUESTIONS for REFLECTION

1. What are your thoughts about the ethics of accepting gifts from students? Are there circumstances where it would be improper to accept a gift from a student? If so, what are they?
2. Should a teacher never be friendly with students? If so, where is the line drawn on how friendly? If not, wouldn't teaching suffer?
3. Although there are no explicit guidelines that prohibit friendships from developing once a student is no longer a student of the teacher, do you think it would ever be appropriate? Why or why not?
4. What are the ethical considerations if a teacher has his or her own child as a student? Should a teacher avoid having them as students? Why or why not?

SEXUAL BOUNDARIES

There are **no** circumstances in which sexual activity between a teacher and a student is acceptable. Sexual activity between a student and teacher is always detrimental to the student's best interest, regardless of what rationalization or belief system a teacher might choose to use to excuse it. Although most codes of ethics and conduct state that a teacher "recognizes that a privileged relationship with students exists and refrains from exploiting that

---

6. Ibid.

relationship,"[7] the Saskatchewan Teachers' Federation's *Code of Ethics* is the only Canadian code that explicitly addresses the issue in the commentary on Article 9 "Dealing with Individual Students":

> It is not appropriate for teachers to engage in romantic or sexual relationships with their students. Such liaisons represent a breach of the teacher–student relationship and may undermine the trust that students and parents should be able to have that all teachers will use the authority and closeness they have with their students in ways that are consistent with that relationship. The onus is on teachers, as adult professionals, to ensure that their behaviour does not encourage romantic or sexual feelings in their students or indicate that they reciprocate such feelings.

The majority of teachers who sexually exploit their students are males, experiencing personal problems such as loneliness or marital discord, who misinterpret their student's friendliness or efforts to please as romantic or erotic. Many of those teachers report being genuinely in love with their female junior and high-school student. Others report seeing nothing wrong with their behaviour and that their actions were misinterpreted by students. This latter group appears to be acting in a sexually aggressive manner in response to their personal problems. A minority are calculating and predatory paedophiles that chose teaching in order to gain access to prepubescent children.[8]

It is obviously difficult to know exactly how often teacher–student sexual contact occurs, and there has been very little research done in this area. In one of only two studies to survey students, 25 percent of girls and 10 percent of boys in Grades 8 through 12 reported being sexually harassed by a teacher or school staff member at some point during their schooling.[9] In the other study, which used a broader definition of sexual harassment, 82 percent of female and 18 percent of male students reported experiencing sexual harassment, with 14 percent reporting having sexual intercourse with a teacher.[10] In the only Canadian study to date, from a review of Ontario cases over a 5-year period 47 teachers

7. British Columbia Teachers' Federation *Code of Ethics*; Federation of Nunavut Teachers' *Code of Ethics*; Manitoba Teachers' Society *Code of Professional Practice*; New Brunswick Teachers' Association *Code of Professional Conduct*; Newfoundland and Labrador Teachers' Association *Code of Ethics*; Saskatchewan Teachers' Federation *Code of Ethics*; Yukon Teachers' Association *Code of Ethics*.

8. Shakeshaft, C. & Cohan, A. (1995). Sexual abuse of students by school personnel. *Phi Delta Kappa, 76*, 512–520.

9. American Association of University Women, 1993

10. Wishnietsky, D.H. (1991). Reported and unreported teacher–student sexual harassment. *Journal of Educational Research, 3*, 164–169.

(46 men and 1 woman) were charged with sexual assault of a student.[11] Approximately half of the cases, representing 0.06 percent of all male teachers in the province, resulted in a conviction.

Because of the unequal balance of power and influence inherent in a professional relationship, it is impossible for a student to give meaningful consent to any sexual involvement with his or her teacher; student consent and willingness to participate in a personal relationship does not relieve teachers of their duties and responsibilities for ethical conduct in this area.

While the rule is simply stated and readily understood —"Do not have intimate personal relationships with students"—it is important to understand the reasoning behind the rule to appreciate the breadth of its application. As already discussed, a teacher's role arises in part through delegation by the parent; the decision of *R. v. Forde*[12] summarizes this as follows:

> Insofar as persons in the profession of the accused, teachers, it's quite apparent that they hold a special role in the life of young people. In our society the role of the teacher is second in importance only to the parent. I dare say that the parent views the teacher as being in his or her place while the child is away from the control of the parent. The parent entrusts the teacher with the parent's responsibilities, preparing the youths to compete and to contribute and to develop their individual talents in this very difficult world, both in our own community, in our national community and in the international community, an extremely difficult time for young people and their parents. The role, therefore, of the teacher, in my opinion, has to be seen in the context of what challenges face teachers and young people in our community in the context to which I've just referred.

Two consequences flow immediately from this delegation of power. First, teachers owe a responsibility to the parent independent of any responsibility owed to the student. The parent, having given over the right of control and direction over the child to the teacher, is owed a duty that the teacher not exercise that power in a manner directly contrary to what would be appropriate for a parent. Some have suggested that because of this delegation the question of consent to sexual relationships is as irrelevant as it would be in the case of a parent exploiting a child;[13] this is perhaps an oversimplification given that only portions of the parental role are transferred over to a teacher, and only for a finite time. Nevertheless, a parent can sue a teacher regardless of the student's wishes: thus, in *Young v. B.C.*

---

11. Dolmage, W.R. (1995). Accusations of teacher sexual abuse of students in Ontario schools: Some preliminary findings. *Alberta Journal of Educational Research, 16*, 127–144.

12. [1992] O.J. No. 1698

13. Case comment on *R. v. Audet, Lex View* Issue No. 1.0, Bensen and Miller.

College of Teachers[14] the Court found liability against the teacher for engaging in a relationship that the student was in favour of but the parents were not.

The second aspect is that a special relationship arises between the teacher and the student where the former is placed in a "position of authority" or a "position of trust." A position of authority is broader than merely the legal right to control another person's activities; it also includes the power that arises simply by virtue of the unequal status between the teacher and student.

Being in "a position of trust" is a related but different concept; the courts have defined it as:

> One needs to keep in mind that what is in question is not the specialized concept of the law of equity, called a "trust". What is in question is a broader social or societal relationship between two people, an adult and a young person. "Trust", according to the Concise Oxford Dictionary (8th ed.), is simply "a firm belief in the reliability or truth or strength of a person". Where the nature of the relationship between an adult and a young person is such that it creates an opportunity for all of the persuasive and influencing factors which adults hold over children and young persons to come into play, and the child or young person is particularly vulnerable to the sway of these factors, the adult is in a position where those concepts of reliability and truth and strength are put to the test. Taken together, all of these factors combine to create a "position of trust" towards the young person.[15]

This is not intended to be an exact, or exhaustive, definition of the phrase; rather it is up to the individual trial judge hearing a case to assess whether in that particular factual situation a position of trust exists.

In 1984 the *Badgley Report on Sexual Offences Against Children and Youths* was tabled in Parliament which resulted in section 153(1) of the *Criminal Code*, R.S.C., 1985, c. C-46 being enacted. That section provides that:

> 153. (1) Every person who is in a position of trust or authority towards a young person or is a person with whom the young person is in a relationship of dependency and who
>
> (a) for a sexual purpose, touches, directly or indirectly, with a part of the body or with an object, any part of the body of the young person, or
>
> (b) for a sexual purpose, invites, counsels or incites a young person to touch, directly or indirectly, with a part of the body

---

14. *Young v. British Columbia College of Teachers*, [2001] B.C.J. No. 405

15. *R. v. Audet*, [1996] 2 S.C.R 171, approvingly citing Blair, J. in *R. v. P.S.*, [1993] O.J. No. 704

or with an object, the body of any person, including the body of the person who so invites, counsels or incites and the body of the young person, is guilty of an indictable offence and liable to imprisonment for a term not exceeding five years or is guilty of an offence punishable on summary conviction.

(2) In this section, "young person" means a person fourteen years of age or more but under the age of eighteen years.

The Supreme Court of Canada decision of *R. v. Audet*[16] provides an interesting example of how this provision is applied. The twenty-two-year-old physical education teacher during the summer of 1992 encountered by chance a former Grade 8 student of his in a club. At the time of the meeting the student had just turned 14. She was accompanied by two cousins, both in their twenties. At no time did Mr. Audet provide alcohol to the student, but he witnessed her consume three beers bought by her cousins. Having spent the evening together the group went to a cottage at the suggestion of one of the other adults. Mr. Audet left the party, complaining of a headache, and laid down in a bedroom that had two beds. The student shortly thereafter joined him in the same bed and fell asleep; during the night the pair had oral sex, to which the student consented, although it was agreed at trial that the teacher initiated the touching. During the course of the oral sex the student became uncomfortable and begged him to stop, which Mr. Audet did immediately.

At the trial level[17] Mr. Audet was acquitted. The Court noted that the event took place during the summer holidays, that at no time did he procure alcohol for her, that he did not suggest that she accompany them to the cottage, and that although there were two beds in the room the student chose to lay down beside the teacher. The Court also noted:

> It must also be recalled that Mr. Audet was only 22 years old. In my view, there is an enormous difference between a 22-year-old teacher and a teacher, let's say, who is 52 years old, and a young girl 14 years old. In my opinion, it is reasonable to conclude that a young 14-year-old girl feels more comfortable with a young man 22 years old than with a 52-year-old man.

It was the Trial Court's view that although the student subsequently regretted the activity, at the time she was unaware of any authoritative power that in any way obliged her to participate in the sexual acts.

The Court of Appeal in a split decision[18] upheld the trial judgement; in a strong dissent Ayles, J.A. wrote that the *Criminal Code* provision must be read not in terms of relative power between the student and teacher, but rather in the

---

16. *R. v. Audet*, [1996] 2 S.C.R. 171

17. (1993), 142 N.B.R. (2d) 382

18. (1995), 155 N.B.R. (2d) 369

relative status between them (part of his reasoning was based on the slightly different wording of the French and English versions of the section). The question of consent, in his view, was irrelevant given the role conferred on teachers by society.

The Supreme Court of Canada was also split in their reasoning with the majority finding that the teacher should be convicted. It noted that section 153 created three categories of persons: those in a position of trust towards a young person, those in a position of authority towards a young person, and those with whom the young person is in a relationship of dependency. The requisite elements of the offence are that the Crown must establish that the accused falls within one of the three categories, that the acts of the accused fall within those enumerated, and that the complainant was a young person as defined by s. 153(2). Unlike cases of sexual assault, where consent is at issue, under this provision it is irrelevant or as was stated by Woolridge, J. in *Hahn No. 2*[19]:

> The implication from the wording of s. 153 is that notwithstanding the consent, desire or wishes of the young person, it is the adult in the position of trust who has the responsibility to decline having any sexual contact whatsoever with that young person.

The Court declined to find that a teacher would always be in a position of trust or authority over a student. This was a factual decision where such factors as the relative ages of the complainant and accused, the evolution of the relationship, and the status of the accused in relation to the young person could all be taken

QUESTIONS for REFLECTION

1. Is it acceptable for a teacher to initiate a sexual relationship with an adult student who is enrolled in another school district and there is no possibility that the teacher will ever have her as a student? Why or why not?
2. What are the ethical implications of a teacher having a sexual relationship with the parent of one of her or his students? Would it be different if sexual contact occurred after the child was no longer a student of the teacher? Why or why not?
3. For psychiatrists, sexual contact with patients is always considered professional misconduct because of the imbalance of power inherent in the relationship. Should the same standard apply to teachers, regardless of the age of the student? Why or why not? Is the power inherent in the teaching relationship different than that of medical professionals?
4. Imagine for a moment that our society did not frown upon sexual intimacies between adults and minors. Would such behaviour still be considered unprofessional? Why or why not?

19. (1990), 86 Nfld. & P.E.I.R. 33

into consideration. Having said that, the Court noted that while it was hypothetically possible that a teacher may not fall within one of the three enumerated categories, in most cases common sense would lead one to conclude that they do.

MAINTAINING BOUNDARIES

In general, when faced with a situation in which the expectations of one's professional role may be in conflict with those of another role, consideration of the following questions may be helpful when deciding how best to proceed:

- Would my actions work against the student's best interest?
- Would this action benefit me beyond what I would normally receive as a teacher?
- Would this action have a negative impact on my teaching?
- Would this action have a negative impact on my ability to be an effective role model?

If the answer to any of these questions is "yes," it would be wise to delay the decision and engage in a thorough ethical decision-making process (see Chapter 12).

Maintaining sexual boundaries is a much more personal and sensitive matter. There may be times when you experience feelings of attraction to a student. If one wants to remain professional and thereby put the best interests of the student first, such feelings should not be acted upon. It is vital to acknowledge these feelings as soon as possible and take action to prevent the relationship from developing into a sexual one.

Before sexual contact occurs there are often a number of changes in a professional's behaviour that alter the professional role boundaries toward more personal role expectations. One should be alert to such signs that suggest you may be starting to treat a particular student differently; ignoring established conventions that help to maintain professional boundaries could lead to boundary violations. These may include sharing personal problems with the student, offering to drive a student home, meeting the student outside of school hours or when no one else is around, and meeting a student in non-school settings. Such risky situations should be avoided and proper boundaries fastidiously guarded.

If you are struggling with sexual or romantic feelings toward a student, assistance should be sought as soon as possible. Talking to a trusted colleague or mentor, or seeking professional help from a qualified mental health practitioner can be most helpful. If it is the student who has been sexualizing the relationship, steps should be taken to address the situation calmly yet firmly as soon as possible. Again, sharing concerns with a trusted colleague can be helpful.

False accusations of sexual misconduct against teachers can certainly occur. There are a variety of appropriate ways of using touch to communicate nurturing, understanding, and support such as a pat on the back or shoulder, a hug, or a handshake. Such touch can, however, also be interpreted as sexual or intrusive, necessitating careful and sound professional judgement. Teachers must be cautious and respectful when any physical contact is initiated, recognizing the diversity of individual and cultural norms with respect to touching, and cognizant that such behaviour may be misinterpreted. Similarly, students may experience personal references and discussion of sexual matters very differently due to a variety of factors including gender, cultural or religious background, or personal trauma such as sexual abuse. The following considerations may help to avoid misunderstandings:

- Am I mindful of cultural and individual differences regarding personal space and physical contact?
- Do I avoid making comments about a student's appearance, body, or clothing?
- Do I refrain from making sexualized or sexually demeaning comments to a student or about anyone else?
- Do I refrain from criticizing students' sexual preferences?
- Am I particularly mindful of "affectionate" behaviour with a student such as hugging or kissing?
- Do I avoid talking about my sexual preferences, fantasies, problems, activities, or performance?
- Do I seek consultation regarding seductive students and assert my professional boundaries?

False allegations, whether they relate to teaching methods or sexual misconduct, have a devastating impact on both the teacher's professional and personal life. Particularly in instances where sexual misconduct is alleged the matter often receives widespread publicity and the teacher is "tried in the press" with little opportunity to respond. A review of the Canadian, English, and American literature suggests that there are no figures that assess what percentage of such allegations are false; having said that in all three of the countries teaching associations have identified false allegations as being one of their greatest concerns in this area. In England, the problem has been perceived to be so significant that the National Association of Schoolmasters Union of Women Teachers sought a revision of the law that would allow them to sue students or their families for wrongful accusation and to protect the teacher's anonymity during investigation; in making the demand they noted that in the 1,782 allegations made against their members in the past ten years, only 69 lead to convictions.[20] In Canada, many boards of education have addressed the problem of false allegations by publishing information circulars. These publications set out that in the instance of a false allegation the penalties can be severe: including, in the case of students, suspensions; for employees, dismissal; and for other adults or volunteers, banning them from the school premises in addition to bringing civil actions against them.[21]

---

20. As reported in *The Independent*, April 15th, 2004, page 18.

21. See, for example New Brunswick Department of Education's "Information for Parents and Pupils about the Policy for the Protection of Pupils in the Public School System from Misconduct by Adults."

If the allegation is by a fellow teacher then a complaint of professional misconduct will require an investigation to be undertaken, and some recourse may be achieved in this manner. In most cases, however, the allegation comes from a non-employee and legal steps must be undertaken. If the allegations are ongoing it may be appropriate to seek an injunction from the courts restraining the person from speaking on the matter;[22] in many instances such an injunction is ignored or the damage has already been done such that lodging a civil suit is appropriate.

In Canada the courts have awarded substantial damages in cases where the wrongful allegation was made maliciously against a teacher[23] and the teacher's ability to fulfil his or her professional duty was maligned.[24] Without delving too deeply into this complicated but fascinating area of the law, it should be pointed out that in the absence of malice some otherwise defamatory statements may be protected by law, in particular under child welfare acts.

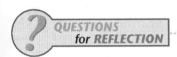

QUESTIONS for REFLECTION

1. If you found yourself experiencing sexual feelings toward a student, whom could you speak to about it? Do you think a fellow teacher would feel they could speak to you if they had such feelings? What do your answers tell you about yourself?

2. You know that a fellow teacher has an excessively intimate, albeit non-abusive, relationship with a student in which they share a keen interest in the theatre. There is absolutely no evidence that the teacher shows the student any favouritism in class, but other students are well aware of the relationship and complain to you that they are not receiving their fair share of time and attention. What are your ethical concerns in this situation?

3. Do you know anyone who was falsely accused of sexual misconduct? How do you feel about how the authorities handled it? How did fellow teachers treat your colleague? Would you do anything different now based on your observations and experiences?

4. If we accept for the moment that sexual relationships with all students are unprofessional, how long should a person be considered a student? What if you meet an ex-student who has been out of school for many years and is now an adult? Would it make a difference if the ex-student told you they still have a crush on you after all these years? Why or why not?

---

22. This was done, for example, in *Campbell v. Cartmell*, [1999] O.J. No. 3553 where a disgruntled teacher was making false allegations against the school board officials, including sexual impropriety, forgery, and theft.

23. *D.F. v. A.S.*, [2001] Q.J. No. 3273

24. *Kohuch v. Wilson*, [1988] S.J. No. 682; *McKerron v. Marshall*, [1999] O.J. No. 4048

Summary

Ethical practice depends upon the teacher always acting in the best interest of the student. In exchange for doing so the teacher receives payment in the form of a salary. When the teacher has an additional personal or professional relationship with the student that includes additional expectations, either on the part of the student or the teacher, the primary professional relationship can be jeopardized. There are many circumstances that represent multiple relationships and boundary crossings, and while not always unethical, they should be handled professionally. Sexual involvement with a student is the most obvious and blatant form of boundary violation and is always unethical. It is also illegal in most instances. Sexual involvement with someone who was a student but is no longer is less straightforward, but it is always unethical for as long as the student is vulnerable to exploitive influence by the teacher.

Questions for Discussion

1. If you found yourself disliking a student intensely, how might you deal with the situation?
2. Is it ever possible to be completely objective in relation to a student? If not, at what point does subjectivity become a problem? If so, what is the role of your personal feelings toward a student? Is it a problem if a teacher is scrupulously unbiased?
3. Returning to the scenario at the beginning of the chapter, have your thoughts changed? If so, in what way? If not, why not?

Further Reading

American Association of University Women. (1993). *Hostile hallways: The AAUW survey on sexual harassment in America's schools*. Washington, DC: Author.

Piddocke, S. (1993). Sexual liaisons between teachers and students: Four Board of Reference cases. *Education and Law Journal, 5,* 53–69.

Robbins, S. L. (2000). *Protecting our students: A review to identify and prevent sexual misconduct in Ontario schools*. Ministry of the Attorney General (Ontario).

CHAPTER 8
THE RIGHTS OF STUDENTS

You are the teacher who is responsible for overseeing the students' preparation of the school newspaper. One of the students indicates that she intends to run an article in which students rank the teachers in the school in terms of how well they teach and how much fun their classes are, and she will include selected comments from student surveys about the teachers.

1. *How much control should you exercise over the paper? Does it make a difference if the newspaper forms part of an assignment?*

2. *Is it fair to censor the students?*

3. *Do you have an obligation to protect your fellow teachers' (or your own for that matter) reputation from this review?*

4. *Would it make a difference if the school were not directly involved in the publication—for example a student's Web site?*

What is referred to as students' rights encompasses a number of different concepts. In its broadest interpretation, one may be speaking of rights that (arguably) exist even were they not codified by law. For example, almost everyone would recognize that infants have the right to be nurtured and cared for by their parents (or guardians) and teachers, and that this right exists even in countries that have no laws that specifically address it (sometimes called "natural rights" or "fundamental rights"). In its narrowest interpretation one may be speaking only of rights that are set out by statute and protected by law (legal rights). The most obvious example of the latter would be those rights set out in the *Charter* that are granted to everyone, including children, in Canada. *Charter*-protected rights are to a very large degree inalienable; they are "subject only to such reasonable limits prescribed by law as can be demonstrably justified in a free and democratic society"[1] and to the opting out clause, section 33. Still important, but more prone to legislative change would be rights contained within other provincial and federal statutes, such as human rights codes or the right to an education[2] contained within school acts.

A somewhat wider interpretation of legal rights would include international agreements that Canada has ratified. In the case of students, the most important agreement is the *Convention on the Rights of the Child*[3] that came into force on September 2nd, 1990. Article 28 of that document provides:

> 1. State Parties recognize the right of the child to education and with a view of achieving this right progressively and on the basis of equal opportunity, they shall, in particular:

> (a) Make primary education compulsory and available free to all;

> (b) Encourage the development of different forms of secondary education, including general and vocational education, make them available and accessible to every child, and to take such appropriate measures such as the introduction of free education and offering financial assistance in case of need;

---

1. *Canadian Charter of Rights and Freedoms*, s.1

2. For example, the *Alberta School Act*, R.S.A. 2000, c. S-3., s.8 provides that an individual who meets certain criteria has a right to access an education program.

3. *Convention on the Rights of the Child*, U.N. Doc. A/RES/44/25 (1989)

(c) Make higher education accessible to all on the basis of capacity by every available means;

(d) Make educational and vocational information and guidance available and accessible to all children;

(e) Take measures to encourage regular attendance in schools and the reduction of dropout rates;

2. State Parties shall take all appropriate measures to ensure that school discipline is administered in a manner consistent with the child's human dignity and conformity with the present Convention . . .

Article 29 provides, in part, that:

1. State Parties agree that the education of a child shall be directed to . . .

(b) The development of respect for human rights and fundamental freedoms, and for the principles enshrined in the Charter of the United Nations;

(c) The development of respect for the child's parents, his or her own cultural identity, language and values, for the national values of the country in which the child is living, the country from which he or she may originate and for civilizations different from his or her own;

(d) The preparation of the child for responsible life in a free society, in the spirit of understanding, peace, tolerance, equality of the sexes, and friendship among all peoples, ethnic, national and religious groups and persons of indigenous origin.

The *Convention* is enforceable under international law but does not form part of the laws of Canada, per se, unless it is incorporated into the national law.[4] Its importance, however, is that in interpreting the *Charter* provisions the courts will be guided by those conventions not only because they are international commitments that Canada has made but that they set a benchmark against which to measure the protection provided by the *Charter*.

---

4. Troope, Stephen J. (1996). "The Convention on the Rights of the Child: Implications for Canada," in M. Freeman, ed. *Children's Rights: A Comparative Perspective*. Dartmouth: Brookfield.

The Rights of Students

An even broader definition of students' rights would include statements of principle enshrined within the codes of ethics of the teaching profession. For example the B.C.T.F. *Code of Ethics* provides that:

1. The teacher speaks and acts towards students with respect and dignity, and deals judiciously with them, always mindful of their individual rights and sensibilities.

There is, of course, no *Charter* right, or for that matter any other law, that a student is to be spoken to with respect and dignity; yet this expression of what constitutes proper conduct of a teacher is important, not only because failure to abide by it could constitute a disciplinable offence by a teacher but also because it creates an expectation of a certain environment in which a student and teacher operate.

This expectation that people treat each other as individuals, worthy of consideration as thinking, caring entities underlies the broadest sense of students' rights. It is a way of thinking that has moved from educational philosophy[5] to the administration of education.

WHAT THE CODES SAY

"A member shall regard the dignity, liberty and integrity of each student under his/her supervision and endeavour to convey to a student some understanding of his/her own worth."

—*From the P.E.I.* Code of Ethics

RIGHTS AND THE MINOR

Whether one is speaking of natural rights or legal rights it is typically accepted that the rights of a student are somehow prescribed by their age. Thus, while the philosopher John Stuart Mill, for example, argues the thesis that "the sole end for which mankind are warranted, individually or collectively, in interfering with the liberty of action of any of their number, is self-protection," he goes on to limit it by observing that "It is, perhaps, hardly necessary to say that this doctrine is meant to apply only to human beings in the maturity of their faculties. We are not speaking of children, or of young persons below the age which the law may fix as that of manhood or womanhood."[6] In much the same way, while the *Charter* guarantees certain rights to all (including children), children are not treated equally under the

---

5. See, for example, Watkinson, A. (1999). *Education, Student Rights and the Charter.* (Saskatoon: Purich Publishing).

6. "On Liberty," 1869

law as if they were adults, based on the extent to which they are developmentally lacking in the ability to take proper care of themselves.[7]

Every jurisdiction in Canada has set a legal age of majority. In most jurisdictions that age is 18, although in some it is 19. Individuals of the age of majority are considered to be adults and capable of making decisions for themselves. Below the age of majority, competence is not assumed and the child's parent or guardian has a legal duty to provide care and supervise them. It should be recognized that the acceptance of the late teens as being an appropriate age to be viewed as adult is a relatively recent construct; in Western Europe in the late 18th century children were often expected to "make it on their own" at the age of 8[8] and were viewed as adults.

The law also recognizes the principle of a *mature minor*. Minors can be considered "mature," and thereby provide their own consent, if they have sufficient understanding and intelligence to enable them to fully appreciate the activity being proposed. Although chronological age is only one of several factors to be considered, court precedent suggests a benchmark—a minor would likely not be considered a mature minor before the age of 15.[9] Minors aged 15 years and older of average intelligence are able to understand what they are agreeing to as well as adults do. Indeed, on some characteristics they cannot be distinguished from young adults of the age of majority.[10] If the minor student's capacity and understanding of the activity is sufficient to warrant being treated as a mature minor, therefore, his or her consent should be sought not only because the law recognizes their right to have input, but also because in so doing you are acknowledging the core ethical principle of autonomy. In some instances, of course, there may be a conflict between what the mature minor views as the proper course of action, and that of his or her parents. Although the courts in Canada have not decided the issue in the context of education, there is some case law that in some circumstances the minor's view is paramount.[11]

Other legal exceptions may apply to the normal requirement for parental consent and teachers should be aware of the legislation in their jurisdiction. In Alberta, for example, students under the age of 18 may be considered "independent" as defined in the *School Act* and thereby be responsible for making their own educational decisions.

---

7. The concept of rights as limited by age is discussed at length in the context of punishment in the next chapter.

8. Stewart, D. (2002) Rights of children: educational and legal implications for schools: an Australian perspective. *B.Y.U. Education and Law Journal*, 255–272.

9. *C. (J.S.) v. Wren*, [1986] A.J. No. 1167.

10. Adelman, H.S., Lusk, R., Alvarez,V., & Acosta, N.K. (1985). Competence of minors to understand, evaluate, and communicate about their psycho-educational problems. *Professional Psychology: Research and Practice, 16*, 426–34. Also Lewis, C.C. (1981). How adolescents approach decisions: Changes over grades seven to twelve and policy implications. *Child Development, 52*, 538–44.

11. *C. (J.S.) v. Wren*, [1986] A.J. No. 1167 (mature minor allowed abortion against parents' wishes); *Gillick v. W. Norfolk and Wisbech Area Health Auth.*, 3 WLR 830 (1985), a case involving the right of a student to information of birth control without her parents' knowledge from a clinic.

Once parental consent for their minor child to participate in educational activities is obtained, the teacher should provide the student with as much information as he or she is able to understand and obtain the child's agreement to proceed. An immature minor student who does not want to participate in activities that his parents have consented to on his behalf should be provided as much choice as possible around aspects of the activity that are negotiable, and every effort made to secure the student's agreement. Ultimately, if the minor student steadfastly refuses to agree to participate in the activity, it may be that there will be little, if any, benefit to the student and the parents should be so informed. No teacher should force a student to participate in an activity that does not help the student.

QUESTIONS for REFLECTION

1. To what extent should a child's rights be considered ahead of parents' rights to decide how their child ought to be raised? What examples are you familiar with and how have these affected your answer?
2. How should a teacher go about deciding how to include students in setting standards for behaviour in the classroom? What role does age play?
3. How does a school administrator's decision differ from a teacher's when setting standards for a school? How ought principles versus practicalities (remember Chapter 1) be valued?

RIGHT TO AN EDUCATION

Under the *Charter* "everyone has the right to life, liberty, and security of the person and the right not to be deprived thereof except in accordance with the principles of fundamental justice."[12] The scope of this clause goes far beyond a mere freedom of physical restraint; it has been interpreted by the Supreme Court to encompass the right to make fundamental personal decisions that are rooted in the basic concepts of human dignity, autonomy, and privacy. Of particular interest is that the section has also been held to be a guarantee of right to an education. In *R. v. Kind*[13] the judge observed:

> I am of opinion that a child's right to education is included in the liberty guaranteed to it in section 7 of the Charter. However, in its role of protector and guardian of these rights on behalf of all parents, the government of this province has assumed the obligation of educating all children of school age in this province

---

12. S.7

13. *R. v. Kind*, [1984] N.J. No. 243; although this is a lower court decision the authors believe that likely this portion of the decision would be followed by the higher courts, particularly in light of the U.N. Resolution on the Child and American case law on the subject.

out of public funds. It is indeed a legitimate goal of the state to insist upon minimum education standards for all children within reasonable limits.

If a child has a *Charter* right to an education, then a school administrator's decision to suspend a student may become the subject of greater scrutiny by the courts. Traditionally, the courts have shown considerable reluctance to become involved with schools' internal discipline decisions unless the parties specifically invoke the *Charter*. In *Haines v. Neudorf*[14] the Court dismissed an application for judicial review on the basis that the school board was entitled to prolong a suspension of a female student who was alleged (and the facts of which were not disputed at the hearing) of having provided sexual favours for a number of male students in the back of a bus. The Court ruled that the suspension was within the powers of the board and noted that the Court was not asked to determine if the decision was right or wrong. In closing, however, the Court did observe that the argument had not been raised as to whether the principle of natural justice had been violated in this case. The Court's observation suggests that the school probably failed to give the student the opportunity to be heard and present a defence in the face of a ten-day suspension. To date, however, the issue has not come before the Supreme Court of Canada, although lower courts have awarded damages for breach of natural justice following expulsion without hearing under a school's "zero tolerance" policy.[15]

As part of their mandate to provide for the protection of some students, school administrators often have to consider limiting the rights of other students to an education. The case of *Hawreluik v. Shamrock School Division No. 38*[16] provides a troubling example of a case where these conflicting rights come into play. A number of children were charged under the *Young Offenders Act* with multiple counts of sexual assaults on other students at the school. The board wrote to the parents of the accused advising them that their children were being put on "short bounds," which severely restricted their movements during school hours. The board justified the restrictions on the basis that it prevented intimidation and/or retaliation against the alleged victims and would prevent the laying of baseless allegations against the alleged offenders, while still allowing the students to attend school.

Judicial review of these restrictions was sought *prior* to the criminal trial, and thus prior to any decision as to whether the students were guilty or innocent. The Court held that the board acted within its duties to "administer and manage the educational affairs of the school division" and to "exercise general supervision and control over the schools of the division" and on that basis the restrictions were within the authority of the board. However, no claim was made that the board had failed to adhere to the requirements of natural justice

---

14. [1995] S.J. No. 314

15. *Edward Gianfrancesco and Jessica Gianfrancesco (by her litigation guardian, Edward Gianfrancesco) v. The Junior Academy Inc* [2003] O.J. No. 931.

16. [1987] S.J. No. 108

in limiting the students without offering them the opportunity of a hearing. The Court very pointedly stated:

> On this application the board does not have to justify the necessity of the "short bounds" placed on the applicants. It is not for me to decide the rightness or wrongness of the decision of the board. I do not sit on appeal from the board. I am only asked to determine whether the board possessed the authority under the Act to impose the restrictions.

The difficulty in determining whether the board was, in fact, right in its decision can easily be seen. On one hand, the board has a responsibility to protect the other students in the school and to administer the school in a way that makes it, so far as possible, a safe place in which to learn. However, there was also a significant curtailment of rights of the alleged offenders without them having been found guilty of any offence, or indeed having the opportunity to present their side of the case in any formal way. While the Court did not have to determine the "rightness" of the board's decision it did, as an aside, note that:

> If the board perceived a potential conflict between certain students, for whatever reason, the board most certainly had the power to restrict, in a reasonable manner, the movement of students so as to prevent any possible confrontation. It is not uncommon for the courts, for example, when granting bail to impose a condition upon an accused that he or she refrains from contact with the alleged victim. The action by the board amounts to no more than that.

Given the seriousness of the allegations it would seem likely that even if the Court had to decide the issue it would have found that the board acted in

QUESTIONS for REFLECTION

1. Do you think the board in *Hawreluik* made the right decision? Why or why not? Do you think the board properly respected the rights of the accused children? Alternatively, had they not restricted their liberty, how would the rights of the alleged victims be respected?
2. What other sorts of conflicts can you imagine (or have you experienced) between a student's right to an education and a teacher's responsibility to maintain the educational climate of the classroom? (This issue will be dealt with again in Chapters 9 and 11.)
3. What ethical values (remember Chapter 1) are relevant to the conflicts you identified in question #1?

a reasonable manner, given that the accused students, while subject to constraint in their activities, were still allowed to attend the school. It is very much doubtful, however, that it would have been reasonable for the same board to suspend the students pending the outcome of their criminal trial.

PRIVACY

Privacy is the right of an individual to choose the time, circumstances, and extent of his or her personal presence, property, thoughts, feelings, or information being shared with or withheld from others. It is a basic human right guaranteed in the *Charter of Rights and Freedoms* and is considered essential to human dignity and freedom of self-determination.

Unlike section 7 of the *Charter*, section 8, which provides that "everyone has the right to be secure against unreasonable search and seizure," has received considerable judicial commentary in the context of students' rights. The leading case is the Supreme Court of Canada's decision in *R. v. M.R.M.*[17] where a vice-principal had been advised by a number of students that another student, aged 13, had been dealing drugs on school property and that he would be carrying drugs at a school dance that evening. The vice-principal arranged for an R.C.M.P. officer to be present when he asked the student to empty his pockets and roll up his pant leg. A bag of marijuana was found hidden in the student's sock. The student was charged with possession.

The key issue in the resulting criminal trial was whether the search by the vice-principal was reasonable, given that no warrant had been obtained beforehand. At trial level the Court found that the search was contrary to the *Charter* and the evidence was thrown out, resulting in the case against the student being dismissed. This decision was reversed on appeal,[18] largely on the basis that the school administrator had a statutory duty to control the activities in the school and that the student, knowing this, had a diminished expectation of privacy.

The first issue the Supreme Court addressed was whether the student had a reasonable expectation of privacy, and if so, to what degree? The Court had little trouble finding that the student had a reasonable expectation for privacy of his body and the contents he carried, and that this expectation was not displaced merely because he was in a school. However, a student would be aware that a school is supposed to be a safe environment in which discipline is enforced, and thus students may at times be required to submit to searches and have items seized. Because of this the Court held that school authorities need only establish that there are reasonable grounds to believe that there has been a breach of school regulations or discipline and that a search would disclose evidence. Reasonable grounds may be established through information provided by a student who is considered to be credible, from information received from more than one student, or from the teacher or principal's own observations.

---

17. [1998] 3 S.C.R. 393

18. (1997), 159 N.S.R. (2d) 321

The search itself must also be reasonable in light of the circumstances[19]: when a student is suspected of carrying a weapon a search that is immediate, thorough, and extensive is reasonable; whereas the belief that a student is carrying chewing gum, contrary to a school policy, would not justify such a search. The gender of the student is also relevant; a male teacher should not perform a search of the person of a female student in less than extraordinary circumstances. Finally, the search should be as minimally intrusive as possible; thus performing a strip search before asking the student to reveal the content of a backpack would be unjustified.

One important factor in the *R. v. M.R.M.* case was that the police officer stood by silently while the search was being conducted. Had the officer conducted the search the argument that the search was for the enforcement of school policies, and not part of a criminal investigation, could not have been made. Thus, where a high school resource officer, dressed in his police uniform and acting on information obtained through a *Crime Stoppers* program, requested that the occupants of a car parked on school property exit the car and place any narcotics they had on the vehicle, the evidence was excluded on the basis that there was a *Charter* violation.[20]

In the cases involving searches of lockers there is an even lower expectation of privacy, particularly where, as is common today, students are told that the lockers are school property and can be searched by the school. Even in the absence of such a policy, locker searches are considered acceptable so long as the school administrator had reasonable cause for the search.[21] A blanket search of all lockers for the vague purpose of finding evidence of some misdoings would likely not constitute a reasonable search.

In many of the school search cases there has been a concomitant argument that the students' *Charter* right on being detained to be informed of the reason and to be given the right to obtain counsel[22] had been violated. In *R. v. M.R.M.*[23] the Court held that even the compelled attendance of a student in a principal's office could not be viewed as "detention" as envisaged by s. 10(b); "detention" in the context of the Act meant not between students and a school but rather between the state and an individual usually in the context of a criminal investigation. However, if the student was brought to the office for the purpose of investigating a criminal offence then the section might apply.

In the event that the police are called into the school to confront a student with a crime the parents should be advised; this was one of the coroner's

---

19. One of the most egregious examples of an unreasonable search occurred in Indiana where the entire student body of 2,780 students was subject to drug sniffing dogs, with four junior high school girls being stripped naked and interrogated. No drugs were found. *Doe v. Renfrew*, 631 F. 2d 91

20. *R. v. S.B.*, [1996] O.J. No. 4724

21. *R. v. W. (J.J.)*, [1990] N.J. No. 73

22. S. 10

23. Ibid., fn. 17

recommendations after a high school student committed suicide when threatened with charges after certain improper suggestions were made in the school yearbook about the sexual conduct of the staff.[24]

QUESTIONS
for REFLECTION

1. At what point do you think respect for privacy should give way to safety of others? To the safety of the individual student, for example in the case of suicide? To what extent do you think your own experience—or lack of experience—with such circumstances influences your answer?

2. A criticism[25] of the *R. v. M.R.M.* case is that it stands for the proposition that a student loses his or her natural rights at the school door. Do you agree with this criticism? If not, why should a student attending a school dance have fewer rights than a student standing on the street adjacent to the school? If so, how would you advise the administrator about how to maintain proper order in the school?

3. Do you agree with the Court's use of a "reasonable expectation of privacy" as a way of determining whether the student's rights had been violated? If an individual is ignorant of personal rights, do those rights cease to exist? What other rights can you envisage being impacted by this line of thinking?

CONFIDENTIALITY

The importance of confidentiality is derived first from the ethical principle of respect for autonomy in that it acknowledges that each person has the right to decide who has access to his or her private information. The concept of confidentiality grows out of the much broader concept of an individual's right to privacy.

Teachers are required to honour student confidentiality; teachers should not gossip about a student nor share student information with people other than the student's parents or legal guardians without proper consent. The rationale for this position is respect for the student's autonomy and welfare; children as young as six years of age are sensitive to issues of privacy and become more sensitive to control over their personal information with age. Teachers also have an obligation to prevent invidious comparisons between students, pejorative labels, ridicule, and the like. Further, when confidentiality is violated students usually feel betrayed and the teacher's effectiveness as someone to turn to for help is greatly diminished.

24. Green, S. "Schools Must Keep Parents Informed, Inquest Says," *Globe and Mail*, July 11, 1998.

25. See, for example, AvRuskin, "In defence of young persons: Search and seizure in schools; A scholarly reduction of a young person's rights." *Ontario Criminal Trial Lawyers Association Newsletter*, 8(6), 19.

OTHER CASES OF NOTE

Can a student's assigned autobiography be compelled into a court proceeding against their wishes? See *Children's Aid Society of Haldimand-Norfolk v. C.C.,* [2004] O.J. No. 2274.

An important exception to this is, of course, in instances of suspected child abuse. All jurisdictions in Canada, with the exception of the Yukon, have legislation making it mandatory to report such suspicions. And all of these, with the exception of Saskatchewan, make the individual who fails to report vulnerable to criminal prosecution.

WHAT THE CODES SAY

"It shall be unethical for a teacher to fail to notify the Minister of Health and Community Services, as per the terms of the Family Services Act, where he or she has information causing him or her to suspect that a child has been abandoned, deserted, physically or emotionally neglected, physically or sexually ill-treated, or otherwise abused."

—*From the New Brunswick Teachers' Association* Code of Ethics

The issue of confidentiality is even more complicated, however, because minors are not fully autonomous individuals in the eyes of our society or their parents. If the minor's parents have given consent for their child to participate in educational activities, what will and will not be disclosed should be clarified with them and the child. Legally, the parent or guardian who consents to activities on the minor student's behalf has the right to know the nature of those activities. Thus, a minor should not be promised that information would be kept from a parent who has legal custody.

OTHER CASES OF NOTE

Different considerations may apply to a student's conversation with a guidance counsellor—the courts have held that in some circumstances these records cannot be obtained by a parent given the confidential nature of the relationship between the counsellor and student. *Children's Aid Society of Ottawa v. N.S.,* [2005] O.J. 1070

If a child requests certain confidences, the degree to which confidentiality can be honoured is directly related to whether or not the child is sufficiently competent to warrant being treated as a mature minor. If so, the parent or guardian no longer has the right of access to the student's confidential information. If not, the teacher must still deal with the matter of limits to confidentiality. That is, the student must be informed that his or her parents or guardians do have the right of access to all information that is kept in school records. Regardless of whether the student agrees to have information disclosed to a parent, the student should be informed about what information will be shared.

The issue of confidentiality is one that is troubling to many school officials, given the conflicting interests of protecting the privacy of the youth and ensuring that a school environment is safe and productive. The Supreme Court of Canada recognized this in *R. v. T. (V.)*[26] when they cited with approval:

> It is apparent that there is a level of societal ambivalence in Canada about the appropriate response to young offenders. On the one hand, there is a feeling that adolescents who violate the criminal law need help to enable them to grow into productive, law-abiding citizens. . . . On the other hand, there is a widespread public concern about the need to control youthful criminality and protect society.[27]

The *Youth Criminal Justice Act* attempts to address this by restricting access to records and preventing the media from publishing the names of youth offenders. However, the *Act* allows the disclosure of information without prior court approval by a Crown prosecutor, a police officer, a provincial director, or a youth worker to, among others, representatives of a school board for the purposes of ensuring compliance with the terms of a youth court order, to ensure safety of staff, students, or other persons or to aid in the rehabilitation of the youth.[28] When such information is released to the school it must be kept confidential, revealed only to those employees who need to know for the purposes for which it was released, and destroyed once that purpose is passed. The information is not to be kept with other information; thus, it cannot be kept with the general information concerning a student's academic record.[29]

A student's school record is also confidential; teachers should ensure that student's grades and materials submitted in class are kept private. Many of the education acts set out the limited conditions under which the information can be divulged to a third party[30] subject to the waiver of this right by the student himself[31] or in appropriate cases by the guardian or parent. As well, teachers may be restrained by their code of ethics; the *Code of Professional Practice* of The Manitoba Teachers' Society (revised A.G.M., 1995), for example, sets out in extensive detail not only the requirements of confidentiality but also its basis.

---

26. [1992] 1 S.C.R. 749

27. Bala & Kirvan. (1991). *The Young Offenders Act: A revolution in Canadian juvenile justice* (pp. 80–81). Toronto, ON: Ontario Criminal Trial Lawyers Association.

28. S. 125(6)

29. S. 127(7)

30. See, for example s. 266(2) of the *Education Act*, R.S.O. 1990, c. E.2, ss. 265(d), 266(2) [am. 1991, vol. 2, c. 10, s. 7(2)], (10) and the discussion thereon in *R. v. Keukens* 23 O.R. (3d) 582

31. *R. v. Keukens* (1995), 23 O.R. (3d) 582

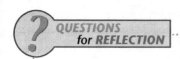
1. In the case of suspected child abuse we have decided as a society that the best interest of the child—in the form of being protected from abuse—takes precedence over the right of the child or the family to decide. Are there any other situations where society overrides the rights of individuals to express their right to autonomy?
2. Thinking back on your own experience as a student, what conversations do you remember having that you felt your teacher should not share with others? What do you think were the most influential factors that shaped how important it was for you?

FREEDOM OF SPEECH

One of the hallmarks of a free and democratic society is the promotion of freedom of speech and as such this is recognized as being a "fundamental freedom" within the *Charter of Rights*.[32] In education, certain freedoms are necessary to prevent teaching from degenerating into a propagation of official dogmas and ideologies. The seminal case on freedom of speech post-*Charter* arose in a school setting with the charging of James Keegstra,[33] a high school teacher, with the wilful promotion of hatred through his teaching that Jewish people were "treacherous," "subversive," "sadistic," "money-loving," "power hungry" and "child killers" who sought to destroy Christianity. Students who espoused different views in assignments were marked down. In that case the Supreme Court of Canada, following a long line of precedent, adopted an expansive definition of "expression" that "if the activity conveys or attempts to convey a meaning, it has expressive content and prima facie falls within the scope of the guarantee." Assuming this requirement is met, the second part of the test for a breach of this *Charter* right was a determination as to whether the impugned action restricts such speech regardless of its content. If both requirements are met the issue then turns on whether such a restriction is demonstrably justified in a free and democratic society,[34] which in the case of Mr. Keegstra the *Criminal Code* provisions were found to be.

A different result was reached in the case of *Lutes v. Prairie View School Division No. 74*[35] where a Grade 9 student was given a month-long noon hour suspension for singing a popular rap song "Let's Talk about Sex." The song was

---

32. S. 2

33. *R. v. Keegstra*, [1990] 3 S.C.R. 697

34. *Charter*, s. 1

35. 101 Sask. R. 232

sung during the lunch break, off school premises, in the presence of the school director. The school wrote to the parents that the song had been banned in the school and the students blamed the director for this. The student's act had been rude and disrespectful and if the noon hour suspension were not adhered to he would be suspended altogether.

In fact, the song had not been banned, and the lyrics, when examined, were not found to be offensive but rather had an educative value on the dangers of AIDS. The case proceeded on two grounds; first that the conduct was outside school hours and off premises, and secondly that it violated the student's right to free speech. On the first ground the Court found that as the student was bussed to school the school was responsible for him from the moment he embarked on the bus in the morning to when he left in the evening. On the second ground the Court rejected the school's argument that the student was being disciplined for being rude and found that the conduct censured (the singing of the song) was protected free speech and ordered that the student could seek damages from the school.

It is an interesting question as to whether freedom of speech could be applied to dress codes; in an effort to control gang actions within schools some boards have banned the wearing of certain jewellery or colours of shoe laces. In Canada, pre-*Charter* there is little doubt this would be within the right of the school authorities as demonstrated by the oft-cited case of *Ward v. Blaine Lake School Board*[36] in which an 11-year-old, in conjunction with 20 others, was suspended because his hair was longer than that allowed by the school appearance code. The Court held:

> I am of the opinion that the power of prescribing within reasonable limits the extent of cleanliness required of pupils attending school, the extent of clothing they should wear, their general appearance, including hair grooming, was within the powers of the Board under the heading "administering and managing the educational affairs of the school district" and "exercising a general supervision and control over the schools of the unit." In these days of the so-called "permissive society" one does not need to indulge in much in the way of flights of imagination to envisage how difficult it would be to conduct a class of boys and girls where they could wear as little or as unusual clothing as some children or some parents might see fit. This would include not only care and cleanliness and covering of various parts of the body but preventing of unusual types of dress and hair styling which might be calculated to distract the pupils from their work in the classroom or adversely affect a proper and reasonable air of discipline in the school.

---

36. [1971] S.J. No. 70

Were the case to be decided today likely the matter of hair length would be viewed as trivial to the administration of a school and a different result would be reached. However, the fact that what was once a matter of serious dispute[37] becomes trivial over time warns of the need to not be overzealous in our justifying rights infringements in the name of proper school management.

The individual teacher is in the "front line" position to determine how custodial and bureaucratic rules are enacted in the classroom. The extent and nature of institutional control varies considerably from school to school and, to a lesser extent, from classroom to classroom within a school. Teachers, and students, typically feel considerable pressure to maintain appropriate decorum in the classroom. Decisions about what is appropriate are rarely made by the students themselves, or the teacher for that matter. Often they are made by administrators and, in many cases, previous administrators. Ultimately, the question of freedom of speech and expression for students addresses what we want our students to learn. If students are denied the opportunity to express their thoughts and ideas in the classroom, what kind of citizens will they be? Will they internalize the skills and dispositions necessary for exercising political and civil rights? And will they think beyond pursuing questions of their own welfare and consider the welfare of others?

QUESTIONS for REFLECTION

1. How important do you think it is that students have the opportunity to express their need for more time to complete their work? Do you think this is even an issue of freedom of speech? Why or why not?
2. What characteristics of a situation are most important to you when deciding how much latitude to give students when expressing their views?
3. During the Vietnam War the U.S. Supreme Court upheld the right of students to wear black armbands signifying their opposition to the war on the basis of freedom of speech (*Tinker v. Des Moines Independent Community District*, 393 U.S. 50 3 (1969)). To what extent is a student's choice of clothes an expression of free speech? Should "offensive" outfits be protected?

---

37. Watkinson (supra, fn. 5) indicates that there are more than 150 U.S. cases on hairstyles in public schools (at p. 86).

Summary

Students' rights can arise from a number of different sources, including our beliefs on the basic entitlement of all humans, laws and statutes, and codes of ethics. However, the rights of a student may be limited by a number of different factors, including their age and developmental abilities, the need to administer schools, and the rights of others. An important source of rights for students are those contained within the *Charter*; including the right to an education (and not to be unreasonably deprived thereof), the security of the person, and the right of free speech. When circumstances require that a student's rights are restricted, teachers should endeavour to do so in the least intrusive manner possible.

Questions for Discussion

1. When does the school's role of socialization give way to respect for the individual preferences and rights of the student? What ethical and legal principles are relevant to your point of view?
2. To what extent should the rights of the individual child take precedence over the rights of parents to decide how their child should be raised? Don't forget to provide ethical and legal justification for your position.
3. If a student turned in a class paper in which the assignment was to produce a work of fiction, but the content contained a graphic, detailed description of a plan to bomb the school, would you alert law-enforcement authorities? Why or why not?

Further Reading

Cohen, C.P. (1989). United Nations: Convention on the rights of the child. *International Law Journal, 28*(6), 1448–1454.

Gilbert, C.B. (1999). We are what we wear: Revisiting student dress codes. *B.Y.U. Education and Law Journal, 199*, 2–21.

Hart, S.N., & Pavlovic, Z. (1991). Children's rights in education: An historical perspective. *School Psychology Review, 20*(3), 345–360.

Howe, R.B. (2001). Do parents have fundamental rights? *Journal of Canadian Studies/Revue d'etudes canadiennes, 36*(3), 61–78.

King, M. (1982). Children's rights in education: More than just a slogan? *Educational Studies, 8*(3), 227–238.

CHAPTER 9
DISCIPLINE AND PUNISHMENT IN THE CLASSROOM

Your class is being particularly unruly today. From the beginning of the school year this class of students has been a challenge. For the most part you feel they are a great group of kids. It's just that a few of them tend to get the rest started and the next thing you know the classroom is out of your control. On many a day it seems that no learning occurs. You have not been consistently implementing the school's "zero tolerance" policy with disruptive students, but today might be the day you start.

1. *What role does your belief in the correctness of the school's policy play in your decision of how to act?*

2. *Would it be fair to isolate the students from the other students? Does this constitute a form of punishment?*

3. *How do you balance the rights of the disruptive students versus those of the students who are having their learning disrupted?*

The complexity of the ethical dimensions of classroom life is nowhere more evident than in the issue of the teacher's exercising control in the classroom. In the above example there are at least two possible ways of thinking about the situation. One is that of authority and respect in which children are supposed to do as the teacher says and it is the teacher's job to establish authority through the administration of punishments for disrespect. Another way is in terms of control and order; the children are out of control and it is the teacher's job to restore order so that learning can occur. The teacher's authority is set aside and classroom management techniques to be implemented (organizing where students sit, the raising of hands to ask questions, etc.) take precedence. Students are seen as confused and undirected, rather than rowdy and disobedient. Each of these ways of thinking about discipline and punishment prompts different ways of teaching. And each gives rise to its own ethical issues.

When confronted with such situations, teachers—especially new or trainee teachers—often feel reluctant to impose order on the classroom for fear of disrespecting the students' autonomy. Yet, as any teacher with any experience can well attest, a classroom of students left to their own devices will soon become so chaotic that the only autonomy any student can exercise is to contribute to the chaos.[1] The teacher's responsibility is to decide how to impose a framework of established limitations such that each student is able to learn, without completely disregarding their individual rights. Teachers must decide how to responsibly exercise *authority*.

AUTHORITY

Power is a constant in classrooms. It resides neither completely within an individual or the group; it is in the complex interplay between them. Power is both personal and social; while it is thus misleading to say that the teacher "has" power, it is also misleading to say that power arises completely out of social structures. Rather, the individual characteristics of the teacher are expressed within the social expectations of the teacher's role. It is the expression of power in the relationships between teacher and student that gives rise to ethical issues.

So what do we mean when we speak of power in the classroom? Power is the ability of one person to get another to do something they would not otherwise do. Getting students to do things they would not otherwise do is a pretty good description of what teachers do every day. What makes this an ethical issue is twofold: teachers get students to do things that are in the students' best interests and will benefit them (beneficence), and there are limits on how much power anyone—including teachers—ought to use in order to achieve even legitimate ends (nonmaleficence).

---

1. Smith, R. (1985). *Freedom and discipline.* London: Allen & Unwin.

The basis of a teacher's authority ultimately comes from being good at fostering student autonomy—that is, from being a good teacher—and from having a broader and richer understanding of societal standards. In this way a teacher is justified in passing judgement on how students ought to behave in order to be good citizens. Thus a teacher is obligated to use her or his authority to *educate* and must be prepared to explain and justify the use of punishment and the enforcement of rules. While the busy ebb and flow of the classroom does not always allow time for explanation, justification must exist in the mind of the teacher and be based on more than mere whim or personal preference. This is also why the example that the teacher sets is so central to the teacher's role (see Chapter 5). Society and students alike benefit when a child comes to obey rules through an appreciation of good and sensible reasons for doing so, rather than simply doing as one is told.

WHAT THE CODES SAY

"The member will strive to show consistent justice and consideration in all his or her relationships with pupils."

—*From the Federation of Nunavut Teachers'* Code of Ethics

QUESTIONS for REFLECTION

1. How do you come to be aware of your community's ethical values and standards?
2. How comfortable (or uncomfortable) are you with being an authority figure in the classroom? How does this affect your teaching?
3. What are your thoughts on the position that "students should learn to respect authority because they will have to respect authority as adults"?

PUNISHMENT

As we have discussed, teachers have an obligation to influence the morality of children toward what is desired by the community at large.[2] It follows, therefore, that any punishment dispensed ought to be in response to behaviour that is legitimately prohibited. Punishment ought to contribute to and protect the educational development of students toward being good citizens. Punishment that is educative is ethically and legally defensible.

Punishment is not brute force coercing one person to the will of another who is more powerful. Neither is it the deliberate infliction of harm. Punishment

---

2. The extent to which punishment is used toward this end is equally subject to the community's ethical values.

is the deliberate infliction of a disadvantage for a wrong voluntarily committed. Teachers, parents, police, and courts of law are appropriate arbitrators of punishment under certain conditions. Each routinely and legitimately exercises a right to punish children. Punishment is meant to decrease the likelihood that the wrong is committed again by *enhancing the offender's autonomy* through presenting a choice of offending again and paying the price, or obeying the rule and reaping the benefit. Properly implemented, punishment is a matter of maintaining moral order: to make a moral point in the mind of the punished, not merely to alter behaviour.

The accepted core ethical principle of justice (see Chapter 1) also dictates that any punishment meted out should not exceed the harm caused by the student's misdeed; it ought not be excessive. The guiding ethical principles of beneficence and nonmaleficence (see Chapter 1) also dictate that a teacher's punishment of a student be educative; the intention should be to remind the student of the community's ethical values. If this does not occur then the student is merely the victim of a system of control, which demeans the student's autonomy and abandons the school's educative responsibility.

Traditionally in our society parents have been viewed as having the right to discipline children, short of what would constitute child abuse. Abuse of children by *any* person (be it parent, teacher, or other family member) is a serious problem[3] in Canada and one that has received widespread attention in recent years. Except in the most blatant instances there is, however, little consensus as to what constitutes the line between a teacher disciplining a child and abuse.

Because of this historical view that parents have the right to discipline their children, and that teachers also have this right by way of delegation,[4] the very controversial *Criminal Code* section 43 was enacted in 1892 whereby:

> 43. Every schoolteacher, parent or person standing in the place of a parent is justified in using force by way of correction toward a pupil or child, as the case may be, who is under his care, if the force does not exceed what is reasonable under the circumstances, R.S., c. C-34, s.43.

The intent of section 43 is to allow what in law would normally constitute an assault, to be permitted by a teacher if the child's conduct merits punishment and that punishment is reasonable in the circumstances.[5] It is important to emphasize that the section, rather than providing an excuse for conduct

---

3. It is difficult to provide accurate numbers but the *Canadian Incidence Study of Reported Child Abuse and Neglect* found that there were 135,573 investigations in 1998 of which 45 percent were confirmed cases.

4. *R. v. Robinson* (1899), 7 C.C.C. 52

5. *R. v. Haberstock* (1970), 1 C.C.C. (2d) 433

that would normally constitute an assault, provides a justification for it;[6] this is not merely a matter of semantics but a profound social commentary.

Although the section was enacted in the late 1800s the reasoning behind it in fact dates back to English common law (and before that Roman law), which also allowed corporal punishment by husbands against wives, by employers against adult servants, and by masters against apprentices.[7] Today, only in the case of children does the law condone such corrective behaviour. Although the section applies a standard of reasonableness, a cross sampling of recent cases involving acquittals under the section show that there are divergent views as to what would be reasonable. Thus, a leather belt, a ruler, or wooden paddle employed by a family member to discipline a child have all been found to be acceptable under the section. In the case of teachers using a karate demonstration on four Grade 10 students,[8] pushing a student against a blackboard and slapping another on the head,[9] and an attempt to kick a 12-year-old then holding him against the wall and slapping him in the stomach[10] have all been deemed acceptable.

Many individuals in our society have long been opposed to corporal punishment in any form as educative, arguing that its potential for harm outweighs any corrective benefits. The seminal 1968 Ontario Hall–Dennis report on education observed "the use of physical punishment as a motivating factor in learning is highly questionable." Reflective of this view a number of provinces, beginning with British Columbia in 1973, amended their education acts to ban corporal punishment in the public school systems. In those provinces that did not ban corporal punishment some school boards did so on their own volition. However, even in those instances where the board or the Minister of Education had not acted, *criminal* liability was still avoided by s. 43.

With the passing of the *Charter* it was inevitable that s. 43 would be the subject of a court challenge and in 1998 one was commenced by the Canadian Foundation for Children, Youth and the Law[11] who argued that s. 43 was unconstitutional by virtue of the "life, liberty and security," "cruel and unusual punishment," and "equality before the law" provisions of the *Charter* (sections 7, 12 and 15, respectively). A number of other interested parties were granted "intervener" status, including the Canadian Teachers' Federation and the Coalition for Family Autonomy, both of whom argued, for different reasons, against the repeal of the section. The CTF, while against corporal punishment, were opposed to the repeal of the section for the limited objective of allowing

---

6. *R. v. Levesque* 2001 ABQB 822

7. Factum of appellant of Children Foundation

8. *R. v. Wetmore*, [1996] N.B.J. No.15 (Q.B.).

9. *R. v. Plourde*, [1993] N.B.J. No. 487 (Prov. Ct.)

10. *R. c. Caouette*, [2002] J.Q. no. 1055 (C.Q.)

11. *Canadian Foundation for Children, Youth and the Law v. Canada (Attorney General)*, [2004] S.C.J. No. 6

Discipline and Punishment in the Classroom **119**

a defence where a teacher needs to intervene to prevent physical violence or control a situation. The Coalition argued that the repeal would result in an infringement of parental liberty rights regarding child rearing and that current child protection laws in Canada were adequate to address any concerns about child abuse.

The ethical issues raised in this lawsuit are profound, not only in relation to the rights of parents, educators, the state, and children but also because they provide a unique insight into the ethical quandary of punishment in the classroom setting. Because of this it is worthwhile to understand the contrasting positions[12] of the Coalition, the Canadian Teachers' Federation, and the Foundation.

The Coalition for Family Autonomy (representing, among others, the Home School Legal Defence Association of Canada) started with the proposition that while they condemn the abuse of children, parents are the primary educators of children and, as such, have an obligation and right to use reasonable force for disciplinary purposes. The role of the family, they argued, is fundamental to Canadian society; it is a natural, not legally created, right. The authority of parents to raise their children, including that of disciplining, arises from this natural element—it predates the development of the Canadian political and legal system—and there is thus a natural (as opposed to merely legal) presumption of family autonomy. State intervention is justified only in instances of necessity, and only to the most minimal extent necessary.

A child's liberty or rights as an autonomous individual are circumscribed by age; even the 19th century liberal philosopher John Stuart Mill restricted his concept of liberty to adults[13] as was pointed out in the intervener's argument. Age is often used as a discriminating factor in determining what rights an individual has; such as voting, the right to consume alcohol, and the right to drive an automobile.

The elimination of s. 43 would, in effect, criminalize not only instances of corporal punishment but any form of physical discipline; thus a parent or teacher restraining a child from hitting another, or holding a child to prevent her or him from running out into a busy street, would, but for s. 43, run the risk of being charged with assault. The requirement of reasonableness within the section, combined with the existing laws on child abuse, strikes an appropriate balance between the need to protect the child and the autonomy of the family unit.[14]

Although the argument of the Coalition was focused primarily on the rights of parents, including those who home school, the rights of a teacher, as a delegated individual, would be essentially the same. Certainly the narrow reading of the rights of a child, and the right to use corporal punishment where

---

12. We are indebted to the factums filed by the parties to this lawsuit in formulating the ethical issues.

13. Mill, J.S. (1991). *On Liberty.* Oxford: Oxford University Press, at p. 14

14. It would be incorrect to assume that under this argument all corporal punishment would be ruled out; only that which was not "reasonable" and "corrective."

reasonable and for corrective purposes, would extend to a teacher. Unanswered, however, is the difficult question of how to apply this reasoning of delegated parental authority to a classroom setting where each of the children has parents with their own views on punishment.

The Canadian Teachers' Federation at the outset stated that they did not condone corporal punishment by teachers; however, there are a set of physical interventions that have been decriminalized as a result of s. 43 and are common and appropriate in the classroom setting. These include removing a child from a classroom, taking a non-cooperative child to the principal's office, gaining a child's attention during the course of a verbal reprimand, or restraining a cognitively impaired child. The CTF took no position on whether s. 43 is unconstitutional, but argued that if it were it was demonstrably justifiable.

The CTF noted that the maintenance of discipline was essential for effective learning, and that disregard of teachers' instructions was becoming increasingly prevalent, particularly for occasional (substitute) teachers. This problem is exacerbated by the number of special needs children in the classroom who have been integrated into the classroom despite having severe behavioural management problems. These children pose a particular problem for educators; often physical restraint is necessary to prevent these students from hurting themselves or others.

Even trivial physical interventions by teachers often form the basis of a parental complaint, or a police investigation of a child abuse allegation. In these instances s. 43 is used as a "screening tool" by the police; its removal would make teachers more susceptible to unjustified allegations and would severely limit their ability to maintain classroom discipline.

Unlike the Coalition, the CTF focused on society's interest in education, and by extension the maintenance of discipline in the classroom. This interest included the right to use limited physical force. In the absence of s. 43 a teacher faced with an unruly student would be forced either to call the police or contact the principal and request that the child be put off school property; neither alternative would be manageable in the day-to-day environment of the classroom. The presence of s. 43 allowed a teacher to use reasonable, corrective force; it did not condone conduct tantamount to abuse of children.

The position of the Canadian Foundation for Children, Youth and the Law was neatly encapsulated in the opening remarks of their written argument to the Supreme Court of Canada:

> Hitting people breaches fundamental rights of respect for human dignity and physical integrity. Children are people too. The existence of a special defence to justify assaulting children for correction breaches their right to equal protection of the law. Hitting children to punish them for misbehaviour is harmful to children and of no benefit to their education: "it is never okay to spank children; it is a bad idea and it doesn't work," says Health Canada. Yet the Attorney General seeks to

justify such assaults in order to protect parents and teachers who mistakenly believe that assaulting children is necessary for their own good.

A number of ethical judgements underlie this line of reasoning. First, unlike the Coalition, the Foundation assumes that children have autonomous rights independent of their age; these are separate from any rights that they derive from their parents. Beyond that they are "fundamental" in the sense that they exist with or without the courts' approval or recognition. Their inclusion as *Charter* rights offers a degree of protection but does not create these rights.

Secondly, the section of the *Criminal Code*, in its application to children, denies them the equal protection of the law from assaults based solely on their age. If such treatment could be justified, it cannot be done on the basis that it is for the benefit of the child or is for an educative purpose.

To a degree this argument is misleading in that it focuses on corporal punishment; whereas the section would cover any form of physical interference with a child's liberty or well-being as was argued by the Canadian Teachers' Federation. However, in answer to that the Foundation argued that the section was overly broad and applied differently across Canada; in effect they were asking the Court to repeal the provision and allow new legislation which would be clearer as to the degree of physical restraint that was allowed. Such legislation, it was argued, should follow the prevailing view of many countries including all of Europe (in the case of all schools) and the majority of U.S. states (in the case of public schools) that corporal punishment should not be allowed in an educative environment. The example of England was provided where corporal punishment in the school system was banned and restraint only used in proscribed circumstances.

Both the trial level and appellate courts rejected this submission. One of the concerns both courts had was the impact on family life if such conduct was criminalized. The Appellate Court noted that the section does not encourage or sanction such conduct and that it was limited to non-abusive physical punishment that is intended to and can achieve correction of the student's behaviour. That Court conceded that the law, by its application to students, infringed on the equality provision but was clearly justified by section 1 of the *Charter*.

The unanimity exhibited by the lower courts is not seen at the Supreme Court of Canada level, however. Of the nine judges presiding, three of the judges disagreed with the majority decision either in whole or in part. The majority decision stressed the requirement that the force used be "reasonable"; that requirement ruled out any conduct that would constitute "cruel and unusual punishment." While the Court noted the importance of the need to address the best interest of the child, it fell short of finding that this was fundamental to our societal notion of justice and therefore section 43 of the *Criminal Code* was not contrary to section 7 of the *Charter*. Finally, the argument that the section was unconstitutional by virtue of treating children in an unequal way from adults was rejected on the basis that the equality provision did not require identical treatment under the law, only equal treatment. The test in determining whether treatment was "unequal" is whether a reasonable person with the claimant's attributes and in their circumstances would conclude that the law marginalizes them or treats them as less worthy on the basis of irrelevant considerations. This is a problematical test to apply to children; the best one can do is to adopt the perspective of a reasonable adult acting on behalf of the child, who keeps in mind the child's views and developmental needs. The repeal of the law, the Court noted, would result in the criminalization of conduct that most would consider far below the level of an assault; for example, placing an unwilling child in a chair for a five-minute "time out."

The broadest dissenting argument was that of Justice Deschamps who found that by its very nature the section violates the equality provisions of the *Charter* as it distinguishes between individuals on the basis of age. It is a significant violation in that, by removing a child's protection under the *Criminal Code* assault provisions, there is a serious risk of physical harm to children, who are recognized in our society as being a vulnerable group. The law, far from having the ameliorative effect claimed, in fact perpetuates the view that children are property rather than human beings and are subject to the wills of their parents and, by extension, teachers, no matter how misguided.

Reaction to the judgement has been mixed; some commentators have viewed it as furthering society's acceptance towards child abuse while others have viewed it as a strong statement on the right of parental autonomy.[15] In any event, teachers maintaining discipline in the classroom continue to be protected by s. 43 subject to the requirement that the force is reasonable in the circumstances.

Determining what constitutes "force which is reasonable in the circumstances" must be done on a case-by-case basis. The courts will assume that any punishment inflicted is reasonable and for sufficient cause until the contrary is shown;[16] the onus is on the complainant to establish the contrary. However, if it can be shown that the punishment was motivated by anger or was intended simply to cause physical harm, the teacher's actions will not be protected by s. 43. The punishment meted out must also be proportional to the behaviour. Thus in a case where two students had already been involved in three separate fights with each other on the same day, a teacher stepping in and physically separating them during the course of which he slapped them on their faces with an open palm was held to be acting reasonably in the circumstances.[17] The Court noted that the fighting was not an isolated incident, and that the teacher did not have a lot of time to consider alternatives.

15. Benson, I. & Miller, B. (2002). Should spanking your child be a criminal act? *Lex View*, No. 50.

16. *R. v. Imbeault* (1977), 17 N.B.R. (2d) 234. This case continues to be followed, most recently in *R. v. Godin*,[1996] N.B.J. No. 148; as societal norms change it may be that the courts reject this proposition. To date the rebuttable presumption persists.

17. *R. v. Godin*, 1996

Whether punishment is warranted is not purely an objective test. In *R. v. Haberstock*[18] a teacher slapped a student for name-calling that had occurred three days earlier. The teacher had been supervising the playground Friday afternoon when a group of students leaving on a school bus shouted names at him. The teacher's reprimand occurred at the earliest opportunity the following Monday. When it was determined that the child was in fact innocent, criminal charges were brought against the teacher. The Court found that the teacher's action was reasonable and justified by an honest belief that the student was guilty.

In contrast, in *R. v. Kanhai*[19] the defendant teacher was administering a twelve-minute running test where students were required to either run or jog during its duration. The student repeatedly walked despite being instructed otherwise. At the end of the test the teacher told the student that they would have "an appointment," and then proceeded to grab him by the hair and usher him into his office. There was no evidence that the student talked back or resisted in any way. During the course of this the teacher gave the student a "firm head rubbing against the door."

What troubled the Court was not just the degree of force used but rather the more fundamental question as to whether there were any reasonable grounds for the teacher to punish the student. The use of force is protected under section 43 only if it is used "by way of correction." The Court held that the punishment was not justified because the student was complying with the teacher's reprimand.

For some students there can never be a situation where force can have a corrective benefit. When a 21-year-old profoundly retarded individual (his I.Q. was less than 20 and he was incapable of speech) was struck for spilling milk, the punishment was not protected by s. 43 because the person administering the punishment knew that the recipient was incapable of remembering the punishment within minutes of it taking place.[20] On the same reasoning the courts have held that a child under the age of 2 years cannot be punished as a form of correction. While some have suggested that punishing a mentally handicapped child is never justified, the courts have been reluctant to state that all persons with a mental handicap cannot be punished.[21]

Whether the amount of force used is reasonable is to be assessed given the circumstances at the time of the incident. The Court has laid down guidelines,

---

18. *R. v. Haberstock*, 1970

19. *R. v. Kanhai*, [1981] S.J. No. 1353

20. *R. v. Ogg-Moss*, [1984] 2 S.C.R. 173. The case involved a care worker in a home for developmentally challenged individuals; the accused argued that he fell within the section on the basis of either being a teacher or person standing in the place of a parent. The Court rejected this submission but noted that even were it accepted the hitting could not be construed as educational or corrective given the mental capacity of the resident. This reasoning would undoubtedly apply to teachers.

21. *R. v. Ogg-Moss*, 1984

however, that any pain inflicted must be temporary in nature, that no serious injury results, that any punishment that threatens to cause injury to life or limb or disfigures the child is unreasonable and unlawful, and that it not be prolonged past the endurance of the child.[22]

So far we have spoken only in terms of court rulings; most of the Codes of Conduct have as a disciplinable offence being "physically, verbally, emotionally or sexually abusive" of a student.[23] As a broad generalization, only the most extreme physical acts come to the attention of the courts; most complaints are dealt with internally in part because school boards view that their internal standards are higher than that of the courts.[24] Some schools and school boards have implemented a "hands off" or a "safe school" policy that prohibits the use of any physical punishment. Most teachers' codes also go much further than the court cases in that they also cover verbal and psychological abuse.

What constitutes psychological and verbal abuse of a student is, of course, in part dependent upon the age and characteristics of the student. In some instances, criticism that would have been accepted by another student can result in a claim of psychological damage by those who are unduly sensitive. It is inappropriate, for example, to call an elementary or secondary school child a "cretin," "loser," or "simpleton," particularly in circumstances where other children might overhear. Punishments that are overlong, such as requiring a kindergarten student to write the alphabet for two and one-half hours without rest breaks constitutes psychological abuse of a child,[25] as does administering strip searches to Grade 9 students after a quantity of money went missing.[26]

QUESTIONS for REFLECTION

1. Where do you feel the autonomy and dignity of the wrongdoers end, and their accountability begins? What is the importance of their age? Why?
2. Do you believe in the concept of "an eye for an eye"? If so, how closely must "the punishment fit the crime"? If not, what ethical principle or system supports your belief?
3. Should punishment ever be dispensed while you are angry? Why or why not?

22. *R. v. Robinson*, 1899

23. Saskatchewan Teachers' Federation, 2000

24. E.g., *Ontario College of Teachers v. Deagle*, [2001] O.C.T.D.D. No. 19

25. *Ontario College of Teachers v. Uhlig*, [1999] O.C.T.D.D. No. 21

26. *Ontario College of Teachers v. MacDonald*, [2001] O.C.T.D.D. No. 13

CLASSROOM MANAGEMENT

Although typically thought of as a technical problem of establishing and maintaining control, classroom management is very much an issue of authority and therefore ethics. Teachers establish rules, correct infractions, give feedback and rewards, resolve conflicts, and recommend suspensions from school. The task of creating a facilitative classroom climate involves working through complex value issues related to authority, autonomy, responsibility, and task orientation in the classroom. The teacher's job of managing and organizing cannot be separated from teaching and learning, however: students learn as much from how they are taught as from what they are taught.

One of the more challenging aspects of classroom management is the relative effect of punishment and discipline on all of the students involved, whether as actors or audience. Teachers need to be sensitive to the subtle line between disciplining individual students, while at the same time reminding the entire class of what is inappropriate behaviour, and singling out individual students in ways that can be embarrassing or hurtful to them. The ethical teacher is sensitive to the need to correct bad behaviour while protecting the student's dignity, and to ensure that students not centrally involved in the incident are not inadvertently treated unfairly.

Teachers and schools are expected to have enforceable rules that contribute to the decorum necessary for learning. Systems of punishment that are so severe that they diminish the educational function of the school violate the school's primary function and are therefore unacceptable to the community at large. Punishment that makes it impossible for the student to continue in the educative process (i.e., suspension or expulsion) runs contrary to the core value of beneficence. Educators are expected to educate as many students as possible. Therefore, suspension from school should be considered only after all other forms of punishment have been tried and failed or there is good reason to believe that they would fail if employed. Thus every effort should be made to keep the child in school in order to keep the child in an environment where he or she has some access to educational opportunities. A teacher's obligation to be just and considerate in dealing with each student does not undermine the teacher's right, for example under Section 231 of *The Education Act, 1995,* to exclude a student from the classroom in the interests of other students.

Perhaps one of the more difficult issues to come to grips with is where classroom management becomes manipulation. Manipulation involves nonrational, covert processes used to bring about behaviour change. Note how this is inconsistent with our understanding of the teacher's legitimate role of education through rational, overt means. Many a teacher has fallen into the habit of assigning "busywork" that has no legitimate educative ends, so that order might be maintained in the classroom. When the means of learning are separate from the ends, the students are being manipulated. When students are given rational grounds (within their ability to understand), then the means are inseparable from the ends and true education is taking place. For example, students can be given an assignment of learning about life in the trenches of

World War I, act out a play that takes place during trench warfare, read *In Flanders Fields*, and write their own poem, where each learning task complements and indeed enables the other. Ultimately, a teacher should be able to answer the question that most dread: "Why are we doing this?"

If a teacher keeps in mind the idea that students are actively learning as much from how they are treated as they are from the curriculum, then the values of respect for student autonomy and justice are as important, if not more so, than the goals of classroom management. Students learn much more than reading, writing, and arithmetic; they learn how schools are run and, by extension, how authority, power, respect, and responsibility are manifested in our society.

QUESTIONS for REFLECTION

1. How much order do you feel is necessary to have a productive classroom? How much individual preference on the part of teachers is acceptable? Why?
2. Is it acceptable to exclude students from classroom management decisions that affect them? Why or why not? If so, under what circumstances?
3. Is it ever justifiable to employ classroom management practices that are deceitful? Why or why not? If so, under what circumstances?

Summary

Power is a constant in classrooms and teachers must decide how to responsibly exercise authority. Punishment ought to contribute to and protect the educational development of students toward being good citizens. The guiding ethical principles of beneficence and nonmaleficence dictate that a teacher's punishment of a student be educative; the intention should be to remind the student of the community's ethical values. Traditionally in our society parents have been viewed as having the right to discipline children, short of conduct that would constitute child abuse. The intent of section 43 of the *Criminal Code* is to allow what in law would normally constitute an assault, to be permitted by a teacher if the child's conduct merits punishment and that punishment is reasonable in the circumstances. Even trivial physical interventions by teachers often form the basis of a parental complaint, or a police investigation of a child abuse allegation. Because of the power that teachers quite rightly exert over students, conditions are created that are potentially coercive.

Teachers' obligation to be just and considerate in dealing with each student does not undermine their right to exclude a student from the classroom in the interests of other students.

Questions for Discussion

1. To what extent should students be held responsible for their actions? How ought a teacher to handle a student who significantly disrupts classroom decorum through no fault of his or her own, for example?
2. A student approaches you and says that he broke a window. Do you praise him for being honest, punish him for playing with a baseball inside the school, or respond in some other way? Why?
3. What are the ethical pros and cons of a school-wide policy of "zero tolerance"? What are the practical pros and cons? Can these be reconciled? Should they be? Why or why not?

Further Reading

Smith, R. (1985). *Freedom and discipline*. London: Allen & Unwin.

CHAPTER 10
CONTROVERSY IN THE CLASSROOM

You are aware that being called "gay" or "a fag" is one of the worst epithets that one of your junior high students can call another and you are troubled as to how doing so may affect those students who are homosexual. You decide to devote one of your English classes to having the students write about the need for tolerance of homosexuality.

1. What ethical values might be relevant to this situation?

2. Does it matter in what setting you teach (denominational vs. public school, for example)? Why or why not?

3. What is the role of your own attitude toward the issue, if any? Explain.

4. Does it make a difference if you believe that any of the students are, in fact, homosexual? Why or why not?

Given that there are controversial issues in the society that teachers are preparing students for, teaching inevitably involves controversy. But how should teachers deal with controversy? Should controversial issues be avoided? If so, how? If controversial curriculum is taught purposefully, how should it be done and what controversies should be addressed?

THE CONTROVERSIAL

As odd as it may appear, first we must agree as to what we mean by "controversial" in order to discuss the teaching of controversial issues. The initial tendency is often to think of issues that are sensitive and thus are likely to arouse strong feelings on the part of students, their parents, and perhaps other teachers. That is, that controversy is a social event as evidenced by people disagreeing about facts and conclusions on a given issue. The problem with this definition from an educational perspective is that people are often, quite frankly, wrong or ignorant concerning an issue. People can argue all they want about whether the earth is flat; at the end of the day it isn't. The fact that some people may feel strongly about the issue does not make it controversial from an educational perspective.

What makes an issue truly controversial is when contrary views can be held without being contrary to reason.[1] This may arise either from insufficient facts to settle the issue, or disagreement on the relative value of known facts. The establishment of sufficient facts to support the theory of evolution or refute it, for example, may one day settle the question of whether human beings evolved from apes. When deciding whether or not to host a casino in order to raise funds for school expenditures, on the other hand, all might agree that the school could use the funds and a casino will generate much-needed monies, but there can be significant disagreement on whether monies gained from gambling are appropriate for educational aims.

QUESTIONS for REFLECTION

1. Do you agree with the definition of controversy presented in this chapter? Why or why not? If not, what do you propose instead? Why?
2. What are some of the more controversial issues that you have encountered? What made them controversial?
3. How comfortable are you discussing issues that arouse strong feelings? Does your comfort level impact your ability to address controversial issues?

---

1. Dearden, R.F. (1981). Controversial issues and the curriculum. *Journal of Curriculum Studies*, 13(1), 37–44.

THE NEED FOR CONTROVERSY IN THE CLASSROOM

Having determined what is meant by "controversial" the next step is to ask whether controversy is a good thing to introduce into the classroom. Consider the following quotation taken from the Supreme Court of Canada's decision in *Ross*:

> A school is a communication centre for a whole range of values and aspirations of a society. In large part, it defines the values that transcend society through the educational medium. The school is an arena for the exchange of ideas and must, therefore, be premised upon principles of tolerance and impartiality so that all persons within the school environment feel equally free to participate.[2]

If teachers are to educate in a manner that changes (hopefully in a positive manner) the very values of our society then clearly sometimes it will be necessary to teach the uncomfortable and the controversial. While this quote is taken from the Supreme Court of Canada, the sentiments it expresses can be found in many of the codes of ethics for the profession. Thus, the *Code of Ethics* for the Saskatchewan Teachers' Federation states in its preface that, "as a self-governing profession, teaching must demonstrate that teachers are more than mere citizens; they are worthy upholders of the public interest in educating future generations that will shape and re-shape society according to its highest aspirations." The P.E.I. *Code of Ethics* requires that, "a member should recognize a responsibility to promote a respect for human rights"; the same requirement exists for teachers in Ontario under the Ontario Teachers' Federation.[3]

Underlying each of these expressions of the role of education (and educators) is the notion that a teacher has a positive duty to effect positive societal change; even if in so doing controversial ideas may be presented. In the realm of universities this belief is deeply ingrained and supported by the concept of academic freedom. Academic freedom may be characterized as an additional right, beyond any universal claim of freedom of speech, which arises out of the unique role of the education system to facilitate free and open discourse, even when such views are unpopular within the school environment. Claims for academic freedom may be advanced where the subject matter being taught is controversial (for example gay rights, or in some times and places theories of evolution) or where the method used (such as books that are viewed as racist, or language deemed unfit for the student population) is controversial.

In K-to-12 education the concept of academic freedom is much less accepted. Teachers are largely constrained as to what curriculum is taught, and the school boards through approved resources largely dictate the techniques used. Thus, while it is easy to say that, "A good teacher is one who instructs

---

2. *Ross v. New Brunswick School District No. 15*, [1996] 1 S.C.R. 825 at paragraph 42

3. Regulation to the *Teaching Professions Act*

while a great teacher is one who reforms," in practice educational reform can be difficult and is almost always controversial, as the Supreme Court of Canada decision of *Chamberlain v. Surrey School District No. 36*[4] demonstrates.

The British Columbia public school system is predicated on being secular and open to all children of all cultures and family backgrounds. While the Minister of Education specifies the core curriculum material, school boards are empowered to select supplementary educational resource material, subject to ministerial approval.

In 1996 the Surrey School Board was approached by one of their kindergarten–Grade 1 (K–1) teachers, who was also a member of Gay and Lesbian Educators of B.C., for approval of three books dealing with same-sex parents to be used in his family life education course. The Board refused, noting that the curriculum as set out did not specifically include same-sex parenting, and that the matter of homosexuality (which they equated with same-sex parenting) was controversial and unlikely to be supported by the parents in the school district (the district had a large Sikh, Muslim, Hindu, and evangelical Christian population). The possibility of "cognitive dissonance" occurring, given that young children would be exposed to views at odds with that of their parents, was also used in support of the refusal.

At trial level[5] the Board was found to have acted improperly, in that it was motivated by religious views of the parents, and in one case of a member of the Board itself. The matter was remitted to the school board for reconsideration on a strictly secular basis.

The matter was appealed to the B.C.C.A.[6] who reversed the trial level decision on the basis that the matter fell within the Board's jurisdiction. The requirement that education be secular did not, in the Court's view, exclude moral positions that were based on religious faith, so long as it did not receive special consideration by virtue of being religious-based.

The Supreme Court of Canada,[7] in a split decision, allowed the appeal and upheld the trial judge's decision. Writing for the majority, Chief Justice McLachlin observed that the heart of the case was the *School Act*, s. 76, which required that:

> Provincial schools must be conducted on strictly secular and non-sectarian principles [and that] the highest morality must be inculcated, but no religious dogma or creed is to be taught.

The Court noted that this did not mean that the school board was wrong in considering the viewpoint of parents who had a religious objection to the

---

4. *Chamberlain v. Surrey School District No. 36* (2002).

5. [1998] B.C.J. No. 2923

6. (2000), 191 D.L.R. (4th) 128

7. [2000] S.C.J. No. 87

material being allowed in the classroom. Religion forms an important part of many persons' lives and it is unreasonable to expect that it be left at the boardroom door. Where they erred was to allow this viewpoint to override the rights of the minority, including in particular that of same-sex parented families.

The Court observed that families in Canada are diverse in nature, with "traditional" family units, "single family" units, families with step-parents, interracial parents, foster and adopted families, same-sex families, and families with different religious or cultural backgrounds all being present in society and all warranting equal consideration and respect. Inevitably, there will be moral objections to some of these arrangements by some parents; however, if the school is to act in a secular manner and includes a curriculum that requires that a wide spectrum of family models be taught, the board cannot exclude certain lawful family matters simply on the basis that some parents find them morally questionable.

The Court directly refuted the concern of "cognitive dissonance" between what students learned at home and what they were taught in school. The Court did concede that students might suffer such cognitive dissonance; however, such dissonance is neither avoidable nor harmful. Indeed, the Court observed:

> Children encounter it every day in the public school system as members of a diverse student body. They see their classmates, and perhaps also their teachers, eating foods at lunch that they themselves are not permitted to eat, whether because of their parents' religious strictures or because of other moral beliefs. They see their classmates wearing clothing with features or brand labels which their parents have forbidden them to wear. And they see their classmates engaging in behaviour on the playground that their parents have told them not to engage in. The cognitive dissonance that results from such encounters is simply a part of living in a diverse society. It is also a part of growing up. Through such experiences, children come to realize that not all of their values are shared by others.

> Exposure to some cognitive dissonance is arguably necessary if children are to be taught what tolerance itself involves. As my colleague points out, the demand for tolerance cannot be interpreted as the demand to approve of another person's beliefs or practices. When we ask people to be tolerant of others, we do not ask them to abandon their personal convictions. We merely ask them to respect the rights, values and ways of being of those who may not share those convictions. The belief that others are entitled to equal respect depends, not on the belief that their values are right, but on

the belief that they have a claim to equal respect regardless of whether they are right. Learning about tolerance is therefore learning that other people's entitlement to respect from us does not depend on whether their views accord with our own. Children cannot learn this unless they are exposed to views that differ from those they are taught at home.

The matter was remanded back to the Surrey School Board to be considered according to the criteria laid out in the Board's own regulations, the curriculum guidelines, and the broad principles of tolerance and sectarianism underlying the *School Act*.

Six months later the Surrey School Board met to reconsider the books; they were again rejected on a number of bases, including poor grammar (one of the books—*Asha's Mums*—used both the Canadian and American spelling of favourite)[8]; another book was rejected on the basis that it raised the issue of dieting, which the board felt was risky for the age group and clumsily done. The Board, however, emphasized that it was not against homosexual parents and that they were currently looking for books on the topic for inclusion in the curriculum.

In part, underlying the dispute in the *Chamberlain* case are, as we discussed in the previous chapter on discipline and punishment, the various beliefs as to the role of schools, and by extension, teachers; if one accepts that a school's authority arises *in loco parentis* (that is the school in effect "stands in" for the parent), then the particular views of the majority of parents in the community on homosexuality, and the need not to undermine parental authority, is a compelling argument. In this particular instance, the case is complicated because the majority of parents of children in the classroom supported the inclusion of the books (as did many other members of the community at large) although some did not.

WHAT THE CODES SAY

"The member will strive for friendly and cooperative relationships with the home."

—*From the preamble to the Federation of Nunavut Teachers'* Code of Ethics

Alternatively, if one accepts that a school's primary purpose is to indoctrinate a community's societal values then a case could be made for the School Board acting as it did in considering both the requirements of the *School Act* and the particular views of the community in which the school was located.

---

8. Board chair Mary Polak, as quoted in "School board rejects books with gay parents for bad grammar," C.B.C. News, Fri. 13 June, 2003, 18:08:04.

It is arguable that this was the approach adopted by the majority of the Supreme Court of Canada who recognized both the role of the School Board's regulations, which presumably reflected the views of the community, and the larger purposes set out in the provincial *Act*.[9] Under this theory of education teachers might trade off some level of "controversy" (in the sense of disagreement) with the parents if they felt that in so doing they were supporting the larger community requirements of, for example, tolerance to alternative parent arrangements.

However, if one accepts a theory of education where a free interplay of ideas is promoted, as was suggested in the *Ross* quotation, the reasoning of the Court is more difficult to accept. Under this model,

> the child is presented with objective conceptions of divergent viewpoints and theories, and thereby given the opportunity to determine for himself, with appropriate parental guidance, the validity of the various positions. While, under the indoctrination theory, the child is the passive recipient of a consistent pattern of thought, in the open classroom, the child actively considers and chooses among diverse views. Adherents to this model see the greater stimulation of the students' reasoning abilities as the primary advantage, and contend that such advantages outweigh the model's dangers. It is inevitable that the student will be exposed to differing views in some contexts, whether it be a class, media, or personal encounter, and therefore it can be argued that the school is the preferable arena for exposure, the child there having the benefit of the teacher's objective guidance.[10]

Under such a view the diversity argument would strongly support the position of introducing atypical parental arrangements in the school through the books, even though parents of the students, or even the community in which the school was located may disagree. Each of the three theories of education is supported both by educational theorists and by court decisions. One cannot say that one is "better" than the others; at best one can only recognize that the issue is a true controversy in that it depends upon the values one places on the known facts.

---

9. The majority of the Court observed that parental involvement was important and their concerns accommodated, but not at the expense of the statutory requirement to teach diversity and tolerance (para. 33).

10. Fritz, M. What will we tell the children? A discussion of current judicial opinion on the scope of ideas acceptable for presentation in primary and secondary education. *56 Tul. L. Rev.* 960

1. Given that the teacher in *Chamberlain* was a member of GALE do you think he was right in attempting to introduce a controversial issue in which he had a personal interest into his classroom? Is there a risk of the classroom being used as a "soapbox" by teachers? Can a teacher be both an advocate and impartial at the same time?
2. Is the age of the children being taught relevant? Would your views be different if the teacher had been teaching teenagers?[11]
3. The Supreme Court of Canada focused on the need for the school to be responsive to the wide range of different types of families in Canada (including same-sex). Should a teacher place a higher priority on this than the views of the community in which the teacher teaches?
4. Do you think the reasoning in this case would apply to a teacher in a religious school that does not approve of homosexuality, or alternatively same-sex parenting? Does the need for tolerance arise out of the secular nature of the public school system or out of a wider value of tolerance in society at large?

CONTROVERSIAL TEACHING METHODS

In *Chamberlain* we saw a situation where the subject matter to be taught was controversial; sometimes as was noted at the outset of this chapter the controversy may be more about how something is taught rather than what is taught. The Prince Edward Island case of *Morin v. Prince Edward Island Regional Administrative Unit No. 3 School Board*[12] provides a useful example of this situation. Mr. Morin, an untenured junior high teacher, was responsible for a Grade 9 language arts program. He taped a documentary, *Thy Kingdom Come, Thy Will Be Done* about fundamentalist religion in the United States and showed it to a class the next day as the basis for an assignment. The following day some 10 to 15 parents called the school to complain about the film. In response the vice-principal asked Mr. Morin not to show the film without first discussing the matter with the principal, a meeting which took place on the next school day. The principal determined that the material was

---

11. Obviously, the young age of the students played an important factual role in the case. Affidavit evidence was before the Courts from parents opposed to the books stating that they were in the best position to evaluate their children's readiness to discuss such topics, a point that the minority decision of the Supreme Court explicitly accepted. However, in this case the Board did not argue that the books should not be included because they were "age-inappropriate."

12. *Morin v. Prince Edward Island Regional Administrative Unit No. 3 School Board*, [1999] P.E.I.J. No. 76

not suitable, as it would adversely affect the children of fundamentalist parents in the school, that it might not be age-appropriate, and that the project had not been well thought out.

Mr. Morin was on sick leave for a period; when he returned his presence was a matter of considerable dispute. During the homeroom period of the day 7 students out of 29 did not attend. During the first period, 11 of 33 were absent, and by the second period 15 of 29 were absent initially, and 8 more left during the course of the period. During the next period, another homeroom period, the original 7 students did not attend. The day ended with a class in Language Arts, during which 6 students of 29 were absent at the beginning, with more students leaving until, at the end of the period, only 4 students remained.

A Curriculum Committee was established, reviewed the matter extensively and determined that the lesson plan was appropriate in terms of theme, topic, skills, and learning materials but that the project was wanting in terms of preparation. They also criticized it for being questionable in terms of meeting the expectations of parents and students on a sensitive topic, and for its failure to provide an alternative assignment. On that basis, while the assignment was found to be appropriate, it was cancelled until amended to be acceptable to both the teacher and the principal. This was a Pyrrhic victory for Mr. Morin; he was placed on paid leave until the end of the term at which time he was told that his contract would not be renewed.

A prolonged and convoluted series of court cases followed on a number of different issues. The substantive question, however, was whether Mr. Morin's academic freedom and freedom of speech had been infringed upon. The trial judge, who held that the notion of academic freedom is based on tenure in universities and could not be extended to a teacher of non-adult students, rejected Mr. Morin's claim of academic freedom.[13]

This left the simple *Charter* argument that Mr. Morin had an unrestrained right to say as he wished within the classroom. At trial level, the Court rejected this stating that:

> I hold that freedom of expression does not grant teachers at the elementary and secondary public school levels the right to teach whatever they like to their students as a captive audience. Administrators must have broad discretion in regulating what is taught as part of the school curriculum, and a school principal should be entitled to make such decisions, based on reasoned

---

13. The concept of academic freedom in the pre-university environment has received little judicial comment in Canada or for that matter in the United States; the only case the writers are aware of where academic freedom for K–12 educators has been accepted is the Court of Appeals of the Fourth Circuit of *Boring v. Buncombe County Board of Education* 136 F.3d 364 (4th Cir. 1998) where the Court held that the classic formulation that the education system has the right to determine for itself on academic grounds who may teach, what may be taught, how it shall be taught, and who may be admitted to study should apply to K–12 education "unless quite impracticable or contrary to law."

grounds, without fear of lawsuits from dissatisfied teachers who believe they know better than their superiors how to achieve the objectives of the curriculum. Teachers in an elementary or secondary public school have no constitutionally protected right to determine, based on their own personal views, how the aims of the curriculum are to be achieved over the informed judgment of school principals and school boards.[14]

It is important to understand, in legal terms, what the trial judge's finding was; Mr. Morin, as a teacher, had *no* freedom of speech rights within the classroom. This is considerably different from saying that while teachers have freedom of speech this right is justifiably limited within a free and democratic society (under s. 1 of the *Charter*).[15]

The matter was appealed on the basis of the freedom of speech aspect. The Court of Appeal[16] disagreed with the trial judge's reasoning, and found that the actions of the principal restricted Mr. Morin's freedom of expression. The Appellate Court noted that freedom of speech had been given an expansive definition by the courts and was held to include the solicitations of a prostitute, advertising to children, the language of signs in Quebec, the hate propaganda of a teacher, airport regulations prohibiting soliciting on airport premises, and a municipal sign law. It was inconceivable, they concluded, that teachers during the course of their profession had no rights of expression while prostitutes and advertisers did.

The school authorities appealed the matter to the Supreme Court of Canada,[17] who declined to hear the case without providing reasons. Mr. Morin was initially awarded $15,000 in damages; he was not, however, rehired. That award was then appealed by Mr. Morin[18] on the basis that the Board's decision not to rehire him was a result of malice or bad faith. This submission was rejected by the courts; however, they increased the damages for the infringement of his freedom of expression to $75,000 on the basis that the administration's actions were arbitrary. As the Court noted:

> The attitude of the respondent school board that there is no need for justification of such arbitrary action simply reinforces the importance of the Charter right. The principal's position was that showing the film after he said not to would be insubordination. Insubordination in such an employment context would have

---

14. *Morin v. Prince Edward Island Regional Administrative Unit No. 3 School Board*, [1999] P.E.I.J. No. 76, paragraph 89.

15. The School Board in *Morin* explicitly restricted itself to the first argument.

16. *Morin v. Prince Edward Island Regional Administrative Unit No. 3 School Board*, [2002] P.E.I.J. No. 36.

17. [2002] S.C.C.A. No. 414

18. [2005] P.E.I.J. No. 42

serious implications. What is being dealt with in this case is the freedom of teachers to carry out their mandate in a free and democratic society without fear that a whiff of controversy could spell the end of their careers—or result in suspension or other punishment. Is education not well served by a stimulating debate, discussion of different points of view, exposure to different perspectives? Should not teachers be encouraged to challenge their students, to raise topical issues, rather than be intimidated from raising anything that might be controversial?

If the Court had to address the issue of whether restrictions on a teacher's freedom of speech within the classroom could, in theory, be demonstrably justifiable under section 1 of the *Charter* there is little doubt that they would have found that they could be. Where the issue has arisen in the United States the courts there have consistently favoured the right of school boards over teachers to determine what should be taught and how it should be taught. As one commentator summarized the U.S. law "Put simply, in matters of curriculum and instruction, teachers do not enjoy any meaningful constitutional rights in the educational setting."[19] To the extent that teachers have been successful against school boards the cases have typically involved inadequate notice or policies being in place concerning the impugned act. Thus, an English teacher was reinstated after assigning a text that used the word "bastard," and a drama teacher could not be dismissed for choosing plays that involved scenes of drinking and profanity where the school had not provided adequate warning that such conduct was not appropriate.[20]

QUESTIONS for REFLECTION

1. If teachers have a right to freedom of expression in the classroom to what extent can the school board limit this? By their professional organization? At what point does the concept of freedom of expression become meaningless?
2. How might you wish to teach a subject using a controversial means? Consider the instances of book banning in Canada and the United States[21] and some of the books that have been banned.
3. Although Mr. Morin was vindicated by the Courts, and to some degree by the Curriculum Committee, in showing the film was this validation offset by the loss of education time to the students boycotting his classes? To what extent must a teacher temper his choice of materials based on the reaction of his pupils?

19. Uerling, D. F. Academic Freedom in K–12 Education, *79 Neb. L. Rev.* 956 at 960

20. *Keefe v. Geanakos*, 418 F.2d 359, 362 (1st Cir. 1969); *Webb v. Lake Mills Community Sch. Dist.*, 344 F. Supp. 791, 799–800 (N.D. Iowa 1972).

21. Two Web sites of interest are http://freedomtoread.ca and its American Library Association's equivalent www.ala.org/ala/oif/bannedbooksweek/bannedbooksweek

To What Extent Can You Be Controversial in the Classroom?

Neither *Chamberlain* nor *Morin* fully resolve the issue of what limits can be placed on a teacher's choice of material within the classroom. Read together, the two cases suggest that the determination of curriculum lies within the purview of first the province, then the provincial authorities, and finally the school boards acting, in part, as elected representatives of the local community. Very little scope would appear to be available to the individual teacher to deviate from the approved curriculum. Although *Morin* suggests that a claim could be made on the basis of a teacher's *Charter* right to freedom of speech, it is unlikely that this right would prevail over the right of the administration to control what is taught in the classroom.

WHAT THE CODES SAY

"A teacher accepts, within those constraints imposed by other educational authorities, responsibility for the educational opportunities and the quality of instruction given the students in his or her care."

—*From the Manitoba Teachers'* Code of Professional Practice

Administrative control over material does not totally rule out the role of teachers as reformers. As one writer observed, while the power to set curriculum may be beyond that of the individual educator, "that right does not encompass the power to restrict teachers to a verbatim script or an approved party line."[22] Teachers continue to determine how to present the material in the classroom, how to encourage or moderate discussion on it, and how to employ it, in the best instances, as inspiration for free thought. Under this view, while the content of what is taught may be regulated, teachers enjoy substantial latitude in how it is presented.

In Canada, as in the United States, there is considerable concern as to whether this latitude is largely illusory.[23] Most codes of conduct allow for the censoring of a teacher for "conduct unbecoming" which includes controversial speech; the courts have traditionally held that the determination of what constitutes such conduct lies within the expertise of the professional bodies and therefore are loath to interfere[24] in what is arguably an uncertain test. There has been little judicial examination in Canada of what are the

---

22. Wernicke, V. (2003). Teachers' Speech Rights in the Classroom: An Analysis of *Cockrel v. Shelby County School District. University of Cincinnati Law Review 71*, 1471.

23. Daly, Karen "Balancing Act: Teachers' Classroom Speech and the First Amendment," *30 J.L. & Educ.* 1

24. *Kempling v. British Columbia College of Teachers*, [2004] B.C.J. No. 173

rights of a teacher to teach an approved subject in a controversial manner. Some guidance, however, may be provided by the criminal case of *R. v. S.D.*[25] where a teacher was convicted under s. 152 of the *Criminal Code* of two counts of invitation of sexual touching, either directly or indirectly, a person under the age of 14. The teacher, highly regarded within the elementary school, was also the school video manager and head of the drama club. The Ontario curriculum for Grades 1 to 8 includes oral and visual communication and media communication skills, which include advertising commercials and their presentation.

The teacher arranged for a number of girls to be filmed after school sucking on "Blowpop Lollipops" in a suggestive manner while he videotaped them. The existence of the videotape came to light after a complaint made by the Children's Aid Society to the school. In his defence, the teacher claimed that the video was part of a demonstration he was creating on advertising to be used to illustrate questionable techniques and exaggerated claims, and that the students were to create and videotape their own commercials. The Court rejected this defence and gave some indication of what factors will be taken into account when reviewing a controversial means of teaching. First, is there a reasonable connection between the approved curriculum and the method chosen? Here, the connection was tenuous at best, and likely inappropriate for the age group. Secondly, has the teacher discussed this with other teachers and the administration? (Compare this to the *Chamberlain* case where the teacher approached the administration with the proposed books before using them in the classroom.) Thirdly, as the Court observed in *Morin*, the controversial means of teaching should be part of a written lesson plan, rather than an ad hoc decision.

The *Codes of Ethics* for teachers often provide some guidance as to how a teacher is to address controversial topics. The Newfoundland and Labrador Teachers' Association *Code of Ethics*, for example, requires that when discussing controversial topics, including political, racial, or religious ones, that the teaching be as objective as possible. A similar requirement is found in the Nova Scotia Teachers' Union *Code of Ethics*, with the additional requirement that "The teacher should avoid giving offence to the religious and political beliefs and moral scruples of his/her pupils and/or their parents."

OTHER CASES OF NOTE

An interesting case on the need to balance parents' wishes, freedom of religion, and teaching controversial subjects (in this case evolution) and the difficulties in so doing, is the United States decision of *Selman v. Cobb County Sch. Dist.*, 2005 U.S. Dist. LEXIS 432.

---

25. [2002] O.J. No. 5141

1. Can one truly be wholly objective on any topic? What does it mean to be "objective"? Does one have a duty to present all opposing views even if they lack widespread support from experts in the field?

2. Consider, for example the requirement of some U.S. school boards that biology texts have placed in them a disclaimer that evolution is only a theory and should be critically examined like any other theory. Does this undermine the general acceptance of evolution or is this just being objective?

3. To what degree does the Nova Scotia *Code* requirement that a teacher be objective and sensitive to parents' and pupils' views contain two irreconcilable views? How, for example, would a social studies teacher there teach cultural studies in a respectful way where a number of parents and students are racist?

TEACHING CONTROVERSIAL SUBJECTS

It is the *nature* of controversial issues that needs to be understood by pupils and teachers. Teachers need to support the development of citizens who are able to engage effectively with controversial issues. Developing an understanding of the nature of controversy and the ability to deal with it is more important than developing students' understanding of a particular issue *per se*. As Oulton et al. (2004) state:

> The challenge, therefore, when teaching about controversial issues is to recognize that they are often controversial *because* the protagonists from their own worldview are applying reason and thereby arriving at their different perspectives. Students need to explore how it is that individuals can apparently arrive at different perspectives on an issue. Introducing them to multiple perspectives is therefore an essential part of the methods of teaching about controversial issues.[26]

On the issue of the difficulties faced by an individual teacher attempting to teach a controversial topic, the Saskatchewan *Code of Ethics* has perhaps the most developed guidelines:

> The teacher will sometimes deal with controversial topics in the classroom in order to develop the students' ability to think critically and to increase their knowledge of important issues.

---

26. Oulton, C., Dillon, J., Grace, M.M. (2004). Reconceptualizing the teaching of controversial issues. *International Journal of Science Education, 26(4)*, 411–423.

The purpose of introducing such topics is never the indoctrination of students to a particular point of view. It is a professional responsibility of the teacher to present the controversy to students fairly and objectively.[27]

The Saskatchewan *Code of Ethics* should also be recognized for its clear statement that teachers have a role in developing curriculum and that there may be circumstances when the set curriculum does not match the needs of the students, the priorities and goals of the school, or the expectations of the community. In some instances:

> [I]t is the role of the teacher to mediate between them and to achieve for each student the best possible education. With some students or groups of students, it may be necessary for teachers, in consultations with the appropriate parties, to adapt the curriculum or develop an alternative curriculum.[28]

This notion of teachers as mediators is a valuable insight; in effect the teacher plays a conciliatory role between the demands of the community, the needs of the students, and the requirements of the administration in dealing with controversial curriculum. It is ideally a supportive rather than aggressive role, where progress is made less through the grand gesture and more by incremental means. Indeed, teachers should approach such issues by facilitating positive, respectful discussion in a balanced and reasoned way. While there is some debate concerning the role of the teacher's opinion about a controversial issue,[29] there is agreement that teachers ought not impose their beliefs on students when discussing controversy.

This is not to say that teachers should not have an opinion; this is, of course, impossible as well as undesirable when the controversy is an important one in the subject being taught. Rather, teachers should present their reasoning and the facts and values upon which they have drawn their conclusions as a model for students to consider. After all, isn't this what is done with regard to non-controversial curriculum? The skilled teacher facilitates student discovery of established facts and conclusions, but has already tread the path before and is able to act as a guide. Teachers have to make subjective judgements about what information to present, and even if the teacher thinks that they have presented matters as fairly as possible, others may still judge the presentation to be biased. The teacher's conclusions on a controversial issue become problematic when the disputed facts or values of reasoned contrary views are not presented, or not presented fairly. For in such a circumstance the student is lead to believe that this issue is not controversial, or that

---

27. Article 11, section 1

28. Article 14, section 2

29. Compare Campbell, E. (2003) *The ethical teacher*, pp. 78–83, with Watson, B. & Ashton, E. (1995) *Education, assumptions and values*, pp. 80–83.

contrary views are not reasonable. This is what is meant by "indoctrination" in the Saskatchewan *Code of Ethics*, which further provides that:

> All teachers bring their values and beliefs to their interactions with others, including their interactions with students. It may be appropriate for teachers to present their own values and opinions to students in the course of discussing controversial topics, depending on the age of the students, community standards, and the nature of the topic. However, in exercising their professional judgement on the appropriateness of this course of action, teachers must ensure that students have the freedom and are encouraged to draw their own conclusions and form their own opinions.[30]

A teacher who is respectful of students' autonomy and is trying to further educational growth will try to encourage students to develop a tolerance for uncertainty and an appreciation for the limits of knowledge, while still valuing informed and substantiated opinions.

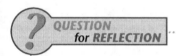

QUESTION for REFLECTION

1. Do you feel that you as a teacher have any ability to teach a controversial subject? What are the limits placed on you? Where do these limits come from?

Summary

The decision, then, to teach controversial subjects is one that almost necessarily requires the support of the school administration. The courts have curtailed the right of the individual teacher to determine what is taught on a number of grounds including the need for consistency in education, and to avoid schools becoming the tools of teachers advancing their own agendas. While how curriculum is taught is left largely to the individual teacher, the *Codes of Ethics* typically require that it be done in a manner that will not bring the profession into disrepute. Although the courts have held that the *Charter* right of freedom of speech exists for teachers, it is likely that the

---

30. Article 11, section 2

administration will be justified in fettering such right in exercising its right of control. Ultimately, what is important is not so much what is taught to the students but rather the promotion of their ability to understand that controversies exist in life, and to facilitate their acceptance of such while they validly support their own beliefs.

Questions for Discussion

1. In *Chamberlain* should the result have been different if the students had been older? If you think that age was relevant do you accept that there may be a sliding scale for theories of education, and that as a child reaches junior high, for example, the wishes of the parents become less important than the benefits seen for open classroom education?

2. As part of a junior high English assignment a teacher recommends other books that students may enjoy, including J.D. Salinger's *A Catcher in the Rye*. A complaint is made that the teacher recommended a text that contains foul language (it is minimal in the book) and conduct unsuitable for exposure to a young adult (there is a short reference to homosexual relationships and a brief passage involving a prostitute). Does the teacher deserve censure? Does it make a difference that the text is widely acknowledged as a modern classic in literature? Would it make a difference if the book was available in the school library? Is there a difference if the teacher says, "The book is recognized as a classic coming-of-age story" or, "This is a book you should read."If so, why?

3. You teach science in a community whose economy is heavily dependent on natural resource utilization. Your personal beliefs are that as a society we are overly dependent upon non-renewable resources and are too consumer-oriented. You have participated in numerous peaceful environmental protests and are known in the community for your "tree-hugging" views. You decide to enhance the curriculum by introducing considerations of sustainability of natural resources and the role of Canada in global greenhouse gas emissions. Is such a modification of the curriculum desirable? Why or why not? On what grounds? Might there be a way of properly introducing such a change? If so, how? If not, why not?

4. Where does prescriptive socialization of students in order to be good members of society end, and autocratic indoctrination begin? Explain and give examples.

Further Reading

Ashton, E., & Watson, B. (1998). Values education: A fresh look at procedural neutrality. *Educational Studies*, *24*(2): 183–193.

Cross, R., and Price, R. (1996). Science teachers' social conscience and the role of teaching controversial issues in the teaching of science. *Journal of Research in Science Teaching, 33,* 319–333.

Oulton, C., Dillon J., Grace, M.M. (2004). Reconceptualizing the teaching of controversial issues. *International Journal of Science Education, 26(4),* 411–423.

Werner, W. (1998). Whatever happened to controversy? *Canadian Social Studies, 32,* 117–120.

CHAPTER 11
DIVERSITY, EQUITY, AND FAIRNESS

One of the students in your class has a very limited attention span. If you teach the child one-on-one you can make meaningful progress, but in so doing you have much less time for the other students in your class and feel that you are short-changing them. Alternatively, if you teach as you normally would the special-needs student becomes disruptive and clearly is gaining very little from the class.

1. How would you go about deciding whose rights you place paramount—the special-needs child as an individual or the 25 other students?

2. What considerations should factor into your decision?

3. Do you think this is really your problem at all, or one that should be the responsibility of the school's administration?

There have always been students in Canadian schools who are "different" from the norm. Yet Canada's demographic landscape is changing at a rapid pace; persons long considered "minority" (neither First Nations, English, nor French) will become the numerical majority in the next few decades. And Canadian society has asked that schools be more inclusive of students with diverse educational needs. This means that teachers will increasingly have to teach students with cultural backgrounds quite different than our own, and with a bewildering variety of educational challenges (e.g., learning disabilities, poor motivation, gifted). How should a concern for fairness affect the way teachers respond to this problem? As in the example at the beginning of the chapter, is it fair to give preferential treatment to the least able student?

At the same time, teachers increasingly find themselves having to "make do" with less than in the past. Society asks schools to streamline their operations in the interests of efficiency and prudent resource management. In focusing upon the larger aggregate, however, teachers are frequently forced to ignore various inequities, and violations of fairness in the classroom can result.

Equity and fairness issues are concerned with ensuring that all people have access to resources and are treated fairly, regardless of their status within society or any other irrelevant attributes. Teachers are responsible to the societies in which they live and work and by extension to the welfare of all members of those societies. A just society is one where human rights and liberties are safeguarded, resources are equally distributed, and there is extensive public involvement in societal decision making. The societal expectation of teaching as a profession is that its members will prepare students to be valuable members of society through instruction and example (see Chapter 5). Given this central role that teachers play in society, considerations of diversity, equity, and fairness are an inherent aspect of a teacher's professional identity.

TEACHING ACROSS CULTURES

Culture refers to the set of shared meanings that form the structure of social interactions by providing members a set of norms for acceptable behaviour. Note that the concept of culture applies to a broad range of groups who share a set of norms, and that assignment to a particular cultural group cannot be made without knowledge of the individual's subjective experience. While often associated with nationality, geographical ancestry, and religious affiliation, there are many other characteristics by which people identify themselves as belonging to a group, such as age, gender, sexual orientation, and (dis)abilities.

The idea of a *minority* refers to a culturally defined group that does not have access to power equal to the dominant cultural group within a society. Such a group is typically, though not necessarily, numerically smaller than the dominant cultural group. Women, for example, are considered a minority even though they are numerically superior to men, due to their not having equal access to power in our society. Minority status is often loosely assigned by way of visible physical characteristics commonly associated with geographical ancestry, such as skin colour. The imprecision of such a grouping is usually further compounded by the use of the term *race* to categorize individuals who share common physical characteristics and to imply a vague concept of genetic lineage that, in reality, does not exist.

In order to understand the necessity of adopting a respectful approach to teaching across cultures, one must accept that not everyone has equal access to power in our society. In particular, many cultural groups have been subjected to oppression and mistreatment, and the prejudicial attitudes and behaviours that allow such violations to occur are far from extinct. Even teachers, who obviously tend to pride themselves as being fair and tolerant, may inadvertently perpetuate practices that disadvantage persons from minority groups. This is because teachers, just like every other member of a society, internalize the norms of behaviour of our culture. These norms provide information not only about how to behave in order to remain a part of the group, but also provide information about who is not a part of the group. Potentially harmful errors of professional practice can result from either of these two information sources.

In order for cultural norms to be useful for guiding our behaviour and making sense of our world, we assume that others from our same cultural group share our circumstances, opportunities, and worldview. Teachers tend to be tolerant and accepting people and thus are particularly prone to assume that their ideas and practices are equally applicable to anyone regardless of cultural background. This mistaken assumption can render a teacher ill-prepared to teach effectively with culturally diverse students. When a minority student does not respond positively to teaching, for example, it is not uncommon to see the fault as residing in the student. At worst, the student is viewed as deficient. What is typically not considered is a mismatch between the cultural worldview inherent in the curriculum and that of the student. Teachers who strive to treat everyone the same, therefore, risk harming them because teaching students from other cultures may require differential approaches. Treating people differently is not necessarily preferential, especially when it provides for equal access and opportunity for an education.

The other function of cultural norms is to define who is and who is not a member of the group. If another person is seen as not of the group, then we do not assume that they share the same values as we do and we turn to whatever knowledge we possess about the group as a whole. That is, one can fall into the trap of not paying attention to individual characteristics of students from culturally diverse groups. This manifests itself in the expectation that all persons from a culturally diverse group are different in the same way as persons from one's own culture. Sometimes these expectations are that persons of minority groups are inferior—the more common usage of the concept of discrimination—but it is not necessarily so. While generalizations about persons from a particular cultural group may be statistically accurate (or inaccurate; the argument is the same), culture shapes but does not determine identity.

In order to be effective teachers of students who are different from them, teachers should focus on *openness, awareness, knowledge,* and *curriculum.* Ethical teachers foster an *attitude of openness* toward other cultural views of the world and a tolerance for divergent views of right and wrong. Teachers need to be willing to accept that others will not have the same worldview as they do and to tolerate the discomfort felt when others base their decisions on different standards than one's own. This is, in essence, the ultimate expression of respect for a student's dignity as a person.

Second, ethical teachers strive to become more *aware of their own values, assumptions, and biases* about human beings; the lessons they learned from their own upbringing and culture. Some of the predominant values from a Euro-Canadian cultural background that are relevant to teaching are an emphasis on the individual, an action-oriented approach to problem-solving, the "Protestant" work ethic, the scientific method, and rigid time schedules. These values are not universally endorsed and should not be held as the standard against which others are judged.

Third, ethical teachers strive to *gain knowledge of other cultures* and the biases, values, and assumptions about human behaviour arising out of the various diverse cultures within Canadian society. Such knowledge is particularly crucial when students are struggling with the expectations of their cultural heritage that are in conflict with those of Canadian culture. Obviously, it is not possible to become knowledgeable about *all* cultures of all of the students one might ever come into professional contact with. But the ethical teacher strives to gain knowledge about the cultures of the students being taught.

Fourth, ethical teachers strive to *develop culturally appropriate curricula.* Standard teaching methods may not sufficiently address the needs of students from minority cultures. In particular, teachers should be willing to foster students taking ownership of their own personal history. This is not to say that curricula should be tailored to specific cultural groups of students. Rather, differences in cultural heritage can be honoured, varieties of values understood, and worldviews tolerated.

GAY, LESBIAN, AND TRANSSEXUAL STUDENTS

In a typical high school classroom of 25 students, two or three of those students will be gay, lesbian, or transgendered.[1] Non-heterosexual students are more likely to commit suicide, to drop out of school, and to have dramatically lower self-esteem; two-thirds report hearing homophobic remarks frequently and one in five have been physically assaulted in school.[2]

At a professional level some efforts had been made in some of the codes of conduct to explicitly recognize that teaching be done without prejudice to sexual orientation[3]; other codes are silent on sexual orientation but refer, in

---

1. It is difficult to calculate the percentage with exactitude (nor is it particularly useful to do so); the figures given correspond with the numbers reported by the *Vancouver Sun* (13 June 1996), and are lower than those reported in "Being out: Lesbian, Gay, Bisexual & Transgendered Youth in BC: An adolescent health survey," which was cited by the Supreme Court of Canada in the *Trinity* decision (at paragraphs 83 and on).

2. These statistics are taken from the *Trinity* case.

3. ATA Code of Professional Conduct, s. 1; Saskatchewan *Code of Ethics* Article 9(3)

general terms, to the need to recognize differences in students.[4] The difficulty with those codes that do not address the issue of sexual orientation directly is that there can be a tendency to assume that if a goal (including the acceptance of homosexuality) is not specifically mentioned then it is of lesser or no importance, or in extreme cases a topic to be avoided.[5] Some school boards have also taken significant steps to support gay, lesbian, and transgendered teachers and students through implementing support programs and policy statements, as well as providing teacher resources.[6]

In the case of public schools the courts have found a positive duty to provide a safe and supportive learning environment for all students; this arises not only through provincial legislation,[7] but also through a broader view of what the purpose of a school is:

> A school is a communication centre for a whole range of values and aspirations of a society. In large part, it defines the values that transcend society through the educational medium. The school is an arena for the exchange of ideas and must, therefore, be premised upon principles of tolerance and impartiality so that all persons within the school environment feel equally free to participate. As the Board of Inquiry stated, a school board has a duty to maintain a positive school environment for all persons served by it.[8]

A school board that fails to take adequate steps to provide such an environment can be found liable. In *Ross*[9] the Supreme Court of Canada adopted the Board of Inquiry's finding that:

> In such situations it is not sufficient for a school board to take a passive role. A school board has a duty to maintain a positive school environment for all persons served by it and it must be ever vigilant of anything that might interfere with this duty.

---

4. For example, Ontario College of Teachers' *Standards of Practice for the Teaching Profession* refers to the need to know how "cultural heritage, language, family, gender, community and other factors shape experience and impact on learning."

5. This issue arose in the *Chamberlain* case in the context of a curriculum that did not specifically address sexual orientation; while the Director of the Curriculum Branch recognized that a teacher could address sexual orientation under the curriculum, the school board did not.

6. A list of some resources can be found at the GALE Web site http://www.galebc.org

7. For example, the Supreme Court of Canada relied upon the wording of the Preamble of the *B.C. School Act.*

8. *Ross v. New Brunswick School District*, [1996] 1 S.C.R. 825 (at paragraph 42)

9. Supra

While *Ross* involves the firing of an anti-Semitic teacher, the principle applies to "poisoned environments" created for gay, lesbian, and transgendered students. The British Columbia Court of Appeal addressed the positive requirement of school boards (and by extension teachers) to create "discrimination-free" school settings in the unusual case of *North Vancouver School District No. 44 v. Jubran*[10] where a student (who was not homosexual) was subject to prolonged verbal abuse by other students who repeatedly called him a "homo," "faggot," or "gay." Mr. Jubran complained to the British Columbia Human Rights Tribunal[11] who awarded him damages against the school board on the basis that he was discriminated against because of his sexual orientation. The Supreme Court overturned this decision,[12] noting that as neither Mr. Jubran nor his tormentors believed he was homosexual the provision of the Code had no application. The Court of Appeal, in turn, reversed that decision and restored the original finding of the Tribunal.

The School Board had made a number of attempts to deal with the harassment, including meeting with Mr. Jubran, his parents, and uncle to discuss the issue, meeting with the other students involved and warning them of escalating consequences should the behaviour continue, and imposing one detention and two suspensions. These steps appeared to be successful in stopping the behaviour of the particular students disciplined, but the harassment continued from other students. Other steps eventually taken included putting into place a formal Code of Conduct for the school, a copy of which was sent home with the students and discussed with them during assemblies. The principal contacted a consultant and workshops were held with the teaching staff on the issue and a peer counsellor program was set up. The Court of Appeal was critical of the delay in implementing some of these changes, and noted that materials were available from other provinces' school boards and from the Gay and Lesbian Educators of British Columbia for a number of years prior to the incidents occurring.

In the case of public sacred schools the law is considerably more difficult and at this time there is no ready answer as to the rights of gay, lesbian, and transgendered students to be free of a poisoned environment. Any discussion, however, would have to start with the recognition that there are competing *Charter* rights under the equality section, the freedom of religion and the freedom of expression section, as well as protection offered under the provincial *Human Rights Code*[13] both to sexual and religious freedoms. The approach taken by the Supreme Court to date, as illustrated in the *Trinity College* decision (see Chapter 5), is to draw a distinction between the freedom to hold beliefs and the freedom to act on them; in the majority's view in the absence of proof that the religious views were creating a poisoned environment (as in *Ross*) the

---

10. *North Vancouver School District No. 44 v. Jubran*, [2005] B.C.J. No. 733 (B.C.C.A.)

11. [2002] B.C.H.R.T.D. No. 10

12. (2003), 9 B.C.L.R. (4th) 338

13. But most have exceptions for religious views.

holding of those views was protected by the *Charter*. As the Court observed the BCCT "does not require public universities with teacher education programs to screen out applicants who hold sexist, racist or homophobic beliefs. For better or for worse, tolerance of divergent beliefs is a hallmark of a democratic society."

As a result, in the *Trinity College* case, the Court held that in the absence of proof that students graduating from the program posed a greater risk of creating a classroom environment intolerant of gay, lesbian, or transgendered students, the program had to be accredited. The Supreme Court was very careful to limit their finding to the public (non-secular) school system. In applying the principles of *Ross* they specifically restricted it to a teacher in a public school.[14] More tellingly they noted that while the requirement to sign the Community Standards pledge of the school would prevent gay, lesbian, and transgendered students and staff from applying, potential applicants would also be aware that is was a religious based school. Such schools are not only common in Canada, they are protected by the constitution as part of the historic compromise that made Confederation possible. Based on that it is unlikely, at this point in history, that the Supreme Court of Canada would find a religious school with a bona fide belief against homosexuality was contrary to the *Charter* even if the school, for example, indirectly excluded staff and students on that basis.

Having said that, there is one lower court decision[15] that runs contrary to this conclusion. Mr. Hall was a 17-year-old Catholic high school homosexual student who sought approval[16] to bring his male date to the high school prom. The principal of the school refused on the basis that a prom as a romantic event was a form of sexual activity, and that if permission was granted this would in effect be an endorsement by the school of homosexuality. The school board subsequently supported this decision on the basis that in so doing it was upholding the doctrine of the Catholic faith.

Mr. Hall was successful in applying for a Court injunction requiring the school to allow him to bring his boyfriend to the prom on the basis that the school's position was contrary to the equality of the *Charter*. The Court noted that within the Catholic Church there was a diversity of views on homosexuality, and that the prom was a social not religious event. Justice MacKinnon concluded by observing that:

> The idea of equality speaks to the conscience of all humanity—
> the dignity and worth that is due each human being. Marc
> Hall is a Roman Catholic Canadian trying to be himself. He is
> gay. It is not an answer to his s. 15 Charter rights, on these
> facts, to deny him permission to attend his school's function

---

14. *Trinity*, at paragraph 37

15. *Hall (Litigation guardian of) v. Powers* 59 O.R. (3d) 423

16. All students were required to have permission from the school to bring dates who were not members of the school.

with his classmates in order to celebrate his high school career. It is not an answer to him, on these facts, to suggest that he can exercise his freedom of disassociation and leave his school. He has not, in the words of the Board, "decided to make his homosexuality a public issue" . . . There are stark positions at each end of the spectrum on this issue. It is one of the distinguishing strengths of Canada as a nation that we value tolerance and respect for others. All of us have fundamental rights including expression, association, and religion. Sometimes, as in this case, our individual rights bump into those of our neighbours and of our institutions. When that occurs we, as individuals and as institutions, must acknowledge the duties that accompany our rights. Mr. Hall has a duty to accord to others who do not share his orientation the respect that they, with their religious values and beliefs, are due. Conversely, for the reasons I have given, the principal and the Board have a duty to accord to Mr. Hall the respect that he is due as he attends the prom with his date, his classmates and their dates.

One of the key issues in the case was whether the school board's decision was protected from the *Charter* by the constitutional guaranteed religious freedoms for denominational schools enshrined in s. 93(1) of the *Constitution Act, 1867* (see Chapter 2). Considerable evidence was presented by the Board including evidence from the Bishop responsible for the region in which the school was located as to the Catholic doctrine on homosexuality and in particular how allowing Mr. Hall to attend the prom with his boyfriend would be contrary to those beliefs. The Court's rejection of this evidence through its acceptance that there was no unanimity of belief in the Catholic Church has troubled some commentators.[17] Whether the case was correctly decided is largely a matter of opinion, and would require personal knowledge of the evidence before the Court, but it does highlight the unclear state of the law.

In the case of private schools there is the additional argument that the *Charter* does not apply. This argument is likely not going to be successful in that private schools exist in part to implement public education and thus must be approved by the provinces.[18] In a case of such delegated duties the Supreme Court of Canada has said that the *Charter* does apply, as "Governments should not be permitted to evade their Charter responsibilities by implementing policy through the vehicle of private arrangements."[19]

The challenge facing the courts in resolving the competing interests of those who approve (or are tolerant) of gay, lesbian, and transgendered persons and those who, for a variety of reasons, have moral objections to them is not

---

17. See, for example, "Second-Guessing the Bishop: Section 93, the Charter, and the "religious government actor" in the Gay Prom Date Case," Zoe Oxaal, *66 Sask. L. Rev.* 455 (2003)

18. This view was supported by the *Hall* decision (supra).

19. *Eldridge v. B.C.*, [1997] 3 S.C.R. 624

easy, particularly in light of the constitutionally guaranteed religious protections. Some religious groups in response to criticism have stated that they disapprove of the act, and not the individual; many people (and most GLT individuals) believe sexual orientation, however, is not a choice and as such this distinction is intellectually not compelling. It is analogous to stating that you don't object to black people, just the colour of their skin. Both the public at large and the law are increasingly recognizing families and relationships that are different from the heterosexual norm in Canada. To be silent in the classroom on the subject may be little better than to be openly critical; for alternative sexuality students, time and silence is suffering.

WHAT THE CODES SAY

The teacher teaches in a manner that respects the dignity and rights of all persons without prejudice as to race, religious beliefs, colour, sex, sexual orientation, gender identity, physical characteristics, age, ancestry or place of origin.

—*From the Alberta Teachers' Association* Code of Professional Conduct

FIRST NATIONS

Members of the First Nations have been equally ill-served in the education system. The *Hawthorn Report*[20] summarized their plight in this way:

> It is difficult to imagine how an Indian child attending an ordinary public school could develop anything but a negative self-image. First, there is nothing from his culture represented in the school or valued by it. Second, the Indian child often gains the impression that nothing he or other Indians do is right when compared to what non-Indian children are doing. Third, in both segregated and integrated schools, one of the main aims of teachers expressed with reference to Indians is "to help them improve their standard of living, or their general lot, or themselves," which is another way of saying that what they are and have now is not good enough; they must do and be other things.

Although the *Hawthorn Report* dates from 1967, the problems it highlights are strikingly valid today. The education of First Nations children has been a failure: The British Columbia Ministry of Education's statistics in 1998 on First Nations students revealed that their graduation rate was a dismal 32 percent, with a pronounced over-representation in special needs. Absenteeism and dropout rates are significantly higher than the norm of the

20. Hawthorn, H. (1967). *A survey of contemporary Indians of Canada*, Volume II. Ottawa: Queen's Printer.

wider population with very low numbers of First Nations students registering for Grade 12 academic Math and English.

Since the *Hawthorn Report* there have been a number of commissions and reports promulgated[21] that have been remarkably similar in tenor. Many of the recommendations involve large scale political change, including First Nations control[22] over education, recognition of aboriginal languages as an official language, and allowing bands to determine labour relations rather than having outside union rules being applied to the community.[23]

Even without, or prior to, these fundamental changes there is a significant role to be played by education authorities. Some of the *Codes of Ethics* have attempted to redress some of the challenges faced by the First Nations community by addressing their unique needs and status. Thus, the Saskatchewan *Code of Ethics* contains the clause that:

> The history and culture of Saskatchewan's First Nation and Métis require recognition by those within the province's education system. Teachers should endeavour to understand and accommodate the special educational needs of Aboriginal students.[24]

In this short passage two important concepts are recognized: First, that there is a need in the education system to recognize the history and culture of the First Nations and Métis. Even more important than empowering First Nations students by emphasizing the worth of their traditions, such a change in the curriculum would provide a more balanced and respectful view of the role of First Nations in Canada's history.[25] As part of this recognition must be the preservation of First Nations languages that have been identified as "by far the most significant factor in the survival of indigenous knowledge."[26]

The second aspect is the responsibility of teachers at an individual level to recognize the challenges faced by some First Nations students. In many cases

---

21. A useful survey can be found in D. Jeffrey's *Summary Report of Selected First Nations Education Documents*, presented to the AGM of the B.C. Teachers' Federation Task Force on First Nations Education, January 1999.

22. This understates to a degree what may be sought; many reports have recommended that the jurisdiction of education of First Nations be transferred directly to the First Nations with the only federal involvement being that of funding: cf. National Indian Brotherhood, Assembly of First Nations, 1988. *Tradition and Education, Towards a Vision of Our Future* (Volumes 1, 2, 3). Ottawa: Assembly of First Nations.

23. *Traditions and Education, Towards a Vision of Our Future*

24. The Teaching Profession of Saskatchewan *Code of Ethics*, Article 10(2)

25. The benefits to all Canadians of a more balanced curriculum were pointed out in the 2002 report to the Minister's National Working Group on Education "Our Children— Keepers of the Sacred Knowledge."

26. Supra, at p. 22

they may come from depressed socio-economic conditions, or are hampered by parents who are unable to provide strong family support due to a number of effects including the lasting impact of residential schooling. In addition to the failure of many curricula to adequately address the role of First Nations, standardized tests and pedagogy militate against the success of the First Nations student.

First Nations people being seriously under-represented in the profession of teaching exacerbates these difficulties; across Canada aboriginal people represent 3.9 percent of the population but the numbers in teaching are a third of that percentage.[27] Because of this low representation it is important for non-First Nations teachers to educate themselves on First Nations culture. A number of the teaching professional organizations have taken important steps towards this goal[28] and identified what teachers should be aware of in teaching about the First Nations.

Teachers should begin with the premise that First Nations children, like all children, can succeed. In defining success in education, however, there is a tendency for the majority to view their role as "raising up" the minority culture to the level of the dominant culture.[29] But as we have seen, success in education is to become a good member of society without having to sacrifice one's cultural identity.

An important part of the preservation of cultural identity is involving families and elders in their children's education. There is a significant level of distrust among First Nations of the school system and this has been attributed as the cause of many First Nations parents being reluctant to visit schools.[30] Schools have been seen as paying little, if any, attention to First Nations culture; their efforts have been characterized as being a "diets, dance, and dress" approach, which furthers the myth that there was one First Nation as opposed to a large number of separate cultures and languages living independently. In addition to local resources, many of the teaching federations have produced resource material for teachers that should be assessed.

QUESTIONS for REFLECTION

1. To what cultural group(s) do you feel you belong? Why?
2. How do you feel that your own cultural heritage has influenced your identity? How does this influence you as a teacher?
3. To what extent do you think the core curriculum in your school system is culturally bound? How might it be improved from the perspective of diversity?

---

27. Supra, figures taken from 1996 census of Canada.

28. For example, the BCTF's 1999 Task Force on First Nations Education.

29. Historically, this has also occurred in the education of blacks in America.

30. Supra, footnote 29 at p. 6

EQUITY AND FAIRNESS IN TEACHING

The issues of equity and fairness have usually been thought of as the concern of policy planners and politicians. Yet teachers are in the "front line" of decisions involving demand for educational opportunities. Like it or not, deciding how they should be distributed in a fair and equitable manner is a teaching issue.

The issue of fairness is central to the profession of teaching. Not only do teachers have to make decisions about how to allocate their time among their students based on students' needs, merit, and what they deserve, teachers are typically the first non-familial adults children meet in a position of authority. Children thus learn what to expect from society in terms of justice and fairness. Of course life—society—is not always fair and just, and some might suggest that unfair treatment in school will do children no harm and may even better prepare them for the "real" world. "A perfect teacher does not prepare a child for an imperfect world" the argument goes. While there is certainly some truth to this point of view, if children receive grossly unfair treatment at school they are certainly less likely to expect or promote fairness once they become full-fledged members of society.

The basic ethical requirement of equity is that persons who are equal in whatever aspects that are relevant to a decision must be treated as equals. While fine in theory, this rarely helps much in decision making because it is often difficult to agree on what aspects are relevant to deciding how to distribute resources. In Canada we have historically adopted the principle that everyone has the right to equitable access to an education. The framework for realizing this principle is that of "fair opportunity."[31] Fair opportunity says that no persons should receive services on the basis of undeserved advantageous attributes (because no persons are responsible for having these attributes) and that no persons should be denied services on the basis of undeserved disadvantageous attributes (because they similarly are not responsible for having these attributes).

Imagine that an educational system offers a high-quality education to all children with basic abilities, regardless of such attributes as gender or minority status, but not to children with attributes that interfere with the realization of their basic abilities. Such a system would be unjust because children are not responsible for their disadvantageous attributes. The fair opportunity rule leads to the conclusion that they should receive an education suitable to their needs and opportunities, even if it costs more.

Our society, obviously, does not allocate unlimited finances to pay for education. In the normal course of allocating limited resources to students, therefore, likelihood of success if the service were to be provided to the particular individual(s) is considered first, followed by "first come, first served" when likelihood of success is roughly equal for eligible recipients.

Of course, many of the decisions to be made about distribution of resources are not made by individual teachers. As such, teachers are often confronted

---

31. Rawls, J. (1971). *A theory of justice*. Cambridge: Harvard University Press.

with policies that run counter to the ethical principles of autonomy, beneficence, nonmaleficence, fidelity, or justice to the harm of students. To the
extent that students without power suffer oppression in our imperfect system,
teachers have a responsibility to use their knowledge and power to contribute
to change. Most teachers would agree that the broad goal of improving our
educational systems for the benefit of all members of society is desirable. The
role that teaching as a profession should play in bringing about such improve-
ments, however, enjoys much less agreement. The role that an individual
teacher might play in particular circumstances arouses downright dissension.
In fact, responding to social justice ethics in particular cases that involve individual students is very likely to give rise to ethical conflict.

While it may be desirable for the profession to advocate openly for social
change, when individual teachers do so members of the community are very
likely to be offended. Teachers, therefore, need to carefully balance the risks
associated with advocacy for particular social changes with the missed opportunity for social betterment. Teachers must always work to ensure that their
students are treated justly by the systems teachers are a part of. In so doing
teachers should be open about their motives and act in accordance with the
core ethical values of the profession—particularly fidelity (see Chapter 1)—in
all professional, and many personal, (see Chapter 5) activities. When systems
are unjust, the ethical teacher seeks change at the system level.

STUDENTS WITH SPECIAL NEEDS

The challenges faced by children whose abilities are significantly different than
the norm[32] are, in one key respect, different from the other groups discussed
above in that their disability varies from individual to individual. Historically,
children were excluded from the school system if they were "unable by reason
of mental or physical handicap to profit by instruction in an elementary
school."[33] During the 1970s and '80s, following a series of reports,[34] education
authorities began to value deinstitutionalization and reintegration of these
individuals back into the school system. Many of the education acts were
amended to reflect this change,[35] typically with school representatives and the

---

32. Various acts refer to the disabled as "exceptional students," or "special needs"; we will
use the term "disabled" save when speaking of a particular jurisdiction.

33. *The Education Act, 1974*, S.O. 1974, c. 109, s. 34(1).

34. Among others, Ontario. Williston, Walter B. (1971). *A Report to the Minister of Health on
Present Arrangements for the Care and Supervision of Mentally Retarded Persons in Ontario.*
Toronto: Department of Health; British Columbia Royal Commission on Education,
(1988). *The Report of the Royal Commission on Education: A legacy for learners.* Victoria:
Royal Commission on Education.

35. For example, *The Education Amendment Act, 1980*, S.O. 1980, c. 61. made it mandatory for
all school boards to provide programs for exceptional students, with the goal of having
every child in the education mainstream to the extent that it benefited the child.

parents or guardians of the child being involved in determining whether the child could benefit from a regular classroom and what additional assistance was required.[36]

The nature of this assessment changed, somewhat, after the passing of the *Charter* into law, and in particular the equality rights afforded the student with a disability under section 15 changed. The Supreme Court of Canada decision of *Emily v. Brant County Board of Education*[37] faced directly the question of whether section15 of the *Charter* created a presumption that children with disabilities should be placed in mainstream classrooms. Emily was a 12-year-old girl with cerebral palsy; she was unable to communicate through sign, speech, or other adaptive means, was largely confined to a wheelchair, and had significant cognitive difficulties. Although identified as an exceptional student from the outset, she began kindergarten in a regular classroom with the assistance of a full-time aid. This experiment continued for three years at which time, after consultation with Emily's parents,[38] the education authority determined that mainstreaming was not in Emily's best interests. Her parents appealed this decision, ultimately being successful at the Court of Appeal level largely on the basis of a section 15 argument.

The purpose of section 15 of the *Charter* is not merely to prevent discrimination through the attributing of stereotypical characteristics, but also to ameliorate the disadvantages of those who had suffered such discrimination. Thus, in *Andrews v. Law Society of British Columbia*[39] the judge stated that the "accommodation of differences. . . is the true essence of equality." The provision of wheelchair ramps, or the allowing of verbal tests for the seeing impaired, are commonplace examples of the reasonable accommodations that must be provided.

However, in the case of persons with differential abilities the "difference dilemma" may arise in that a course of action that promotes the autonomy of the individual (such as the integration of a disabled child into a regular classroom setting) may at the same time violate the principle of beneficence if the child is hindered in development as a result. The Supreme Court of Canada overturned the Court of Appeal's reasoning that there was a presumption in favour of integration, stating that the best interests of the child must be paramount. In the case of *Emily* the Court accepted as reasonable the tribunal's approach of considering her special needs (including instruction in sign language), her safety (she was prone to placing objects in her mouth), and her degree of integration in the classroom (which was observed to be slight). Parenthetically, it should be noted that placing her in a special class would not remove her from the regular

---

36. A common criticism of this process is that it can be very slow, and many of the acts do not specify a time limit. Some, in fact, do not make the identification mandatory.

37. [1997] 1 S.C.R. 241

38. Where a statute provides that parents are to be consulted, failure to do so will result in the Court overturning the decision. Cf. *Yarmoloy et al. v. Banff School Dist. No. 102*, [1985] Alta. D. 71-01

39. [1989] 1 S.C.R. 143

classroom environment completely; the special class would be integrated with the regular class during portions of the day with a "buddy system" between students with and without disabilities.

The Supreme Court's decision required that "reasonable" accommodation must be made. In determining what is reasonable, education authorities work within the realm of limited budgets and must make difficult and often heart-rending decisions. A number of different approaches have been adopted but in general "reasonable accommodation" is to be interpreted in a means analogous to the "reasonable limits" test of section 1 of the *Charter*.[40] In practice, therefore, a school board must be able to provide a reason for *not* providing accommodation. This reason 1) must be rationally connected to the failure to accommodate; 2) must minimally impair the student's rights; and 3) the effect on the student of failing to accommodate must be proportional to the reason.[41] This is admittedly a difficult practice to apply. Consider for example a school board that denied entrance to a child with special needs who would benefit from a regular classroom, for the reason that the teaching staff had no experience with the disability. First, the fact of the staff's inexperience is unrelated to the fact of the child needing accommodation in order to function in and benefit from a regular classroom. Secondly, not accommodating the child's needs would significantly impair the child's right to an education (see Chapter 8). Thirdly, the inconvenience of providing training for the staff is disproportionately trivial when compared with denying the child's right.

In determining what accommodating measures need to be taken, the educational authority must consider the needs of the individual student rather than taking a blanket approach to children sharing the same disability. In addition, some minimal level of expertise will be required in performing the assessment of the student's needs; a school board whose assessment is done incompetently risks having needs decisions overturned in the courts.[42]

An interesting question arises as to whether a school board could be found negligent for failing to assess a child with special needs. The authors are unaware of any Canadian cases on point, but the issue has been argued successfully in England[43] and liability could be imposed on the individual teacher (in the English context[44]) but this seems unlikely in Canada at this time.

40. *Eldridge v. British Columbia (Attorney General)*, [1997] 3 S.C.R. 624

41. This test was developed in *R. v. Oakes*, [1986] 1 S.C.R. 103, and is referred to as the Oakes test.

42. Stack, R. (2001).Progress and Uncertainty: The Educational Rights of Special Needs Children in British Columbia. *7 Appeal* 42–65

43. Stephenson, C. (2002). "Johnny, I'm sorry. . ."–The duties imposed on teachers and local education authorities, *Health & Safety Law*, 2(1)

44. Supra

1. How different does a student need to be before accommodations should be made? The argument can certainly be made that we are all unique, but where do we draw the line? If children could receive an individualized education tailored to their unique attributes, would we want to do so? Why or why not?

2. What ethical concerns arise when parents refuse to have their child assessed and potentially "labelled" as "special needs," thereby preventing the school from applying for additional funding to pay for accommodations to assist the student? How would it be different—from an ethical point of view—if the parents consented but the child steadfastly refused?

Summary

Ethical problems in teaching may arise when there are differences of culture between teacher and student. Cultural differences can be based on gender, language, nationality, ethnicity, ancestry, age, social status, religion, disability, or sexual orientation. The ethical significance is not the fact of difference in itself, but that the teacher may fail to recognize the student's different worldview or individuality, thereby failing to teach effectively or actually causing harm. Teachers are cultural beings just like any other, but their professional status requires that they address their students' needs by being more sensitive to diversity. Ethical teachers should cultivate an attitude of respect for others' individuality, make every effort to be aware of their own worldview, gain knowledge of their students' individuality, and teach in a manner respectful of diversity. The profession of teaching is concerned with the well-being of individuals, by assuring that all have equal access to an education, and with the betterment of society and social systems for the benefit of all individuals. Obligations and dilemmas arising out of these values can occur at the level of the individuals and the social systems with which we interact. If a just system is being applied unjustly, teachers should advocate on behalf of their students. If a system is unjust, teachers have a responsibility to take action at the systems level.

Questions for Discussion

1. In some societies the norms differ dramatically from what are considered universal human rights. For example, currently in some countries girls and women are denied education. Can teachers be respectful of students and families from such cultures and still honour those values? How?
2. Considering the core values of the profession described in Chapter 1 (autonomy, beneficence, nonmaleficence, fidelity, and justice), to what extent do you think they are culturally bound? Explain. Should some, or all, be modified to be less culturally bound? If so, how?
3. Do you think that education is fairly distributed among all Canadians? What do you think is the basic level of education that all members of society are entitled to? How would such a level be determined?
4. To what extent do you think teachers have an obligation to promote social change? Explain.
5. How could you bring cultural artefacts into the classroom in order to facilitate learning, understanding, and acceptance of other cultures, while avoiding merely provoking curiosity?

Further Reading

Davies, S. (1999). From moral duty to cultural rights: A case study of political framing in education. *Sociology of Education, 72* (1), 1–21.

Ghosh, R. & Ray, D. (1995). *Social Change and Education in Canada*, 3rd ed. Toronto: Harcourt Brace.

Lipkin, A. (1999). *Raising Gay/Lesbian Issues in the Classroom*. GLSEN Education Dept. Resource.

Smith W. (1997). Integration: New procedures set in Quebec. *Canadian School Executive*, November, 3–7.

Smith, W. (1997). The placement of students with disabilities and the best interest standard. *Education and Law Journal, 8*, 251–254.

CHAPTER 12
ETHICAL DECISION MAKING

You have been experiencing some rather significant discomfort during the fall term of teaching Social Studies. Some of your students have been raising some persuasive and challenging alternative interpretations of the curriculum. When you approach one of your colleagues you are told to just finish out the term. "What are the odds that the next class will be as clever in quite the same way?" she says. You feel unsatisfied but can't quite put your finger on why.

1. *What individuals or groups ought to be considered in this situation? Who is most central to your decision?*

2. *What feelings are aroused in you by this situation? How might they influence your decision?*

3. *What ethical values are relevant to this situation? Which are most important to you?*

4. *What are the likely consequences of doing nothing? If you were to do something, what might you do? Why?*

As we have discussed, Canadian social systems operate from a normative framework for ethical problem solving that is based on general ethical principles. Ethical principles allow us to articulate an ethical decision that is conclusive, because it is based upon premises—ethical principles—that are accepted as core universal values. Ethical principles allow us to have a common ethical language. Ethical decision making provides us with a common ethical grammar. This grammar is abstract, universal, objective and, most importantly, defensible. This language and grammar provides the basis for professionals to resolve ethical controversies and dilemmas.

Professionals often face circumstances where it is difficult to know how to behave in an ethical manner because the nature of the circumstance is complex or unclear (making it difficult to know how to apply ethical principles) or the applicable principles are in conflict. With the goal of providing a basis for deciding how best to behave ethically, in this chapter we first distinguish between two levels of ethical decision making: intuitive and critical-evaluative. Second, we present an ethical decision-making model that allows for arriving at justifiable ethical decisions when faced with ethically challenging circumstances.

THE ETHICAL DECISION-MAKING PROCESS

We all make ethical decisions every day in our personal and professional lives. The process is usually so rapid that we don't experience having made a decision. This is an *intuitive* ethical decision. Such decisions tend to be spontaneous and emotional without any clear, conscious decision making. This intuitive level of judgement, for example, is the basis for feeling outrage when a fellow teacher harms a student. Intuitive ethical decision making can often lead to an easy solution on how to best behave ethically in a given situation. This is particularly true when one can apply clear-cut guidelines or standards, and when there is no conflict between ethical principles. Our intuitive ethical sense is based upon a lifetime of learning about being moral, of which our training and experience in professional ethics may constitute only a very small part (especially so in the case of students). In ideal circumstances, intuitive ethical decisions predispose teachers to make sound ethical choices and to act in ethically appropriate ways. In ambiguous, confusing, or conflicting situations, or when one's personal ethical values are in conflict with community or professional values, however, intuitive decisions may not lead to desirable or defensible professional actions.

Ethical challenging situations are often emotionally distressful, and typically require time-consuming deliberation. In such situations professionals need guidance and justification for their decisions. In order to honour the societal contract that allows teachers to be self-regulating, our profession requires us to be able to justify our ethical decisions according to principles that serve to protect the public. Reliable, justifiable, ethical decisions require that teachers be able to employ *critical-evaluative* ethical decision making.[1] A critical-evaluative decision involves a deliberate process of intensive problem solving based on professional ethical values, principles, and standards and is grounded in a commitment to the protection of the public.

The two different levels of ethical decision making—intuitive and critical-evaluative—are interrelated with each other, with professional values, and with the consequences of our actions. At the immediate intuitive level, teachers' ethical decisions will often lead to an ethical choice of action. Even if they do, however, one's choice must be justifiable on professional ethical grounds applied in a systematic manner. Particularly when confronted with new situations, teachers should proceed through a structured decision-making process such as the one described in detail in the next section of this chapter. As more and more new situations are encountered and this process is repeated, one's personal ethical values become increasingly congruent with professional ethical values through repeated exposure to the values, principles, and standards of the profession and through experience with the consequences of one's choices. Thus ethical decisions that are justifiable and professionally appropriate can become more intuitive with experience.

QUESTIONS for REFLECTION

1. Under what circumstances would you feel tempted to disregard ethical standards in favour of your intuitive judgement? Under what circumstances would you feel justified?
2. Think of someone you know, or know of, who you think of as highly ethical. What qualities or behaviours do they exhibit that make them ethical?
3. Do you agree that ethical judgement is a skill that can be developed? Why or why not?

A MODEL FOR ETHICAL DECISION MAKING

There are many published models for ethical decision making. Each has its own strengths and weaknesses and you may find another model more to your liking. The decision-making model presented here incorporates what we consider to be the strengths of other models (completeness) without their weaknesses (too lengthy or incomplete). The model is comprised of seven steps:

1. Identification of individuals and groups involved or likely to be affected by the decision
2. Identification of relevant ethical values and principles
3. Consideration of personal values, bias, stress, or self-interest

---

1. Kitchener, K. S. (1984). Intuition, critical evaluation and ethical principles: The foundation for ethical decision in counseling psychology. *The Counseling Psychologist, 12,* 43–55.

4. Development of viable alternative courses of action
5. Analysis of alternative courses of action
6. Choice of course of action
7. Evaluation of consequences and response

1. Identification of individuals and groups involved or likely to be affected by the decision

In the simplest case the only parties legitimately concerned with the outcome of an ethical decision would be the teacher and the student. In practice, however, other individuals and groups are almost always involved or affected by our actions. Parents, of course, usually have a pressing interest, as might school administrators or the community at large. In all situations it is important for the teacher to be clear about who has a legitimate right to be considered when professional decisions are being made, and to consider what their preferences and interests are. Equally important in some circumstances can be excluding individuals or groups who do not have the right to be considered.

2. Identification of relevant ethical values and principles

The next question one should ask oneself is, "Does a relevant standard of conduct, ethical principle or standard, or professional guideline exist?" This question obligates a review of relevant professional documents, starting with the code of conduct and code of ethics for one's jurisdiction, professional guidelines, and through to the scholarly ethics literature.

In some situations, especially for pre-service and beginning teachers, the decision-making process may stop at this point when a relevant standard or guideline is found. Even more experienced practitioners may find that a review of their jurisdiction's professional codes turns up standards that they had missed before or forgotten. One may have difficulty recalling specifics when they are hypothetical and it is hard to imagine exactly how they might apply to situations one has not yet encountered.

If there is no single ethical or professional standard that applies, teachers must identify the ethical principles or values that are in conflict or that may apply. Once this has been done, the teacher is sometimes able to identify an overriding or primary ethical principle.

3. Consideration of personal values, bias, stress, or self-interest

Doing the right thing professionally demands a commitment to be of service to others. One might even go so far as to say that an ethical teacher is first and foremost a person of virtue. This does not mean that all teachers must be saints, but teachers should regularly consider how their own interests and "blind spots" are influencing ethical choices. In response to financial stresses, for example, one may make ethical compromises in hopes that no harm will result and a profit can be made. Sometimes a situation will arouse feelings that block one's ability to understand and sort through the problem, such as a teacher who is struggling with his or her own child and finds it difficult to deal with a student who has similar qualities.

Sometimes teachers may be able to resolve the personal issue that is interfering with their conscientious fulfilment of their professional obligations before attempting to make the ethical decision. In other situations it may be possible to recognize that personal biases or stresses are an issue, and acknowledge them as something to remain aware of as one proceeds through the decision-making process. Seeking consultation from a trusted colleague would be well advised in either case.

When teachers become aware of self-interests influencing their decisions they should, quite simply, refrain from acting on those interests. This is not to say that their rights and preferences should be disregarded—they are certainly legitimate parties to the outcome of their ethical decisions—but rather to highlight that they should never benefit at the expense of their students and communities.

4. Development of viable alternative courses of action

In situations when no single ethical principle outweighs the others, a number of ethical actions may be ethically defensible. A review of relevant codes and ethical literature, and consultation with colleagues, may be of benefit. Time can be spent "brainstorming" and generating possible solutions that address the conflicting principles. When at all possible, the affected individuals and groups should be involved in the development of alternative courses of action.

5. Analysis of alternative courses of action

When evaluating the alternative courses of action generated in Step 4, one needs to consider to what extent each alternative:

Satisfies the preferences of the affected parties. Given that promoting human welfare by respecting the dignity of individuals is a teacher's first and foremost ethical value, in particular cases this translates into promoting the preferences of the involved or affected parties. Thus, if no standard exists that directs a teacher's choice, a course of action that satisfies—or at least takes into account—the preferences of affected parties should be developed.

Presents no new ethical problems. The nature of an ethically challenging situation is such that attempts to resolve it can present new problems. In particular, one may feel tempted to do something "a little unethical," such as telling a partial truth, in order to avoid larger ethical issues. Such alternatives are really based on expediency rather than ethical responsibility. One consideration is referred to as the "clean, well-lit room" standard; how would you feel presenting your choice of action to a group of your colleagues in a professional setting? If you imagine yourself feeling uncomfortable, perhaps that alternative is not a good one.

Addresses the ethical principles that are in conflict. This consideration may seem obvious, but it is easy for professionals to focus on more practical issues, such as what would be "good for" the student or community, rather than on the ethical principles that are in conflict, such as autonomy versus beneficence.

Advances one principle over the other(s) in conflict. Again, the nature of making an ethical choice is often that each alternative choice advances one ethical principle while compromising another. The best (or sometimes least undesirable) alternative is often the one that compromises fewer principles or compromises the conflicting principle(s) to a lesser degree than the other alternatives.

Can practically be implemented. Practicality refers to whether or not one could actually put the alternative into effect. Often, for example, teachers would like to change school policies but cannot implement such changes in a particular case. Also, one needs to consider how practical a particular alternative is. One might decide that the best solution to a particular problem is to lobby for a change in government policy, but that would take months if not years even if one were successful. The time and effort that a course of action may require can sometimes be out of proportion to the ethical problem it is intended to resolve.

6. Choice of course of action

After conscientious application of Steps 1 through 5, one ultimately needs to make a choice. Ideally, the choice will be justifiable to others and consistent with one's personal ethical values. It may help to remember that no one can be held to a standard of perfection; one must simply try one's best to do the right thing.

But making a decision is not enough; one must act in order to be able to say one is truly ethical. Remember that even not doing anything is a choice to do nothing. Sometimes taking action can be a relief from the tension of anticipation. Behaving ethically typically results in increased work, pressure, and anxiety, however. It can also sometimes necessitate defying or confronting others who have power over us, such as principals or other administrators. Implementing our choice of course of action therefore often involves additional skills, such as assertiveness, fortitude, and the ability to convey respect for all who are affected by our actions. All reasonable steps should be taken to inform and involve the individuals and groups affected by our actions.

This is not to say that all choices are unpleasant. Coming to an informed ethical decision can provide a sense of professional pride and mastery, and instil confidence in our ability to master future ethical challenges. It can also provoke respect in colleagues and facilitate a more ethical school environment.

7. Evaluation of consequences and response

Evaluation of the consequences of one's actions goes hand in hand with implementation. Ideally, you will be able to follow up with all parties affected by your actions, although this is not always possible. Certainly the most ethical course of action will not always please everyone. But whenever possible you should include the direct participants in the situation in the ongoing process of evaluating whether your actions are ethically appropriate.

Although teachers are expected to consult with others and be guided by professional codes and standards, the responsibility for their actions remains with the individual teacher. Often, their actions bring to light additional dimensions of the situation, which may lead to a redefinition of the problem, necessitating consideration of further alternatives, and so on.

Every experience changes the people involved. Ethical challenges tend to change us rather profoundly. Often the emotional toll prompts a teacher to conclude, "I'm never going to provide that type of service (or teach that type of student, etc.) again!" Such a reaction, although understandable, is ultimately counterproductive. In fact, what tends to happen when teachers adopt such an attitude is that they become more rigid in their interactions with students and have less access to their personal–professional resources. Taking time to reflect on what one has learned from the situation is probably the best way to preventing future problems:

- Are there things that I would do differently next time?
- Am I as familiar as I would like to be with ethical codes, standards, and literature?
- Do I have a professional network with whom I can effectively consult?
- Are there changes that I could or should make in my professional practices that may prevent future occurrences of similar problems?
- Are there changes that could or should be made in the policies and procedures of the institution that may prevent future occurrences of similar problems?

QUESTIONS for REFLECTION

1. How would you decide which colleague(s) to consult with about an ethical decision?
2. What are some of the personal impediments that you have encountered when trying to do what you felt was ethical? How might you anticipate and deal with them in the future?
3. Do you agree that ethical decisions ought to be held to the same standards of evidence as other types of decisions, such as medical diagnosis or weather forecasting? Why or why not?

APPLYING THE MODEL TO A HYPOTHETICAL CASE

You are an English teacher in a Saskatchewan urban high school. One of your students, who you find very intelligent but do not particularly like, comes to class wearing a T-shirt with "White Power" written across a clenched fist on it. You find the slogan distasteful, and a few other students have complained that it makes them uncomfortable. A problem in your school is that the First Nations and white students do not "mix" and there have been some instances of racial tension both in the school and in the community surrounding it.

When you ask Ed to not wear the T-shirt to class he objects. The following day your principal receives a phone call from his irate father who indicates that either Ed is allowed to wear the shirt or he will be kept home from school. The father is adamant that the shirt is "free speech," and further accuses you of being hypocritical as you have allowed other students to wear, without comment, shirts indicating that they support gay marriage.

While the administration supports your decision in general terms you are asked to justify your position, particularly in light of the fact that the school has not implemented a dress code.

This hypothetical situation raises a number of different issues. One—but not necessarily the only—possible line of reasoning using our model of ethical decision making would go as follows.

1. Identification of individuals and groups involved or likely to be affected by the decision

Obviously both Ed and his father have a direct interest in the outcome. You also feel that the other students' views that they feel uncomfortable with the shirt must be considered. It follows that the school administration has an interest because the educative environment is affected. You as a teacher also have an interest in the outcome. Finally, schools exist within the larger community, which will always have a stake in how children are taught.

2. Identification of relevant ethical values and principles

From the point of view of Ed and his father the ethical value of autonomy— Ed's right to freedom from control by others—is front and centre in this situation. Ed chose to wear a T-shirt with a controversial slogan on it. Ed's father states that he wants his son to be able to wear the shirt in school; again, an expression of desire for autonomy. From an educative perspective of beneficence—contributing to the well-being of others—you want to help Ed consider how freedom of choice is limited by the degree to which our choices threaten the autonomy of others. The Saskatchewan *Code of Ethics* advises that, "In allowing students to form and express their own judgements, the teacher is responsible for ensuring that students are making judgements on the basis of adequate knowledge of the topic" and that you have a duty "To respect the right of students to form their own judgements based upon knowledge." You are concerned that the statement conveyed via Ed's shirt is not one of compassion and tolerance for others and that he may not understand that his choice of slogan is a moral position.

The other students' well-being (autonomy and beneficence) are at issue in this situation in that they feel uncomfortable. There is an underlying threat inherent in Ed's slogan that may cause students to feel personally afraid, as well as arousing fear of promoting a more hostile school climate. Beneficence and nonmaleficence are also relevant because of the lessons the other students will learn about justice by observing how you handle the situation.

The school has an interest in promoting the autonomy of students through free speech, as well as an over-riding obligation to provide an inclusive, safe environment for learning (beneficence and nonmaleficence)—you wonder if the other students' feelings of "discomfort" suggest that this environment is being imperilled.

Your own opinion is that the T-shirt slogan shows a lack of tolerance, a disrespect of others, as well as being suggestive of a more sinister agenda of white supremacy. While you want to respect Ed's choice (autonomy), you want to behave with integrity by also being true to your own beliefs (fidelity); as a teacher you have a responsibility to be a moral exemplar (beneficence and nonmaleficence). In dealing with the situation in its entirety you want to respect the dignity and autonomy of all parties involved, and behave in a fair and reasonable manner (justice).

The community at large always has an interest in how children are prepared to become members of society. Issues of tolerance and freedom of expression are important—though often controversial—societal values. The community will expect that you and the school administration deal with this situation in a manner that serves the common good (beneficence and nonmaleficence).

3. Consideration of personal values, bias, stress, or self-interest

The fact that you do not personally like Ed is a potential source of bias—would you have the same reaction to the shirt if it was worn by a student who you liked better? You also recognize that you support (or at least do not openly condemn) students who engage in free speech in support of alternative marriages. You wonder if a First Nations student wore a similar shirt in support of native rights, would your reaction be the same?

4. Development of viable alternative courses of action

In this situation you recognize that part of the issue is determining what Ed thinks the slogan on his shirt represents; you view that as more important in the circumstances than what his father might think. Having said that, you also must weigh Ed's interpretation against the understanding that others (including yourself) might have of its connotation. One course of action, therefore, is to arrange to meet with Ed privately and discuss the slogan. Alternatively or additionally, you could invite his father to be part of this or another conversation. Considering the school as a whole, you could also use this situation as an opportunity for learning about the limits of freedom of expression in society vis-à-vis tolerance and respect for others.

Of course, at some point you have to consider the course of action of "laying down the law" and forbidding Ed to wear the shirt, or simply allowing him to do so without further comment from you.

5. Analysis of alternative courses of action

In the best possible scenario a conversation with Ed would result in him coming to understand the impact that his shirt's slogan has on others, and deciding that he wants to have a more tolerant and respectful relationship with his fellow students and the community at large. This would promote all of our core ethical values (autonomy, nonmaleficence, beneficence, fidelity, justice) and compromise none of them. Of course, such a conversation could also uncover that he wants to express non-tolerant views and does not want to explore other points of view, or that he is unwilling to compromise his desire for unfettered choice of clothing, requiring you to consider another course of action.

By expanding the conversation to include Ed's father, you are respecting his right to be involved (autonomy) and his involvement may help to resolve the matter (beneficence). His objection to your position that his son ought not to wear the T-shirt to school may be based on a limited understanding of the broader implications and he may then be able to positively influence his son. There may also be some other, unstated, reason or concern underlying his position that is amenable to an open respectful conversation with you. On the other hand, the meeting may be acrimonious and unproductive, leaving the issue unresolved.

Using this situation as an opportunity for a classroom project could facilitate a dialogue among the students—Ed included—that would promote their learning about the issues and the development of a more tolerant climate in the school (beneficence). On the other hand, you are concerned that it might have the effect of isolating Ed from some of his classmates (nonmaleficence). And realistically, having spoken to your colleagues, you are not at all confident that you can design an assignment that would draw out and resolve all the issues involved given how complex and controversial the situation is.

Banning the shirt against Ed's and his father's wishes does not respect Ed's autonomy, would not have any substantive educative value for him (nonmaleficence), and would not promote a moral climate in the school (nonmaleficence) because the principle of justice would be compromised. It would, however, promote the safety of the other students (autonomy, beneficence).

Simply ignoring the matter and allowing the T-shirt to be worn neither respects the views of the other students (autonomy) or the safety and moral climate of the school (nonmaleficence), nor does it promote Ed's development (beneficence).

6. Choice of course of action

At its simplest level, your choice of course of action, in light of all of the above considerations, is to recommend to the school administration that a discussion be held between Ed and his father and the principal and yourself, about the shirt. Prior to that meeting, you would want to do some research on what the slogan represents (its denotation) and what it means to the other students (its connotation), as well as speaking with the principal. During the meeting, you would want to find out if, in fact, Ed is expressing himself. If, for example, Ed indicates he wants to wear the shirt because of its colour or because it promotes controversy, then how it would proceed would be different that if he honestly believed that he was expressing racial pride.

7. Evaluation of consequences and response

Ed and his father's response to the meeting will be pivotal to how you proceed next. This is not to say, of course, "anything goes." Rather, knowledge of the ethical values inherent in this situation forms the framework that guides how to proceed and, if necessary, defend your choice of action. Either Ed or his father may bring forth new considerations that prompt other courses of action; you must be mindful that an essential part of this dialogue is your willingness to modify your point of view during the course of it.

WHAT THE CODES SAY

The teacher is willing to review with colleagues, students, and their parents/guardians the quality of service rendered by the teacher and the practices employed in discharging professional duties.

—*From British Columbia Teachers' Federation* Code of Ethics

QUESTIONS
for REFLECTION

1. Are there other courses of action that you would consider for this situation? What are they?
2. Do you agree with the choice of course of action for this situation? If not, at what step did we go wrong in your opinion?

CONCLUSION

What the above discussion highlights is that making an ethically justifiable decision involves appreciating how our professional ethical values are inherent in our choice of action, as well as being respectful of and incorporating the point of view of the individuals involved. The resolution of a conflict can (as in this case) be both difficult and potentially unpleasant. Yet during the course of working through the elements a greater appreciation of the complexity of the issue, and of one's own feelings, is often achieved.

The ethical decision-making model presented here provides a clear and comprehensive framework for sorting through conflicting ethical duties and obligations as a professional teacher. The language of principles and rules can feel somewhat abstract and devoid of inspirational concepts and virtues. The model is, however, very helpful as a guide for applying our ethical values to the problem of deciding how to act in specific situations. Especially in situations where the stakes are high, a careful detailed analysis of an ethical dilemma as a guide for arriving at a publicly defensible decision is in the best interest of the professional, the profession, and the public we serve.

Summary

Ethical decisions should be made after careful deliberation. A seven-step model for making ethical decisions begins with (Step 1) identification of the individuals and groups potentially affected by the decision and moves to (Step 2) identification of relevant ethical principles and standards. In Step 3 teachers consider the influence of personal values, bias, stress, or self-interest, and then (Step 4) develop alternative courses of action. Step 5 involves analysis of each course of action. At Step 6 teachers choose a course of action, then (Step 7) evaluate the results of the course of action, assume responsibility for the consequences of action, and take appropriate and feasible action to prevent future occurrences of the problem. Although the process appears time-consuming at first, it can be shortened by familiarity with codes of ethics, professional guidelines and the ethics literature, maintaining ready access to knowledgeable colleagues with whom to consult, and experience.

Questions for Discussion

1. In your experience, why do teachers not always behave as ethically as they ought to? Are these reasons different than the reasons why non-teachers do not always behave ethically?
2. You may have heard people say (and may have thought so yourself) that ethical decisions really just depend on the situation and cannot be reduced to "rules" or "standards." How would you respond to this point of view after having read this chapter?
3. Under what circumstances would you feel tempted to disregard ethical standards in favour of your intuitive judgment? Under what circumstances would you feel justified in doing so?
4. Do you agree with how the ethical dilemma was resolved in this chapter? Why or why not? If not, how would you resolve it?

Further Reading

Hostetler, K.D. (1997). *Ethical judgment in teaching*. Boston: Allyn and Bacon.

Strike, K.A., & Soltis, J.F. (1998). *The ethics of teaching* (3rd Ed.). New York: Teachers College Press.

Zubay, B., & Soltis, J.F. (2005). *Creating the ethical school: A book of case studies*. New York: Teachers College Press.

Appendix

THE *CANADIAN CHARTER OF RIGHTS AND FREEDOMS*

Whereas Canada is founded upon principles that recognize the supremacy of God and the rule of law:

Guarantee of Rights and Freedoms

1. The *Canadian Charter of Rights and Freedoms* guarantees the rights and freedoms set out in it subject only to such reasonable limits prescribed by law as can be demonstrably justified in a free and democratic society.

Fundamental Freedoms

2. Everyone has the following fundamental freedoms:
   - *(a)* freedom of conscience and religion;
   - *(b)* freedom of thought, belief, opinion and expression, including freedom of the press and other media of communication;
   - *(c)* freedom of peaceful assembly; and
   - *(d)* freedom of association.

Democratic Rights

3. Every citizen of Canada has the right to vote in an election of members of the House of Commons or of a legislative assembly and to be qualified for membership therein.

4. (1) No House of Commons and no legislative assembly shall continue for longer than five years from the date fixed for the return of the writs at a general election of its members.

   (2) In time of real or apprehended war, invasion or insurrection, a House of Commons may be continued by Parliament and a legislative assembly may be continued by the legislature beyond five years if such continuation is not opposed by the votes of more than one-third of the members of the House of Commons or the legislative assembly, as the case may be.

5. There shall be a sitting of Parliament and of each legislature at least once every twelve months.

Mobility Rights

6. (1) Every citizen of Canada has the right to enter, remain in and leave Canada.

   (2) Every citizen of Canada and every person who has the status of a permanent resident of Canada has the right
   - *(a)* to move to and take up residence in any province; and
   - *(b)* to pursue the gaining of a livelihood in any province.

(3) The rights specified in subsection (2) are subject to
    (a) any laws or practices of general application in force in a province other than those that discriminate among persons primarily on the basis of province of present or previous residence; and
    (b) any laws providing for reasonable residency requirements as a qualification for the receipt of publicly provided social services.

(4) Subsections (2) and (3) do not preclude any law, program or activity that has as its object the amelioration in a province of conditions of individuals in that province who are socially or economically disadvantaged if the rate of employment in that province is below the rate of employment in Canada.

Legal Rights

7. Everyone has the right to life, liberty and security of the person and the right not to be deprived thereof except in accordance with the principles of fundamental justice.

8. Everyone has the right to be secure against unreasonable search or seizure.

9. Everyone has the right not to be arbitrarily detained or imprisoned.

10. Everyone has the right on arrest or detention
    (a) to be informed promptly of the reasons therefor;
    (b) to retain and instruct counsel without delay and to be informed of that right; and
    (c) to have the validity of the detention determined by way of *habeas corpus* and to be released if the detention is not lawful.

11. Any person charged with an offence has the right
    (a) to be informed without unreasonable delay of the specific offence;
    (b) to be tried within a reasonable time;
    (c) not to be compelled to be a witness in proceedings against that person in respect of the offence;
    (d) to be presumed innocent until proven guilty according to law in a fair and public hearing by an independent and impartial tribunal;
    (e) not to be denied reasonable bail without just cause;
    (f) except in the case of an offence under military law tried before a military tribunal, to the benefit of trial by jury where the maximum punishment for the offence is imprisonment for five years or a more severe punishment;
    (g) not to be found guilty on account of any act or omission unless, at the time of the act or omission, it constituted an offence under Canadian or international law or was criminal according to the general principles of law recognized by the community of nations;
    (h) if finally acquitted of the offence, not to be tried for it again and, if finally found guilty and punished for the offence, not to be tried or punished for it again; and
    (i) if found guilty of the offence and if the punishment for the offence has been varied between the time of commission and the time of sentencing, to the benefit of the lesser punishment.

12. Everyone has the right not to be subjected to any cruel and unusual treatment or punishment.

13. A witness who testifies in any proceedings has the right not to have any incriminating evidence so given used to incriminate that witness in any other proceedings, except in a prosecution for perjury or for the giving of contradictory evidence.

14. A party or witness in any proceedings who does not understand or speak the language in which the proceedings are conducted or who is deaf has the right to the assistance of an interpreter.

Equality Rights

15. (1) Every individual is equal before and under the law and has the right to the equal protection and equal benefit of the law without discrimination and, in particular, without discrimination based on race, national or ethnic origin, colour, religion, sex, age or mental or physical disability.

    (2) Subsection (1) does not preclude any law, program or activity that has as its object the amelioration of conditions of disadvantaged individuals or groups including those that are disadvantaged because of race, national or ethnic origin, colour, religion, sex, age or mental or physical disability.

Official Languages of Canada

16. (1) English and French are the official languages of Canada and have equality of status and equal rights and privileges as to their use in all institutions of the Parliament and government of Canada.

    (2) English and French are the official languages of New Brunswick and have equality of status and equal rights and privileges as to their use in all institutions of the legislature and government of New Brunswick.

    (3) Nothing in this Charter limits the authority of Parliament or a legislature to advance the equality of status or use of English and French.

17. (1) Everyone has the right to use English or French in any debates and other proceedings of Parliament.

    (2) Everyone has the right to use English or French in any debates and other proceedings of the legislature of New Brunswick.

18. (1) The statutes, records and journals of Parliament shall be printed and published in English and French and both language versions are equally authoritative.

    (2) The statutes, records and journals of the legislature of New Brunswick shall be printed and published in English and French and both language versions are equally authoritative.

19. (1) Either English or French may be used by any person in, or in any pleading in or process issuing from, any court established by Parliament.

    (2) Either English or French may be used by any person in, or in any pleading in or process issuing from, any court of New Brunswick.

20. (1) Any member of the public in Canada has the right to communicate with, and to receive available services from, any head or central office of an institution of the Parliament or government of Canada in English or French, and has the same right with respect to any other office of any such institution where

   (a) there is a significant demand for communications with and services from that office in such language; or

   (b) due to the nature of the office, it is reasonable that communications with and services from that office be available in both English and French.

(2) Any member of the public in New Brunswick has the right to communicate with, and to receive available services from, any office of an institution of the legislature or government of New Brunswick in English or French.

21. Nothing in sections 16 to 20 abrogates or derogates from any right, privilege or obligation with respect to the English and French languages, or either of them, that exists or is continued by virtue of any other provision of the Constitution of Canada.

22. Nothing in sections 16 to 20 abrogates or derogates from any legal or customary right or privilege acquired or enjoyed either before or after the coming into force of this Charter with respect to any language that is not English or French.

Minority Language Educational Rights

23. (1) Citizens of Canada

   (a) whose first language learned and still understood is that of the English or French linguistic minority population of the province in which they reside, or

   (b) who have received their primary school instruction in Canada in English or French and reside in a province where the language in which they received that instruction is the language of the English or French linguistic minority population of the province, have the right to have their children receive primary and secondary school instruction in that language in that province.

(2) Citizens of Canada of whom any child has received or is receiving primary or secondary school instruction in English or French in Canada, have the right to have all their children receive primary and secondary school instruction in the same language.

(3) The right of citizens of Canada under subsections (1) and (2) to have their children receive primary and secondary school instruction in the language of the English or French linguistic minority population of a province

   (a) applies wherever in the province the number of children of citizens who have such a right is sufficient to warrant the provision to them out of public funds of minority language instruction; and

   (b) includes, where the number of those children so warrants, the right to have them receive that instruction in minority language educational facilities provided out of public funds.

Enforcement

24. (1) Anyone whose rights or freedoms, as guaranteed by this Charter, have been infringed or denied may apply to a court of competent jurisdiction to obtain such remedy as the court considers appropriate and just in the circumstances.

(2) Where, in proceedings under subsection (1), a court concludes that evidence was obtained in a manner that infringed or denied any rights or freedoms guaranteed by this Charter, the evidence shall be excluded if it is established that, having regard to all the circumstances, the admission of it in the proceedings would bring the administration of justice into disrepute.

General

25. The guarantee in this Charter of certain rights and freedoms shall not be construed so as to abrogate or derogate from any aboriginal, treaty or other rights or freedoms that pertain to the aboriginal peoples of Canada including

(a) any rights or freedoms that have been recognized by the Royal Proclamation of October 7, 1763; and

(b) any rights or freedoms that may be acquired by the aboriginal peoples of Canada by way of land claims settlement.

26. The guarantee in this Charter of certain rights and freedoms shall not be construed as denying the existence of any other rights or freedoms that exist in Canada.

27. This Charter shall be interpreted in a manner consistent with the preservation and enhancement of the multicultural heritage of Canadians.

28. Notwithstanding anything in this Charter, the rights and freedoms referred to in it are guaranteed equally to male and female persons.

29. Nothing in this Charter abrogates or derogates from any rights or privileges guaranteed by or under the Constitution of Canada in respect of denominational, separate or dissentient schools.

30. A reference in this Charter to a province or to the legislative assembly or legislature of a province shall be deemed to include a reference to the Yukon Territory and the Northwest Territories, or to the appropriate legislative authority thereof, as the case may be.

31. Nothing in this Charter extends the legislative powers of any body or authority.

Application of Charter

32. (1) This Charter applies

(a) to the Parliament and government of Canada in respect of all matters within the authority of Parliament including all matters relating to the Yukon Territory and Northwest Territories; and

(b) to the legislature and government of each province in respect of all matters within the authority of the legislature of each province.

(2) Notwithstanding subsection (1), section 15 shall not have effect until three years after this section comes into force.

33. (1) Parliament or the legislature of a province may expressly declare in an Act of Parliament or of the legislature, as the case may be, that the Act or a provision thereof shall operate notwithstanding a provision included in section 2 or sections 7 to 15 of this Charter.

(2) An Act or a provision of an Act in respect of which a declaration made under this section is in effect shall have such operation as it would have but for the provision of this Charter referred to in the declaration.

(3) A declaration made under subsection (1) shall cease to have effect five years after it comes into force or on such earlier date as may be specified in the declaration.

(4) Parliament or a legislature of a province may re-enact a declaration made under subsection (1).

(5) Subsection (3) applies in respect of a re-enactment made under subsection (4).

Citation

34. This Part may be cited as the *Canadian Charter of Rights and Freedoms*.

List of Cases

Adler v. Ontario, [1996] 3 S.C.R. 609 **(page 20)**

Andrews v. Law Society of British Columbia, [1989] 1 S.C.R. 143 **(page 160)**

Bain v. Calgary Board of Education, [1993] A.J. 952 **(page 74n)**

Boese v. St. Paul's Roman Catholic Separate School District No. 20, [1980] S.J. No. 211; aff'd [1979] S.J. No. 87 **(page 72n)**

Boring v. Buncombe County Board of Education 136 F. 3d 364 (4th Cir. 1998) **(page 173n)**

British Columbia Teachers' Federation v. Vancouver School District No. 39, [2003] B.C.J. No. 366 **(page 47)**

C. (J.S.) v. Wren, [1986] A.J. No. 1167 **(page 101n)**

Caldwell v. Stuart, [1984] 2 S.C.R. 603 **(page 60)**

Campbell v. Cartmell, [1999] O.J. No. 3553 **(pages 74, 95n)**

Canadian Foundation for Children, Youth and the Law v. Canada (Attorney General), [2004] S.C.J. No. 6 **(page 119n)**

Catherwood v. Heinrichs, [1996] B.C.J. 1373 **(pages 72n, 74n)**

Chamberlain v. Surrey School District No. 15, [2002] S.C.J. No. 87; revg. (2000), 191 D.L.R. (4th) 128; revg. [1998] B.C.J. No. 2933 **(pages 23n, 132–135)**

Children's Aid Society of Haldimand-Norfolk v. C.C., [2004] O.J. No. 2274 **(page 108)**

Children's Aid Society of Ottawa v. N.S., [2005] O.J. 1070 **(page 108)**

Cropp v. Potashville School Unit 25, [1977] S.J. No. 328 **(page 75n)**

D.F. v. A.S., [2001] Q.J. No. 3273 **(page 95n)**

Doe v. Renfrew, 631 F. 2d 91 **(page 106n)**

Donohue v. Copiage Union Free School, Court of Appeal, New York (1979), 47 N.Y. 2d, 375 **(page 77n)**

Dziwnka v. The Queen in Right of Alberta (1971) 25 D.L.R. (3d) 12 **(page 72)**

E.D.G. v. Hammer, [2003] S.C.C. 52 **(page 76)**

Edward Gianfrancesco and Jessica Gianfrancesco (by her litigation guardian, Edward Gianfrancesco) v. The Junior Academy Inc., [2003] O.J. No. 931. **(page 103n)**

Egan v. Canada, [1995] 2 S.C.R. 513 **(page 57n)**

Eggertson v. Alberta Teachers' Association, [2003] A.J. No. 384 **(page 48n)**

Eldridge v. British Columbia (Attorney General), [1997] 3 S.C.R. 624 **(page 154)**

Emily v. Brant County Board of Education, [1997] 1 S.C.R. 241 **(page 160)**

Essex County Roman Catholic Separate School Board v. Porter (1978), 89 D.L.R. (2d) 445, 21 O.R. (2d) 255 (C.A.) **(page 66n)**

Essex County Roman Catholic Separate School Board v. Tremblay-Webster (1984), 5 D.L.R. (4th) 665, 84 C.L.L.C. Para.14, 030, 45 O.R. (2d) 83 (C.A.) **(page 66n)**

Fraser v. Campbell River School District No. 72, [1988] B.C.J. No. 2453 **(page 74n)**

Freer v. Okanagon-Skaha School District No. 67, [2002] B.C.J. No. 2739 **(page 73)**

George v. Port Alberni School District 70, [1986] B.C.J. 1726 **(page 74n)**

Gillick v. W. Norfolk and Wisbech Area Health Auth., 3 WLR 830 (1985) **(page 101n)**

Gosselin (Tutor of) v. Quebec (Attorney General), [2005] S.C.J. No. 15 **(page 21)**

Gould v. Regina (East) School Division No. 77 (1996), 7 C.P.C. (4th) 372 **(page 77n)**

Hahn No. 2 (1990), 86 Nfld. & P.E.I.R. 33 **(page 92)**

Haines v. Neudorf, [1995] S.J. No. 314 **(page 103)**

Hall (Litigation guardian of) v. Powers (2002), 59 O.R. (3d) 423 **(page 153)**

Hawreluik v. Shamrock School Division No. 38, [1987] S.J. No. 108 **(page 103)**

Haynes (Guardian ad litem of) v. Lleres, [1997] B.C.J. No. 1202 **(page 77n)**

Hoyt v. Hay, [1978] N.B.J. No. 9 **(page 75n)**

J.S. v. Bethlehem Area Sch. Dist., 569 Pa 638 **(page 98)**

James et al. v. River East School Division No. 9 et al. (1975), 58 D.L.R. (3d) 311, [1976] 5 W.W.R. 135; affirmed by the Manitoba Court of Appeal at 64 D.L.R. (3d) 338, [1976] 2 W.W.R. 577 **(page 72n)**

Keefe v. Geanakos, 418 F.2d 359, 362 (1st Cir. 1969) **(page 139)**

Kempling v. British Columbia College of Teachers, [2004] B.C.J. No. 173 **(pages 59n, 140n)**

Kohuch v. Wilson, [1988] S.J. No. 682 **(page 95n)**

Leah Bradford-Smart v. West Sussex County Council, [2002] E.W.J. No. 127 **(page 78n)**

Lutes (Litigation Guardian of) v. Prairie View School Division No. 74, [1992] S.J. 198 **(pages 75n, 110)**

Lutes v. Prairie View School Division No. 74 101 Sask. R. 232 **(pages 75n, 110)**

Mahe v. Alberta, [1990] 1 S.C.R. 342 **(page 35)**

McKay v. CDI Career Development Institutes Ltd., [1999] B.C.J. No. 561 **(page 77n)**

McKay v. Govan School Unit (1967), 60 W.W.R. 513 **(pages 71–72)**

McKerron v. Marshall, [1999] O.J. No. 4048 **(page 95)**

Metropolitan Separate School Board and Ontario Catholic Teachers' Association (1994), 41 L.A.C. (4th) 353 **(page 66)**

Morin v. Prince Edward Island Regional Administrative Unit No. 3 School Board, [1999] P.E.I.J. No. 76 **(pages 136n–139)**

Morin v. Prince Edward Island Regional Administrative Unit No. 3 School Board, [2002] P.E.I.J. No. 36. **(page 138)**

Morin v. Prince Edward Island Regional Administrative Unit No. 3 School Board, [2002] S.C.C.A. No. 414 **(page 138)**

Morin v. Prince Edward Island Regional Administrative Unit No. 3 School Board, [2005] P.E.I.J. No. 42 **(page 138)**

Myers v. Peel, [1981] 2 S.C.R. 21 **(page 70)**

North Vancouver School District No. 44 v. Jubran, [2002] B.C.H.R.T.D. No. 10; (Human Rights Tribunal), [2003] B.C.J. No. 10 (B.C.S.C.) **(pages 78, 152)**

North Vancouver School District No. 44 v. Jubran, [2005] B.C.J. No. 733 (B.C.C.A.); revg (2003), 9 B.C.L.R. (4th) 338; revg. [2002] B.C.H.R.T.D. No. 10 **(pages 78, 152)**

OCT v. Haines, [1999] O.C.T.D.D. No. 12 **(page 63)**

OCT v. Hungerford, [1999] O.C.T.D.D. No. 17 **(page 62)**

OCT v. Knott, [2000] O.C.T.D.D. No. 11 **(page 62)**

OCT v. Kuhn, [1998] O.C.T.D.D. No. 10 **(page 62)**

OCT v. Raciot, [2001] O.C.T.D.D. No. 5 **(page 63)**

Ontario College of Teachers v. D.J., [2000] O.C.T.D.D. No. 45 **(page 43n)**

Ontario College of Teachers v. Deagle, [2001] O.C.T.D.D. No. 19 **(page 125n)**

Ontario College of Teachers v. GWD, [1999] O.C.T.D.D. No. 15 **(page 62)**

Ontario College of Teachers v. H.J.R., [2001] O.C.T.D.D. No. 17 **(page 86n)**

Ontario College of Teachers v J.L., [2001] O.C.T.D.D. No. 12 **(page 86n)**

Ontario College of Teachers v. King, [2003] O.C.T.D.D. No. 59 **(page 67)**

Ontario College of Teachers v. MacDonald, [2001] O.C.T.D.D. No. 13 **(pages 43n, 125n)**

Ontario College of Teachers v. Markson, [2001] O.C.T.D.D. No. 16 **(page 86)**

Ontario College of Teachers v. Newton, [1999] O.C.T.D.D. No. 10 **(page 43n)**

Ontario College of Teachers v. Uhlig, [1999] O.C.T.D.D. No. 21 **(page 125n)**

Ontario Public School Boards Assn. v. Ontario (A.G.) (1999), 175 D.L.R. (4th) 609 **(page 24n)**

Plumb v. Cowichan School District No. 65, [1993] B.C.J. 1936 **(page 73n)**

R. v. Audet, [1996] S.C.J. 61; [1996] 2 S.C.R 171; revg. (1995), 155 N.B.R. (2d) 369; revg. (1993), 142 N.B.R. (2d) 382 **(pages 61n, 89n, 90n, 91–93, 186)**

R. v. Caouette, [2002] J.Q. no. 1055 (C.Q.) **(page 119n)**

R. v. Forde, [1992] O.J. No. 1698 **(page 89)**

R. v. Godin, [1996] N.B.J. No. 148 **(page 123n)**

R. v. Haberstock 18 (1970), 1 C.C.C. (2d) 433 **(pages 118n, 124)**

R. v. Imbeault (1977), 17 N.B.R. (2d) 234 **(page 123n)**

R. v. Jones, [1986] 2 S.C.R. 284 **(page 22)**

R. v. Kanhai, [1981] S.J. No. 1353 **(page 124)**

R. v. Keegstra, [1990] 3 S.C.R. 697 **(page 110n)**

R. v. Keukens (1995) 23 O.R. (3d) 582 **(page 109n)**

R. v. Kind, [1984] N.J. No. 243, 50 Nfld. & P.E.I.R. 332 **(pages 22, 102)**

R. v. Levesque 2001 ABQB 822 **(page 119n)**

R. v. M.R.M. (1997), 159 N.S.R. (2d) 321 **(pages 105, 106)**

R. v. M.R.M., [1998] 3 S.C.R. 393 **(pages 105, 106)**

R. v. Morgentaler, [1988] 1 S.C.R. 30 **(page 34n)**

R. v. Oakes, [1986] 1 S.C.R. 103 **(page 34n)**

R. v. Ogg-Moss, [1984] 2 S.C.R. 173 **(page 124n)**

R. v. P.S., [1993] O.J. No. 704 **(page 90n)**

R. v. Plourde, [1993] N.B.J. No. 487 (Prov. Ct.) **(page 119n)**

R. v. Powell, [1985] A.J. No. 456 **(page 22)**

R. v. Robinson (1899), 7 C.C.C. 52 **(pages 118n, 125n)**

R. v. S.B., [1996] O.J. No. 4724 **(page 106n)**

R. v. S.D., [2002] O.J. No. 5141 **(page 141)**

R. v. T. (V.), [1992] 1 S.C.R. 749 **(page 109)**

R. v. W. (J.J.), [1990] N.J. No. 73 **(page 106n)**

R. v. Wetmore, [1996] N.B.J. No.15 (Q.B.). **(page 119n)**

Robinson v. Calgary School District 19 (1977), 5 A.R. 430 **(page 73n)**

Ross v. New Brunswick School District, [1996] 1 S.C.R. 825 (at paragraph 42) **(pages 64–66, 131n, 151)**

Selman v. Cobb County Sch. Dist., 2005 U.S. Dist. LEXIS 432 **(page 141)**

Shewan v. Abbotsford School District No. 34 (1987) 21 B.C.L.R. (2d) 93, 47 D.L.R. (4th) 106 **(page 61n)**

Smart v. College of the Rockies, [2002] B.C.J. No. 3119 **(page 77n)**

Snell v. Farrel, [1990] 2 S.C.R. 311 **(page 32)**

Stolen v. British Columbia College of Teachers, [1995] B.C.J. No. 1980 **(page 64n)**

Thiessen v. Winnipeg School Division 1, [1967] S.C.R. 413 **(page 75n)**

Thornton v. Prince George, [1976] 5 W.W.R. 240; varied on other grounds [1978] 2 S.C.R. 267 **(page 72n)**

Tinker v. Des Moines Independent Community District, 393 U.S. 50 3 (1969) **(page 112)**

Trinity Western University v. British Columbia College of Teachers, [2001] 1 S.C.R. 772 **(pages 58, 152, 153)**

Vriend v. Alberta, [1998] 1 S.C.R. 493 **(pages 56–57)**

Waldman v. Canada, CCPR/C/67/D/694/1996 **(page 20)**

Ward v. Blaine Lake School Board, [1971] S.J. No. 70 **(page 111)**

Webb v. Lake Mills Community Sch. Dist., 344 F. Supp. 791, 799–800 (N.D. Iowa 1972) **(page 139)**

Wernicke, v. "Teachers' Speech Rights in the Classroom: An Analysis of Cockrel v. Shelby County School District," 71 U. Cin. L. Rev. 1471 **(page 140)**

Williams v. Eady (1893), 10 T.L.R. 41 **(page 70n)**

Yarmoloy et al. v. Banff School Dist. No. 102, [1985] Alta. D. 71-01 **(page 160n)**

Young v. British Columbia College of Teachers, [2001] B.C.J. No. 405 **(pages 89–90)**

References

Adelman, H.S., Lusk, R., Alvarez, V., & Acosta, N. K. (1985). Competence of minors to understand, evaluate, and communicate about their psycho-educational problems. *Professional Psychology: Research and Practice, 16,* 426–34.

Alberta School Act, R.S.A. (2000) c. S-3.

Alberta Teachers' Association. (1999). *Code of conduct.* Edmonton: Author.

American Association of University Women. (1993). *Hostile hallways: The AAUW survey on sexual harassment in America's schools.* Washington, DC: Author.

Anand, S. (2003) Crafting youth sentences: The roles of rehabilitation, pro-portionality, restraint, restorative justice, and race under the Youth Criminal Justice Act. *Alberta Law Review, 40,* 943–963.

Andrews v. Law Society of British Columbia, [1989] 1 S.C.R. 143.

Ashton, E., & Watson, B. (1998). Values education: A fresh look at procedural neutrality. *Educational Studies, 24*(2): 183–193.

AvRuskin, S.J. (1987). In defence of young persons: Search and seizure in schools: A scholarly reduction of a young person's rights. *Ontario Criminal Trial Lawyers Association Newsletter, 8*(6), p. 19.

Axelrod, P. (1997). *The promise of schooling: Education in Canada 1800–1914.* Toronto: University of Toronto Press.

Bain v. Calgary Board of Education, [1993] A.J. 952.

Bala, N. (2002). *Youth criminal justice law.* Toronto: Irwin.

Bala, N. et. al. (1991). *The Young Offenders Act: A revolution in Canadian juvenile justice.* Toronto:University of Toronto Press.

Benson, I., & Miller, B. (1996). Case comment on *R. v. Audet. Lex View,* 1.0.

Benson, I., & Miller, B. (2002). Should spanking your child be a criminal act? *Lex View,* No. 50.

Boese v. Board of Education of St. Paul's Roman Catholic Separate School District No. 20, [1980] S.J. No. 211; aff'd [1979] S.J. No. 87.

Boring v. Buncombe County Board of Education 136 F.3d 364 (4th Cir. 1998).

British Columbia Royal Commission on Education. (1988). *The Report of the Royal Commission on Education: A legacy for learners.* Victoria: Author.

British Columbia Teachers' Federation. (1999) Task Force on First Nations Education. Vancouver: Author

British Columbia Teachers' Federation. (2003). *Code of ethics.* Vancouver: Author.

Caldwell v. Stuart, [1984] 2 S.C.R. 603.

Campbell, E. (1996). Ethical implications of collegial loyalty as one view of teacher professionalism. *Teachers and Teaching: Theory and Practice, 2,* 191–208.

Campbell, E. (1997). Connecting the ethics of teaching and moral education. *Journal of Teacher Education, 48,* 255–263

Campbell, E. (2003). *The ethical teacher.* Maidenhead, England: Open University Press.

Campbell v. Cartmell, [1999] O.J. No. 3553.

Canadian Charter of Rights and Freedoms, Part 1 of the *Constitution Act, 1982,* being Schedule B to the *Canada Act 1982* (U.K.), 1982, c. 11, s. 32.

Canadian Foundation for Children, Youth and the Law v. Canada (Attorney General), [2004] S.C.J. No. 6.

Carr, D. (2000). *Professionalism and ethics in teaching.* New York: Routledge.

Carr, D. (2003). Moral educational implications of rival conceptions of education and the role of the teacher. *Journal of Moral Education, 32,* 219–232.

Catherwood v. Heinrichs, [1996] B.C.J. 1373.

Chamberlain v. Surrey School District No. 15, [2002] S.C.J. No. 87; revg. (2000), 191 D.L.R. (4th) 128; revg. [1998] B.C.J. No. 2933.

C. (J.S.) v. Wren, [1986] A.J. No. 1187

Cohen, C.P. (1989). United Nations: Convention on the rights of the child. *International Law Journal, 28*(6), 1448–1454.

Convention on the Rights of the Child, U.N. Doc. A/RES/44/25 (1989)

Cropp v. Potashville School Unit 25, [1977] S.J. No. 328.

Cross, R., and Price, R. (1996). Science teachers' social conscience and the role of teaching controversial issues in the teaching of science. *Journal of Research in Science Teaching, 33,* 319–333.

D.F. v. A.S., [2001] Q.J. No. 3273.

Daly, K. (2001). Balancing act: Teachers' classroom speech and the First Amendment, *30 Journal of Law & Education,* 1.

Davies, S. (1999). From moral duty to cultural rights: A case study of political framing in education. *Sociology of Education, 72*(1), 1–21

Dearden, R.F. (1981). Controversial issues and the curriculum. *Journal of Curriculum Studies, 13*(1), 37–44.

DeMitchell, T.A. & DeMitchell, T.A. (2003) Statutes and standards: Has the door to educational malpractice been opened? *Brigham Young University Education and Law Journal, 2003*(2), 485–519.

Doe v. Renfrew, 631 F. 2d 91.

Dolmage, W.R. (1995). Accusations of teacher sexual abuse of students in Ontario schools: Some preliminary findings. *Alberta Journal of Educational Research, 16,* 127–144.

Donohue v. Copiage Union Free School, Court of Appeal, New York (1979), 47 N.Y. 2d, 375.

Dziwnka v. The Queen in Right of Alberta (1971), 25 D.L.R. (3d) 12.

E.D.G. v. Hammer, [2003] S.C.C. 52.

The Education Act, 1974, S.O. 1974, c. 109, s. 34(1)

The Education Amendment Act, 1980, S.O. 1980, c. 61.

Edward Gianfrancesco and Jessica Gianfrancesco (by her litigation guardian, Edward Gianfrancesco) v. The Junior Academy Inc., [2003] O.J. No. 931.

Egan v. Canada [1995] 2 S.C.R. 513.

Eggertson v. Alberta Teachers' Association, [2003] A.J. No. 384.

Eldridge v. British Columbia (Attorney General), [1997] 3 S.C.R. 624.

Emily v. Brant County Board of Education, [1997] 1 S.C.R. 241.

Essex County Roman Catholic Separate School Board v. Porter (1978), 89 D.L.R. (2d) 445, 21 O.R. (2d) 255 (C.A.).

Essex County Roman Catholic Separate School Board v. Tremblay-Webster (1984), 5 D.L.R. (4th) 665, 84 C.L.L.C. Para. 14,030, 45 O.R. (2d) 83 (C.A.).

Etzioni, A. (1969). *Semi-professions & their organization.* New York: Free Press.

Federation of Nunavut Teachers. (1999). *Code of ethics.* Iqaluit: Author.

Fraser v. Campbell River School District No. 72, [1988] B.C.J. No. 2453.

Freer v. Okanagon-Skaha School District No. 67, [2002] B.C.J. No. 2739.

Fritz, M. (1982). What will we tell the children? A discussion of current judicial opinion on the scope of ideas acceptable for presentation in primary and secondary education. *Tulsa Law Review, 56,* 960

Gall, G.L. (1995). *The Canadian legal system.* Toronto: Carswell.

George v. Port Alberni School District 70, [1986] B.C.J. 1726.

Ghosh, R. & Ray, D. (1995). *Social Change and Education in Canada,* 3rd ed. Toronto: Harcourt Brace.

Gilbert, C.B. (1999). We are what we wear: Revisiting student dress codes. *Brigham Young University Education and Law Journal, 199,* 2–21.

Gillick v. W. Norfolk and Wisbech Area Health Auth., 3 WLR 830 (1985).

Gould v. Regina (East) School Division No. 77 (1996), 7 C.P.C. (4th) 372.

Grace, E. (1993). Professional misconduct of moral pronouncement: A study of "contentious" teacher behaviour in Quebec. *Education and Law Journal, 5*, 99–142.

Green, S. "Schools Must Keep Parents Informed, Inquest Says," *Globe and Mail*, July 11, 1998.

Guppy, N., & Davies, S. (1998). *Education in Canada: Recent trends and future challenges.* Ottawa: Minister of Industry.

Hahn No. 2 (1990), 86 Nfld. & P.E.I.R. 33.

Haines v. Neudorf, [1995] S.J. No. 314.

Hall (Litigation guardian of) v. Powers (2002), 59 O.R. (3d) 423.

Hart, S.N., & Pavlovic, Z. (1991). Children's rights in education: An historical perspective. *School Psychology Review, 20*(3), 345–360.

Hawreluik v. Shamrock School Division No. 38, [1987] S.J. No. 108.

Hawthorn, H. (1967). *A survey of contemporary Indians of Canada*, Volume II Ottawa: Queen's Printer.

Haynes (Guardian ad litem of) v. Lleres, [1997] B.C.J. No. 1202.

Hogg, P.W. (1982). *Canada Act 1982 annotated.* Toronto: Carswell.

Hostetler, K.D. (1997). *Ethical judgment in teaching.* Boston: Allyn and Bacon.

Howe, R.B. (2001). Do parents have fundamental rights? *Journal of Canadian Studies-Revue d'etudes Canadiennes, 36*(3), 61–78.

Hoyt v. Hay, [1978] N.B.J. No. 9.

James et al. v. River East School Division No. 9 et al. (1975), 58 D.L.R. (3d) 311, [1976] 5 W.W.R. 135; affirmed by the Manitoba Court of Appeal at 64 D.L.R. (3d) 338, [1976] 2 W.W.R. 577.

Jeffrey, D. (January 1999) *Summary Report of Selected First Nations Education Documents*, presented to the AGM of the B.C. Teachers' Federation Task Force on First Nations Education.

Juvenile Delinquents Act, S.C. 1908, c. 40, s. 31

Kant, I. (1959). *Foundations of the metaphysics of morals.* New York: Bobbs-Merrill.

Keefe v. Geanakos, 418 F.2d 359, 362 (1st Cir. 1969)

Kempling v. British Columbia College of Teachers, [2004] B.C.J. No. 173.

King, M. (1982). Children's rights in education: More than just a slogan? *Educational Studies, 8*(3), 227–238.

Kitchener, K. S. (1984). Intuition, critical evaluation and ethical principles: The foundation for ethical decision in counseling psychology. *The Counseling Psychologist, 12*, 43–55.

Kohuch v. Wilson, [1988] S.J. No. 682.

La Forest, G. V. (1997). Off duty conduct and the fiduciary obligations of teachers. *Education & Law Journal, 8,* 119–137.

Leah Bradford-Smart v. West Sussex County Council, [2002] E.W.J. No. 127.

Lewis, C.C. (1981). How adolescents approach decisions: Changes over grades seven to twelve and policy implications. *Child Development, 52,* 538–44.

Lipkin, A. (1999). *Raising Gay/Lesbian Issues in the Classroom.* GLSEN Education Dept. Resource. <http://www.glsen-org/cgi-bin/iowaall/news/record/193.html>

Lutes (Litigation Guardian of) v. Prairie View School Division No. 74, [1992] S.J. 198.

MacKay, W. & Dickinson, G. (1998). *Beyond the "Careful Parent": Tort Liability in Education.* Toronto: Edmond Montgomery.

Mahe v. Alberta, [1990] 1 S.C.R. 342.

Manitoba's Teachers' Society. (2003). *Code of professional practice.* Winnipeg: Author.

Manzer, R.A. (1994). *Public schools and political ideas: Canadian educational policy in historical perspective.* Toronto: University of Toronto Press.

Martel, A. (2001). *Rights, schools and communities in minority contexts: 1986–2002 toward the development of French through education, an analysis.* Ottawa: Office of the Commissioner of Official Languages.

McKay v. CDI Career Development Institutes Ltd., [1999] B.C.J. No. 561.

McKay v. Govan School Unit (1967), 60 W.W.R. 513.

McKerron v. Marshall, [1999] O.J. No. 4048.

Metropolitan Separate School Board v. Ontario English Catholic Teachers' Association (1994), 41 L.A.C. (4th) 353.

Mill, J.S. (1833/1985). *John Stuart Mill on politics and society.* Glasgow: William Collins.

Mill, J.S. (1896/1991). *On liberty.* Oxford: Oxford University Press.

Minister's National Working Group on Education 2002 report to the "Our Children-Keepers of the Sacred Knowledge"; Indian and Northern Affairs, Government of Canada

Morin v. Prince Edward Island Regional Administrative Unit No. 3 School Board, [1999] P.E.I.J. No. 76.

Morin v. Prince Edward Island Regional Administrative Unit No. 3 School Board, [2002] P.E.I.J. No. 36.

Morin v. Prince Edward Island Regional Administrative Unit No. 3 School Board, [2002] S.C.C.A. No. 414.

Morin v. Prince Edward Island Regional Administrative Unit No. 3 School Board, [2005] P.E.I.J. No. 42.

Myers v. Peel, [1981] 2 S.C.R. 21.

National Association of Schoolmasters Union of Women Teachers. As reported in *The Independent*, April 15th, 2004, p. 18.

National Indian Brotherhood, Assembly of First Nations. (1988). *Tradition and education, towards a vision of our future* (Volumes 1, 2, 3). Ottawa: Assembly of First Nations.

New Brunswick Department of Education. (1988). *Information for parents and pupils about the policy for the protection of pupils in the public school system from misconduct by adults*. Fredericton: Author.

New Brunswick Teachers' Association. (2005). *Code of professional conduct*. Fredericton: Author.

Newfoundland and Labrador Teachers' Association. (1974). *Code of ethics*. St. John's: Author.

Noddings, N. (1984). *Caring: A feminine approach to ethics and moral education*. Berkeley: University of California Press.

North Vancouver School District No. 44 v. Jubran, [2002] B.C.H.R.T.D. No. 10; (Human Rights Tribunal) [2003] B.C.J. No. 10 (B.C.S.C.).

North Vancouver School District No. 44 v. Jubran, [2005] B.C.J. No. 733 (B.C.C.A.); revg. (2003), 9 B.C.L.R. (4th) 338; revg. [2002] B.C.H.R.T.D. No. 10.

Nova Scotia Teachers Union. (2002). *Code of ethics*. Halifax: Author.

Nyberg, D. (1990). Teaching values in schools: The mirror and the lamp. *Teachers College Record, 91*, 595–611.

Ontario College of Teachers (1999). *Standards of practice for the teaching profession*. Toronto: Author.

Ontario College of Teachers (2000). *Ethical standards for the teaching profession*. Toronto: Author.

Ontario College of Teachers v. D.J., [2000] O.C.T.D.D. No. 45.

Ontario College of Teachers v. Deagle, [2001] O.C.T.D.D. No. 19.

Ontario College of Teachers v. GWD, [1999] O.C.T.D.D. No. 15.

Ontario College of Teachers v. Haines, [1999] O.C.T.D.D. No. 12.

Ontario College of Teachers v. H.J.R., [2001] O.C.T.D.D. No. 17.

Ontario College of Teachers v. Hungerford, [1999] O.C.T.D.D. No. 17.

Ontario College of Teachers v. J.L., [2001] O.C.T.D.D. No. 12.

Ontario College of Teachers v. King, [2003] O.C.T.D.D. No. 59.

Ontario College of Teachers v. Knott, [2000] O.C.T.D.D. No. 11.

Ontario College of Teachers v. Kuhn, [1998] O.C.T.D.D. No. 10.

Ontario College of Teachers v. MacDonald, [2001] O.C.T.D.D. No. 13.

Ontario College of Teachers v. Markson, [2001] O.C.T.D.D. No. 16.

Ontario College of Teachers v. Newton, [1999] O.C.T.D.D. No. 10.

Ontario College of Teachers v. Raciot, [2001] O.C.T.D.D. No. 5.

Ontario College of Teachers v. Uhlig, [1999] O.C.T.D.D. No. 21.

Ontario Department of Health. *A Report to the Minister of Health on Present Arrangements for the Care and Supervision of Mentally Retarded Persons in Ontario.* By Walter B. Williston. Toronto: 1971.

Ontario Public School Boards Assn. v. Ontario (A.G.) (1999), 175 D.L.R. (4th) 609.

Oulton, C., Dillon J., Grace, M.M. (2004). Reconceptualizing the teaching of controversial issues. *International Journal of Science Education, 26(4),* 411–423.

Oxaal, Z. (2003). Second-Guessing the Bishop: Section 93, the Charter, and the "religious government actor" in the Gay Prom Date Case, 66 *Sask. L. Rev.* 455.

Piddocke, S. (1993). Sexual liaisons between teachers and students: Four Board of Reference cases. *Education and Law Journal, 5,* 53–69.

Piddocke, A., Magsino, R., & Manley-Casmir, M. (1997). *Teachers in trouble: An exploration of the normative character of teaching.* Toronto: University of Toronto Press.

Plumb v. Cowichan School District No. 65, [1993] B.C.J. 1936.

Prince Edward Island Teachers' Federation. (no date). *Code of ethics.* Charlottetown: Author.

R. v. Audet, [1996] S.C.J. No. 61; [1996] 2 S.C.R. 171; revg. (1995), 155 N.B.R. (2d) 369; revg. (1993), 142 N.B.R. (2d) 382

R. c. Caouette, [2002] J.Q. no. 1055 (C.Q.)

R. v. Forde, [1992] O.J. No. 1698.

R. v. Godin, [1996] N.B.J. No. 148.

R. v. Haberstock (1970), 1 C.C.C. (2d) 433.

R. v. Imbeault (1977), 17 N.B.R. (2d) 234.

R. v. Kanhai, [1981] S.J. No. 1353.

R. v. Keegstra, [1990] 3 S.C.R. 697.

R. v. Keukens, (1995) 23 O.R. (3d) 582

R. v. Kind, [1984] N.J. No. 243, 50 Nfld. & P.E.I.R. 332.

R. v. Levesque 2001 ABQB 822

R. v. Morgentaler, [1988] 1 S.C.R. 30.

R. v. M.R.M. [1998] 3 S.C.R. 393; (1997), 159 N.S.R. (2d) 321

R. v. Oakes, [1986] 1 S.C.R. 103.

R. v. Ogg-Moss, [1984] 2 S.C.R. 173.

R. v. Plourde, [1993] N.B.J. No. 487 (Prov. Ct.).

R. v. P.S., [1993] O.J. No. 704.

R. v. Robinson, [1899] 7 C.C.C. 52.

R. v. S.B., [1996] O.J. No. 4724.

R. v. T. (V.), [1992] 1 S.C.R. 749.

R. v. W. (J.J.), [1990] N.J. No. 73.

R. v. Wetmore, [1996] N.B.J. No. 15 (Q.B.).

Rawls, J. (1971). *A theory of justice*. Cambridge: Harvard University Press.

Robbins, S. L. (2000). *Protecting our students: A review to identify and prevent sexual misconduct in Ontario schools*. Ministry of the Attorney General (Ontario).

Robinson v. Calgary School District 19 (1977), 5 A.R. 430.

Ross v. New Brunswick School District No. 15, [1996] 1 S.C.R. 825 (at paragraph 42).

Saskatchewan Teachers' Federation. (2000). *The teaching profession of Saskatchewan code of ethics*. Saskatoon: Author.

Shakeshaft, C., & Cohan, A. (1995). Sexual abuse of students by school personnel. *Phi Delta Kappa, 76*, 512–520.

Shewan v. Abbotsford School District No. 34 (1987), 21 B.C.L.R. (2d) 93, 47 D.L.R. (4th) 106.

Smart v. College of the Rockies, [2002] B.C.J. No. 3119.

Smith, R. (1985). *Freedom and discipline*. London: Allen & Unwin.

Smith W. (1997). Integration: New procedures set in Quebec. *Canadian School Executive*, November, 3–7.

Smith, W. (1997). The placement of students with disabilities and the best interest standard. *Education and Law Journal, 8*, 251–254.

Snell v. Farrel [1990] 2 S.C.R. 311.

Sockett, H. (1993). *The moral base for teacher professionalism*. New York: Teachers College Press.

Stack, R. (2001). Progress and uncertainty: The educational rights of special needs children in British Columbia. *Appeal, 7*, 42–65.

Stephenson, C. (2002). "Johnny, I'm sorry . . ." - The duties imposed on teachers and local education authorities, *Health & Safety Law, 2*(1).

Stewart, D. (2002) Rights of children: Educational and legal implications for schools: An Australian perspective. *Brigham Young University Education and Law Journal*, 255–272.

Stewart, D. & Knott, A. (1988). Schools and the duty of care in relation to student suicide and self-harm: An Australian perspective. *Education and Law Journal, 1*, 218.

Stolen v. British Columbia College of Teachers, [1995] B.C.J. No. 1980.

Strike, K.A., & Soltis, J.F. (2005). *The ethics of teaching* (4th Ed.). New York: Teachers College Press.

Strike, K. A., & Ternasky, P.L. (1993). *Ethics for professionals in education: Perspectives for preparation and practice.* New York: Teachers College Press.

Teacher certification, N.B. Reg. 2004-8.

Thiessen v. Winnipeg School Division 1, [1967] S.C.R. 413.

Thornton v. Prince George, [1976] 5 W.W.R. 240; varied on other grounds [1978] 2 S.C.R. 267.

Tinker v. Des Moines Independent Community District, 393 U.S. 50 3 (1969)

Trinity Western University v. British Columbia College of Teachers, [2001] 1 S.C.R. 772.

Trocme, N. et. al. (1988). *Canadian Incidence Study of Reported Child Abuse and Neglect, Final Report*, Public Health Agency of Canada, Government of Canada.

Troope, S.J. (1996). The Convention on the Rights of the Child: Implications for Canada. In M. Freeman (ed.), *Children's rights: A comparative perspective*. Dartmouth: Brookfield.

Tupper, C. (1896). Debates of the House of Commons, 6th Sess., 7th Parliament, 59 Vict. 1896, col. 2719, at 2724, March 3, 1896.

Uerling, D. F., (2000) Academic freedom in K-12 education. *Nebraska Law Review, 79*, 956.

Vriend v. Alberta, [1998] 1 S.C.R. 493.

Ward v. Blaine Lake School Board, [1971] S.J. No. 70.

Watkinson A. (1999). *Education, Student Rights and the Charter*. Saskatoon: Purich Publishing.

Watson, B. & Ashton, E. (1995). *Education, assumptions and values*. London: David Fulton.

Webb v. Lake Mills Community Sch. Dist., 344 F. Supp. 791, 799–800 (N.D. Iowa 1972).

Werner, W. (1998). Whatever happened to controversy? *Canadian Social Studies, 32*, 117–120.

Wernicke, V. (2003). Teachers' speech rights in the classroom: An analysis of *Cockrel v. Shelby County School District. University of Cincinnati Law Review, 71*, 1471.

Williams v. Eady (1893), 10 T.L.R. 41.

Winch, C. (2004). What do teachers need to know about teaching? A critical examination of the occupational knowledge of teachers. *British Journal of Educational Studies, 52*, 180–196.

Wishnietsky, D.H. (1991). Reported and unreported teacher–student sexual harassment. *Journal of Educational Research, 3*, 164–169.

Yarmoloy et al. v. Banff School Dist. No. 102, [1985] Alta. D. 71-01.

Yates, R. A., Yates, R. W., & Baines, P. (2000). *Introduction to law in Canada*. Scarborough: Prentice-Hall Canada.

Young, J. & Levin, B. (2002). *Understanding Canadian schools: An introduction to educational administration* (3rd ed.) Scarborough, ON: Nelson.

Young v. British Columbia College of Teachers, [2001] B.C.J. No. 405

Young Offenders Act, R.S.C. 1985.

Youth Criminal Justice Act, S.C. 2002, c. 1.

Yukon Teachers' Association. (2004). *Code of Ethics*. Whitehorse: Author.

Zubay, B., & Soltis, J.F. (2005). *Creating the ethical school: A book of case studies*. New York: Teachers College Press.

Credits

Page 78: *Leah Bradford-Smart v. West Sussex County Council,* [2002] E.W.J. No. 127, para. 38. *Quicklaw,* LexisNexis Canada Inc.

Page 132: [2000] S.C.J. No. 87. *Quicklaw,* LexisNexis Canada Inc.

Page 135: Fritz, M., "What will we tell the children? A discussion of current judicial opinion on the scope of ideas acceptable for presentation in primary and secondary education," *56 Tulsa Law Review 960.*

Page 138: [2005] P.E.I.J. No. 42. *Quicklaw,* LexisNexis Canada Inc.

Page 142: Oulton, C., Dillon, J., Grace, M.M. (2004) from "Reconceptualizing the teaching of controversial issues," *International Journal of Science Education,* 26(4), 411-423. http://www.tandf.co.uk

Index